SAFETY PRACTICES IN THE ORGANIC LABORATORY[1]

GENERAL: Never work in the laboratory alone. Perform no unauthorized experiments. Do not use mouth suction to fill pipettes. Confine long hair and loose clothes while working in the laboratory. Wear shoes. Learn the location of and correct use of the nearest fire extinguisher. Learn the location of the safety shower and first aid kit, and be prepared to give help to others.

SAFETY GLASSES: Safety glasses should be worn **at all times** while in the laboratory, whether you actively engage in experimental work or not.

FIRE: Avoid unnecessary flames. Check the area near you for volatile solvents before lighting a burner. Check the area near you for flames if you are about to begin working with a volatile solvent. Be particularly careful of the volatile solvents diethyl ether, petroleum ether, ligroin, benzene, methanol, ethanol, and acetone.

CHEMICALS: Handle every chemical with care. Avoid contact with skin and clothing. Wipe up spills immediately, especially near the balances and reagent shelf. Replace caps on bottles as soon as possible. Do not use an organic solvent to wash a chemical from the skin as this may actually *increase* the rate of absorption of the chemical through the skin. Avoid the inhalation of organic vapors, particularly aromatic solvents and chlorinated solvents. Use care in smelling chemicals, and do not taste them unless instructed to do so. Drinking, eating, or smoking in the laboratory is forbidden.

DISPOSAL OF CHEMICALS: Dispose of chemicals as directed in each experiment's "Cleaning Up" section. In general, small quantities of nonhazardous water-soluble substances can be flushed down the drain with a large quantity of water. Hazardous waste, nonhazardous solid waste, organic solvents, and halogenated organic waste should be placed in the four containers provided.

CAUTION: It has been determined that several chemicals that are widely used in the organic laboratory (e.g., benzene and chloroform) cause cancer in test animals when administered in large doses. Where possible, the use of these chemicals is avoided in this book. In the few cases where suspected carcinogens are used, the precautions noted should be followed carefully. A case in point is chromium in the $+6$ oxidation stage. The *dust* of solid Cr^{+6} salts is carcinogenic. The hazards have been pointed out, and safe handling procedures are given.

[1]Adapted from *Safety in Academic Chemistry Laboratories,* prepared by the American Chemical Society Committee on Chemical Safety, March 1996.

IN CASE OF ACCIDENT[1]

*In case of accident notify the laboratory instructor **immediately**.*

FIRE

Burning Clothing. Prevent the person from running and fanning the flames. Rolling the person on the floor will help extinguish the flames and prevent inhalation of the flames. If a safety shower is nearby hold the person under the shower until flames are extinguished and chemicals washed away. Do not use a fire blanket if a shower is nearby. The blanket does not cool and smoldering continues. Remove contaminated clothing. Wrap the person in a blanket to avoid shock. Get prompt medical attention.

Do not, under any circumstances, use a carbon tetrachloride (toxic) fire extinguisher and be very careful using a CO_2 extinguisher (the person may smother).

Burning Reagents. Extinguish all nearby burners and remove combustible material and solvents. Small fires in flasks and beakers can be extinguished by covering the container with a fiberglass-wire gauze square, a big beaker, or a watch glass. Use a dry chemical or carbon dioxide fire extinguisher directed at the base of the flames. **Do not use water.**

Burns, Either Thermal or Chemical. Flush the burned area with cold water for at least 15 min. Resume if pain returns. Wash off chemicals with a mild detergent and water. Current practice recommends that no neutralizing chemicals, unguents, creams, lotions, or salves be applied. If chemicals are spilled on a person over a large area quickly remove the contaminated clothing while under the safety shower. Seconds count, and time should not be wasted because of modesty. Get prompt medical attention.

CHEMICALS IN THE EYE: Flush the eye with copious amounts of water for 15 min using an eyewash fountain or bottle or by placing the injured person face up on the floor and pouring water in the open eye. Hold the eye open to wash behind the eyelids. After 15 min of washing obtain prompt medical attention, regardless of the severity of the injury.

CUTS: Minor Cuts. This type of cut is most common in the organic laboratory and usually arises from broken glass. Wash the cut, remove any pieces of glass, and apply pressure to stop the bleeding. Get medical attention.

Major Cuts. If blood is spurting place a pad directly on the wound, apply firm pressure, wrap the injured to avoid shock, and get **immediate** medical attention. Never use a tourniquet.

POISONS: Call 800 information (1-800-555-1212) for the telephone number of the nearest Poison Control Center, which is usually also an 800 number.

---

[1]Adapted from *Safety in Academic Chemistry Laboratories,* prepared by the American Chemical Society Committee on Chemical Safety, March 1996.

MULTIPLES OF ELEMENTS' WEIGHTS

C	12.0112	C_{41}	492.457	H_{31}	31.2471	O_6	95.9964	I	126.904	P	30.9738
C_2	24.0223	C_{42}	504.468	H_{32}	32.2550	O_7	111.996	I_2	253.809	P_2	61.9476
C_3	36.0335	C_{43}	516.479	H_{33}	33.2630	O_8	127.995	I_3	380.713	P_3	92.9214
C_4	48.0446	C_{44}	528.491	H_{34}	34.2710	O_9	143.995			P_4	123.895
C_5	60.0557	C_{45}	540.502	H_{35}	35.2790	O_{10}	159.994	OCH_3	31.0345	P_5	154.869
C_6	72.0669	C_{46}	552.513	H_{36}	36.2869			$(OCH_3)_2$	62.0689	P_6	185.843
C_7	84.0780	C_{47}	564.524	H_{37}	37.2949	N	14.0067	$(OCH_3)_3$	93.1034		
C_8	96.0892	C_{48}	576.535	H_{38}	38.3029	N_2	28.0134	$(OCH_3)_4$	124.138	Na	22.9898
C_9	108.100	C_{49}	588.546	H_{39}	39.3108	N_3	42.0201	$(OCH_3)_5$	155.172	Na_2	45.9796
C_{10}	120.111	C_{50}	600.558	H_{40}	40.3188	N_4	56.0268	$(OCH_3)_6$	186.207	Na_3	68.9694
						N_5	70.0335	$(OCH_3)_7$	217.241		
C_{11}	132.123	H	1.00797	H_{41}	41.3268	N_6	84.0402	$(OCH_3)_8$	248.276	K	39.102
C_{12}	144.134	H_2	2.01594	H_{42}	42.3347			$(OCH_3)_9$	279.31	K_2	78.204
C_{13}	156.145	H_3	3.02391	H_{43}	43.3427	S	32.064	$(OCH_3)_{10}$	310.345	K_3	117.306
C_{14}	168.156	H_4	4.03188	H_{44}	44.3507	S_2	64.128				
C_{15}	180.167	H_5	5.03985	H_{45}	45.3587	S_3	96.192	OC_2H_5	45.0616	Ag	107.868
C_{16}	192.178	H_6	6.04782	H_{46}	46.3666	S_4	128.256	$(OC_2H_5)_2$	90.1231	Ag_2	215.736
C_{17}	204.190	H_7	7.05579	H_{47}	47.3746	S_5	160.320	$(OC_2H_5)_3$	135.185		
C_{18}	216.201	H_8	8.06376	H_{48}	48.3826	S_6	192.384	$(OC_2H_5)_4$	180.246	Cu	63.546
C_{19}	228.212	H_9	9.07173	H_{49}	49.3905			$(OC_2H_5)_5$	225.308	Cu_2	127.092
C_{20}	240.223	H_{10}	10.0797	H_{50}	50.3985			$(OC_2H_5)_6$	270.369	Cr	51.996
						F	18.9984	$(OC_2H_5)_7$	315.431	Hg	200.59
C_{21}	252.234	H_{11}	11.0877	H_{51}	51.4065	F_2	37.9968	$(OC_2H_5)_8$	360.492	Pb	207.19
C_{22}	264.245	H_{12}	12.0956	H_{52}	52.4144	F_3	56.9952			Pt	195.09
C_{23}	276.256	H_{13}	13.1036	H_{53}	53.4224	F_4	75.9936	$OCOCH_3$	59.045	Pt_2	390.18
C_{24}	288.268	H_{14}	14.1116	H_{54}	54.4304	F_5	94.992	$(OCOCH_3)_2$	118.090	Se	78.96
C_{25}	300.279	H_{15}	15.1196	H_{55}	55.4384	F_6	113.99	$(OCOCH_3)_3$	177.135	Th	204.37
C_{26}	312.290	H_{16}	16.1275	H_{56}	56.4463	F_7	132.989	$(OCOCH_3)_4$	236.180		
C_{27}	324.301	H_{17}	17.1355	H_{57}	57.4543	F_8	151.987	$(OCOCH_3)_5$	295.225		
C_{28}	336.312	H_{18}	18.1435	H_{58}	58.4623	F_9	170.986	$(OCOCH_3)_6$	354.270		
C_{29}	348.323	H_{19}	19.1514	H_{59}	59.4702	F_{10}	189.984	$(OCOCH_3)_7$	413.315		
C_{30}	360.334	H_{20}	20.1594	H_{60}	60.4782			$(OCOCH_3)_8$	472.360		
				H_{61}	61.4862	Cl	35.453	$(OCOCH_3)_9$	531.405		
C_{31}	372.346	H_{21}	21.1674	H_{62}	62.4941	Cl_2	70.906	$(OCOCH_3)_{10}$	590.450		
C_{32}	384.357	H_{22}	22.1753	H_{63}	63.5021	Cl_3	106.359				
C_{33}	396.368	H_{23}	23.1833	H_{64}	64.5101	Cl_4	141.812	$(H_2O)_{1/2}$	9.00767		
C_{34}	408.379	H_{24}	24.1913	H_{65}	65.5181	Cl_5	177.265	H_2O	18.0153		
C_{35}	420.390	H_{25}	25.1993					$(H_2O)_{1\frac{1}{2}}$	27.0230		
C_{36}	432.401	H_{26}	26.2072	O	15.9994	Br	79.904	$(H_2O)_2$	36.0307		
C_{37}	444.413	H_{27}	27.2152	O_2	31.9988	Br_2	159.808	$(H_2O)_3$	54.0460		
C_{38}	456.424	H_{28}	28.2232	O_3	47.9982	Br_3	239.712	$(H_2O)_4$	72.0614		
C_{39}	468.435	H_{29}	29.2311	O_4	63.9976	Br_4	319.616	$(H_2O)_5$	90.0767		
C_{40}	480.446	H_{30}	30.2391	O_5	79.9970	Br_5	399.52	$(H_2O)_6$	108.092		

BUFFER SOLUTIONS (0.2 *M*, except as indicated)

pH	Components	pH	Components
0.1	1 *M* Hydrochloric acid	8.0	11.8 g Boric acid + 9.1 g Borax
1.1	0.1 *M* Hydrochloric acid		$(Na_2B_4O_7 \cdot 10H_2O)$ per L
2.2	15.0 g *D*-Tartaric acid per L (0.1 *M* solution)	9.0	6.2 g Boric acid + 38.1 g Borax per L
3.9	40.8 g Potassium acid phthalate per L	10.0	6.5 g $NaHCO_3$ + 13.2 g Na_2CO_3 per L
5.0	14.0 g KH-Phthalate + 2.7 g $NaHCO_3$ per L	11.0	11.4 g Na_2HPO_4 + 19.7 g Na_3PO_4 per L
	(heat to expel carbon dioxide, then cool)	12.0	24.6 g Na_3PO_4 per L (0.15 *M* solution)
6.0	23.2 g KH_2PO_4 + 4.3 g Na_2HPO_4 (anhyd., Merck) per L	13.0	4.1 g Sodium hydroxide pellets per L (0.1 *M*)
7.0	9.1 g KH_2PO_4 + 18.9 g Na_2HPO_4 per L	14.0	41.3 g Sodium hydroxide pellets per L (1 *M*)

ATOMIC WEIGHTS

Aluminum	Al	26.9815	Molybdenum	Mo	95.94
Antimony	Sb	121.75	Nickel	Ni	58.71
Arsenic	As	74.9216	Nitrogen	N	14.0067
Barium	Ba	137.34	Osmium	Os	190.2
Beryllium	Be	9.0122	Oxygen	O	15.9994
Bismuth	Bi	208.980	Palladium	Pd	106.4
Boron	B	10.811	Phosphorus	P	30.9738
Bromine	Br	79.904	Platinum	Pt	195.09
Cadmium	Cd	112.40	Potassium	K	39.102
Calcium	Ca	40.08	Praseodymium	Pr	140.907
Carbon	C	12.01115	Rhodium	Rh	102.9055
Cerium	Ce	140.12	Ruthenium	Ru	101.07
Cesium	Cs	132.905	Selenium	Se	78.96
Chlorine	Cl	35.453	Silicon	Si	28.086
Chromium	Cr	51.996	Silver	Ag	107.868
Cobalt	Co	58.9332	Sodium	Na	22.9898
Copper	Cu	63.546	Strontium	Sr	87.62
Europium	Eu	151.96	Sulfur	S	32.064
Fluorine	F	18.9984	Tantalum	Ta	180.948
Gold	Au	196.967	Tellurium	Te	127.60
Hydrogen	H	1.00797	Thallium	Tl	204.37
Iodine	I	126.9044	Thorium	Th	232.038
Iridium	Ir	192.22	Tin	Sn	118.69
Iron	Fe	55.847	Titanium	Ti	47.90
Lead	Pb	207.19	Tungsten	W	183.85
Lithium	Li	6.939	Vanadium	V	50.942
Magnesium	Mg	24.312	Ytterbium	Yb	173.04
Manganese	Mn	54.9380	Zinc	Zn	65.37
Mercury	Hg	200.59	Zirconium	Zr	91.22

ACIDS AND BASES

	Sp. Gr.	% by Wt	Moles per L	Grams per 100 mL
Hydrochloric acid, concd.	1.19	37	12.0	44.0
3 M (124.3 mL concd. acid diluted to 500 mL)	1.05	10.8	3.0	10.9
Constant boiling (252 mL concd. acid + 200 mL water, bp 110°)	1.10	22.2	6.1	22.2
10% (100 mL concd. acid + 321 mL water)	1.05	10	2.9	10.5
5% (50 mL concd. acid + 380.5 mL water)	1.03	5	1.4	5.2
1 M (41.5 mL concd. acid diluted to 500 mL)	1.02	3.6	1	3.6
Hydrobromic acid, constant-boiling (bp 126°)	1.49	47.5	8.8	70.7
Hydriodic acid, constant-boiling (bp 126°)	1.7	57	7.6	97
Sulfuric acid, concd.	1.84	96	18	177
1.5 M (41.7 mL concd. acid diluted to 500 mL)	1.09	14.1	1.5	14.7
10% (25 mL concd. acid + 398 mL water)	1.07	10	1.1	10.7
0.5 M (13.9 mL concd. acid diluted to 500 mL)	1.03	4.7	0.5	4.9
Nitric acid, concd.	1.42	71	16	101
Sodium hydroxide, 3 M solution	1.12	11	3.0	12.0
10% solution	1.11	10	2.8	11.1
Ammonia solution, concd.	0.90	28.4	15	25.6
Acetic acid, glacial	1.05	100.0	17.5	105
Sodium bicarbonate	1.03	4	0.5	4.2
Saturated solution	1.05	8	1	8.3
Sodium chloride, saturated solution	1.20	26	5.3	31.1

Grams of sodium carbonate required to neutralize 1 mL of concd. acid:

0.636 g	1 mL HCl
0.848 g	1 mL HNO_3
1.91 g	1 mL H_2SO_4
0.928 g	1 mL CH_3COOH

CENTIMETER RULER

Macroscale and Microscale Organic Experiments

FIFTH EDITION

SPECIAL EDITION FOR THE UNIVERSITY OF WEST GEORGIA
ORGANIC CHEMISTRY LAB I AND II

Kenneth L. Williamson
Mount Holyoke College, Emeritus

Robert Minard
Pennsylvania State University, Emeritus

Katherine M. Masters
Pennsylvania State University

Houghton Mifflin Harcourt Publishing Company
Boston   New York

Publisher: Charles Hartford
Executive Sponsoring Editor: Richard Stratton
Development Editor: Kate Heinle
Senior Project Editor: Margaret Park Bridges
Manufacturing Manager: Karen B. Fawcett
Senior Marketing Manager: Katherine Greig
Marketing Assistant: Naveen Hariprasad

Custom Publishing Editor: Glen Garett
Custom Publishing Production Manager: Christina Battista
Project Coordinator: Sara Abbott

Cover Designer: Heather Pytel
Cover Image: PhotoDisc

This book contains select works from existing Houghton Mifflin Harcourt Publishing Company resources and was produced by Houghton Mifflin Harcourt Custom Publishing for collegiate use. As such, those adopting and/or contributing to this work are responsible for editorial content, accuracy, continuity and completeness.

Printed in the United States of America.

ISBN-13: 978-0-547-20864-0
ISBN-10: 0-547-20864-2
1059837

1 2 3 4 5 6 7 8 9 – BR – 10 09 08

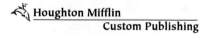 **Houghton Mifflin**
Custom Publishing

222 Berkeley Street • Boston, MA 02116

Address all correspondence and order information to the above address.

Contents

Organic Experiments and Waste Disposal

An unusual feature of this book is the advice at the end of each experiment on how to dispose of its chemical waste. Waste disposal thus becomes part of the experiment, which is not considered finished until the waste products are appropriately taken care of. This is a valuable addition to the book for several reasons.

Although chemical waste from laboratories is less than 0.1% of that generated in the United States, its disposal is nevertheless subject to many of the same federal, state, and local regulations as is chemical waste from industry. Accordingly, there are both strong ethical and legal reasons for proper disposal of laboratory wastes. These reasons are backed up by a financial concern, because the cost of waste disposal can become a significant part of the cost of operating a laboratory.

There is yet another reason to include instructions for waste disposal in a teaching laboratory. Students will someday be among those conducting and regulating waste disposal operations and voting on appropriations for them. Learning the principles and methods of sound waste disposal early in their careers will benefit them and society later.

The basics of waste disposal are easy to grasp. Some innocuous water-soluble wastes are flushed down the drain with a large proportion of water. Common inorganic acids and bases are neutralized and flushed down the drain. Containers are provided for several classes of solvents, for example, combustible solvents and halogenated solvents. (The containers are subsequently removed for suitable disposal by licensed waste handlers.) Some toxic substances can be oxidized or reduced to innocuous substances that can then be flushed down the drain; for example, hydrazines, mercaptans, and inorganic cyanides can be thus oxidized by sodium hypochlorite solution, widely available as household bleach. Dilute solutions of highly toxic cations are expensive to dispose of because of their bulk; precipitation of the cation by a suitable reagent followed by its separation greatly reduces its bulk and cost. These and many other procedures can be found throughout this book.

One other principle of waste control lies at the heart of this book. Microscale experimentation, by minimizing the scale of chemical operations, also minimizes the volume of waste. Chromatography procedures to separate and purify products, spectroscopy methods to identify and characterize products, and well-designed small-scale equipment enable one to conduct experiments today on a tenth to a thousandth the scale commonly in use a generation ago.

Chemists often provide great detail in their directions for preparing chemicals so that the synthesis can be repeated, but they seldom say much about how to dispose of the hazardous byproducts. Yet the proper disposal of a chemical's byproducts is as important as its proper preparation. Dr. Williamson sets a good example by providing explicit directions for such disposal.

Blaine C. McKusick

CHAPTER

1

Introduction

Online Study Center

This icon will direct you to techniques, equipment setups, and online resources at http://college.hmco.com/PIC/williamsonMMOE5e.

PRELAB EXERCISE: Study the glassware diagrams presented in this chapter and be prepared to identify the reaction tube, the fractionating column, the distilling head, the filter adapter, and the Hirsch funnel.

Welcome to the organic chemistry laboratory! Here, the reactions that you learned in your organic lectures and studied in your textbook will come to life. The main goal of the laboratory course is for you to learn and carry out techniques for the synthesis, isolation, purification, and analysis of organic compounds, thus experiencing the experimental nature of organic chemistry. We want you to enjoy your laboratory experience and ask you to remember that safety always comes first.

Synthesis–The Big Picture

Synthesis is a pervasive process in the universe. Science has shown us that our world consists of energy and matter and that both of these are being transformed from one form to another throughout the cosmos (see Fig. 1.1).

- Cosmosynthesis started roughly 14 billion years ago when the Big Bang transformed subatomic particles into hydrogen and helium. These elements condense into stars and are fused by nucleosynthetic reactions to give us the periodic table of elements. Most stars ultimately expand or explode and disperse their product elements into space where they can recondense to form new stars, some with planets around them. For the early Earth, these elements combined into minerals and other substances such as water, carbon dioxide, and nitrogen.
- Biosynthesis on planet Earth has been going on for over 2 billion years. In the process of growth and reproduction, even the simplest single cell organisms can synthesize incredibly complex structural, catalytic, informational, and

■ FIG. 1.1
The three types of synthesis and the steps by which organic chemists study the resulting products. Theory allows correlation of structure to properties and guides the cycle of synthetic design, synthesis, separation/purification, and analysis.

regulatory molecules from simple starting materials such as CO_2, H_2O, and N_2. Organic chemistry's beginnings are based on isolating and studying these natural products such as urea, ethanol, caffeine, or oil of wintergreen (methyl salicylate). The whole field of biochemistry is based on the isolation, structure determination, and reactivity of organic molecules found in living systems.

● Anthrosynthesis is a human activity that produces either known substances economically (e.g., iron, ammonia, and vitamin C) or new substances not found in the cosmos or biology (e.g., aspirin, Splenda, and Teflon). To date, chemists have synthesized or isolated from nature over 20 million different substances, and 99% of these are organic compounds. As you know, this great variety of organic compounds stems from carbon's unique ability to form chains that can be linear, branched, or cyclic and that can have other elements bonded to them to yield myriad structures.

Whether chemists study rocks from the earth, molecules in cells, or products of anthrosynthesis, they almost always separate and study the structure and properties of pure substances (e.g., silica, hemoglobin, or carbon nanotubes) rather than the mixtures (e.g., a shovel of dirt, blood, or soot) typically found in nature or synthetic reactions. Only pure substances will show reproducible data for physical, chemical, and biological properties. Chemists then try to understand the relationship between a compound's structure and its properties and devise a reasonable theory that relates these. If a theory is found to be true, it can be used to design the synthesis of a new substance with enhanced properties such as elasticity, antibiotic activity, or biodegradability. This cycle of Synthesis → Separation/Purification → Analysis → Theory → Synthetic Design is depicted in Figure 1.1. The cycle can be repeated to test and refine the theory and further improve the desired properties. This cycle is at the heart of progress in the pharmaceutical, polymer/plastic, and metallurgy industries.

Once you start your laboratory work, you will soon realize that synthesis involves much more than reacting chemicals. The techniques of separation, purification, and analysis often require considerable time and attention. Therefore, the first part of this lab text is designed to help you understand, apply, and master these techniques. They will then be used repeatedly in the dozens of synthesis and isolation experiments presented in later chapters.

Experimental Organic Chemistry– What Is in It for Me?

You are probably not a chemistry major. The vast majority of students in this laboratory course are majoring in the life sciences or engineering. Although you may never use the exact same techniques taught in this course, you will undoubtedly apply the skills taught here to whatever problem or question your ultimate career may present. Application of the scientific method involves the following steps:

1. Designing an experiment, therapy, or approach to solve a problem
2. Executing the plan or experiment
3. Observing the outcome to verify that you obtained the desired results
4. Recording the findings to communicate them both orally and in writing

You may not always get the desired result the first time when doing an experiment. Do not take this as a personal failure; it is evidence that carrying out an organic reaction can often be trickier than baking a cake (and we all probably had trouble baking our first cake!). Your laboratory instructor is there to provide guidance and advice but not to solve your problems. Learning to think for yourself is the most valuable skill you will take from this course. However, you should not be afraid to ask questions or bounce ideas off your instructor or fellow students. Just formulating the question or talking about your problem often helps you find the answer. To begin troubleshooting a problem, you will need to scrutinize carefully every detail of the approach, therapy, or experimental design; the execution of the experiment; and your observations to see where things might have gone wrong. This process will lead you to an idea or hypothesis about how to change things to make the experiment work. The sequence is then repeated, sometimes many times, until you solve the problem, answer the question, or prove/disprove the idea.

The teaching lab is more controlled than the real world. In this laboratory environment, you will be guided more than you would be on the job. Nevertheless, the experiments in this text are designed to be sufficiently challenging to give you a taste of experimental problem-solving methods practiced by professional scientists. We earnestly hope that you will find the techniques, the apparatus, and the experiments of just the right complexity, not too easy but not too hard, so that you can learn at a satisfying pace.

Macroscale and Microscale Experiments

This laboratory text presents a unique approach for carrying out organic experiments; they can be conducted on either a *macroscale* or a *microscale*. Macroscale was the traditional way of teaching the principles of experimental organic chemistry and is the basis for all the experiments in this book, a book that traces its history to 1934 when the late Louis Fieser, an outstanding organic chemist and professor at Harvard University, was its author. Macroscale experiments typically involve the use of a few grams of *starting material*, the chief reagent used in the reaction. Most teaching institutions are equipped to carry out traditional macroscale experiments. Instructors are familiar with these techniques and experiments, and much research in industry and academe is carried out on this scale. For these reasons, this book has macroscale versions of most experiments.

For reasons primarily related to safety and cost, there is a growing trend toward carrying out microscale laboratory work, on a scale one-tenth to one-thousandth of that previously used. Using smaller quantities of chemicals exposes the laboratory worker to smaller amounts of toxic, flammable, explosive, carcinogenic, and teratogenic material. Microscale experiments can be carried out more rapidly than macroscale experiments because of rapid heat transfer, filtration, and drying. Because the apparatus advocated by the authors is inexpensive, more than one reaction may be set up at once. The cost of chemicals is, of course, greatly reduced. A principal advantage of microscale experimentation is that the quantity of waste is one-tenth to one-thousandth of that formerly produced. To allow maximum flexibility in the conduct of organic experiments, this book presents both macroscale and microscale procedures for the vast majority of the experiments. As will be seen, some of the equipment and techniques differ. A careful reading of both the microscale and macroscale procedures will reveal which changes and precautions must be employed in going from one scale to the other.

Synthesis and Analysis

Synthesis and analysis are two major concerns of the organic chemist, and both are dealt with in this book. The typical sequence of activity in synthetic organic chemistry involves the following steps:

1. Designing the experiment based on knowledge of chemical reactivity, the equipment and techniques available, and full awareness of all safety issues
2. Setting up and running the reaction
3. Isolating the reaction product

4. Purifying the crude product, if necessary
5. Analyzing the product using chromatography or spectroscopy to verify purity and structure
6. Disposing of unwanted chemicals in a safe manner

Each of these steps uses certain laboratory techniques. The experiments at the beginning of this text are designed to teach you these techniques and to help you understand the molecular level principles that underlie them.

1. Designing the Experiment

Because the first step of experimental design often requires considerable experience, this part has already been done for you for most of the experiments in this introductory level book. Synthetic experimental design becomes increasingly important in an advanced course and in graduate research programs. Remember that safety is paramount, and therefore it is important to be aware of all possible personal and environmental hazards before running any reaction. These are more fully discussed in Chapter 2 and are highlighted in each experiment.

2. Running the Reaction

The rational synthesis of an organic compound, whether it involves the transformation of one functional group into another or a carbon-carbon bond-forming reaction, starts with a *reaction*. Organic reactions usually take place in the liquid phase and are *homogeneous*—the reactants are entirely in one phase. The reactants can be solids and/or liquids dissolved in an appropriate solvent to mediate the reaction. Some reactions are *heterogeneous*—that is, one of the reactants is a solid and requires stirring or shaking to bring the reactants in contact with one another. A few heterogeneous reactions involve the reaction of a gas, such as oxygen, carbon dioxide, or hydrogen, with material in solution. Examples of all these reactions are found in this book.

An *exothermic* reaction evolves heat. If it is highly exothermic with a low activation energy, one reactant is added slowly to the other, and heat is removed by external cooling. Most organic reactions are, however, mildly *endothermic*, which means the reaction mixture must be heated to overcome the activation barrier and to

Effect of temperature

increase the rate of the reaction. A very useful rule of thumb is that *the rate of an organic reaction doubles with a 10°C rise in temperature*. Louis Fieser introduced the idea of changing the traditional solvents of many reactions to high-boiling solvents to reduce reaction times. Throughout this book we will use solvents such as triethylene glycol, with a boiling point (bp) of 290°C, to replace ethanol (bp 78°C) and triethylene glycol dimethyl ether (bp 222°C) to replace dimethoxyethane (bp 85°C). Using these high-boiling solvents can greatly increase the rates of many reactions.

The progress of a reaction can be followed by observing a change in color or pH, the evolution of a gas, or the separation of a solid product or a liquid layer. Quite often, the extent of reaction can be determined by withdrawing tiny samples

Chapters 8–10: Chromatography

at certain time intervals and analyzing them by *thin-layer chromatography* or *gas chromatography* to measure the amount of starting material remaining and/or the amount of product formed. The next step, product isolation, should not be carried out until one is confident that the desired amount of product has been formed.

3. Product Isolation: Workup of the Reaction

Running an organic reaction is usually the easiest part of a synthesis. The real challenge lies in isolating and purifying the product from the reaction because organic reactions seldom give quantitative yields of a single pure substance. Any unwanted byproducts need to be removed.

In some cases the solvent and concentrations of reactants are chosen so that, after the reaction mixture has been cooled, the product will *crystallize* or *precipitate* if it is a solid. The product is then collected by *filtration*, and the crystals are washed with an appropriate solvent. If sufficiently pure at that point, the product is dried and collected; otherwise, it is purified by the process of *recrystallization* or, less commonly, by *sublimation*.

More typically, the product of a reaction does not crystallize from the reaction mixture and is often isolated by the process of *liquid/liquid extraction*. This process involves two liquids, a water-insoluble organic liquid such as dichloromethane and a neutral, acidic, or basic aqueous solution. The two liquids do not mix, but when shaken together, the organic materials and inorganic byproducts go into the liquid layer, organic or aqueous, that they are the most soluble in. After shaking, two layers again form and can be separated. Most organic products remain in the organic liquid and can be isolated by evaporation of the organic solvent.

If the product is a liquid, it is isolated by *distillation*, usually after extraction. Occasionally, the product can be isolated by the process of *steam distillation* from the reaction mixture.

4. Purification

When an organic product is first isolated, it will often contain significant impurities. This impure or crude product will need to be further purified or cleaned up before it can be analyzed or used in other reactions. Solids may be purified by recrystallization or sublimation and liquids by distillation or steam distillation. Small amounts of solids and liquids can also be purified by *chromatography*.

5. Analysis to Verify Purity and Structure

The purity of the product can be determined by melting point analysis for solids, boiling point analysis or refractive index for liquids, and chromatographic analysis for either solids or liquids. Once the purity of the product has been verified, structure determination can be accomplished by using one of the various spectroscopic methods, such as ^1H and ^{13}C nuclear magnetic resonance (NMR), infrared (IR), and ultraviolet/visible (UV/Vis) spectroscopies. Mass spectrometry (MS) is another tool that can aid in the identification of a structure.

CAUTION: Never smell chemicals in an attempt to identify them.

6. Chemical Waste Disposal

All waste chemicals must be disposed of in their proper waste containers. Instructions on chemical disposal will appear at the end of each experiment. It is recommended that nothing be disposed of until you are sure of your product identity and purity; you do not want to accidentally throw out your product before the analysis is complete. Proper disposal of chemicals is essential for protecting the environment in accordance with local, state, and federal regulations.

Equipment for Experimental Organic Chemistry

A. Equipment for Running Reactions

Organic reactions are usually carried out by dissolving the reactants in a solvent and then heating the mixture to its boiling point, thus maintaining the reaction at that elevated temperature for as long as is necessary to complete the reaction. To keep the solvent from boiling away, the vapor is condensed to a liquid, which is allowed to run back into the boiling solvent.

Microscale reactions with volumes up to 4 mL can be carried out in a *reaction tube* (Fig. 1.2a). The mass of the reaction tube is so small and heat transfer is so rapid that 1 mL of nitrobenzene (bp 210°C) will boil in 10 s, and 1 mL of benzene (mp 5°C) will crystallize in the same period of time. Cooling is effected by simply agitating the tube in a small beaker of ice water, and heating is effected by immersing the reaction tube to an appropriate depth in an electrically heated sand bath. This sand bath usually consists of an electric 100-mL flask heater or heating mantle half filled with sand. The temperature is controlled by the setting on a variable voltage controller often called a Variac (Fig. 1.2b). The air above the heater is not hot. It is possible to hold a reaction tube containing refluxing solvents between the thumb and forefinger without the need for forceps or other protective device. Because sand is a fairly poor conductor of heat, there is a very large variation in temperature in the sand bath depending on its depth. The temperature of a 5-mL flask can be regulated by using a spatula to pile up or remove sand from near the flask's base. The heater is easily capable of producing temperatures in excess of 300°C; therefore, never leave the controller at its maximum setting. Ordinarily, it is set at 20%–40% of maximum.

Because the area of the tube exposed to heat is fairly small, it is difficult to transfer enough heat to the contents of the tube to cause the solvents to boil away. The reaction tube is 100 mm long, so the upper part of the tube can function as an efficient *air condenser* (Fig. 1.2a) because the area of glass is large and the volume of vapor is comparatively small. The air condenser can be made even longer by attaching the empty *distilling column* (Fig. 1.2c and 1.15o) to the reaction tube using the *connector with support rod* (Fig. 1.2c and Fig. 1.15m). The black connector is made of Viton, which is resistant to high-boiling aromatic solvents. The cream-colored connector is made of Santoprene, which is resistant to all but high-boiling aromatic solvents. As solvents such as water and ethanol boil, the hot vapor ascends to the upper part of the tube. These condense and run back down the tube. This process is called *refluxing* and is the most common method for conducting a reaction at a constant temperature, the boiling point of the solvent. For very low-boiling solvents such as diethyl ether (bp 35°C), a pipe cleaner dampened with water makes an efficient cooling device. A water-cooled condenser is also available (Fig. 1.3) but is seldom needed for microscale experiments.

A Petri dish containing sand and heated on a hot plate is not recommended for microscale experiments. It is too easy to burn oneself on the hot plate; too much heat wells up from the sand, so air condensers do not function well; the glass

Turn on the sand bath about 20 min before you intend to use it. The sand heats slowly.

CAUTION: Never put a mercury thermometer in a sand bath! It will break, releasing highly toxic mercury vapor.

Online Study Center

Photos: Williamson Microscale Kit, Refluxing a Liquid in a Reaction Tube on a Sand Bath; Video: The Reaction Tube in Use

Online Study Center

Video: How to Assemble Apparatus

■ FIG. 1.2

(a) A reaction tube being heated on a hot sand bath in a flask heater. The area of the tube exposed to the heat is small. The liquid boils and condenses on the cool upper portion of the tube, which functions as an air condenser. (b) A variable voltage controller used to control the temperature of the sand bath. (c) The condensing area can be increased by adding a distilling column as an air condenser.

Cool part of tube

Refluxing liquid (Air condenser)

Sand

Heated area

Boiling liquid

Boiling chip

Electric flask heater

(a)

Distilling column

Wet pipe cleaner

Connector stir rod

(c)

(b)

![caution triangle] **CAUTION**: Organic reactions should be conducted in a fume hood with the sash lowered.

dishes will break from thermal shock; and the ceramic coating on some hot plates will chip and come off.

Larger scale (macroscale) reactions involving volumes of tens to thousands of milliliters are usually carried out in large, round-bottom flasks that fit snugly (without sand!) into the appropriately sized flask heater or heating mantle (Fig. 1.4). The round shape can be heated more evenly than a flat-bottom flask or beaker. Heat transfer is slower than in microscale because of the smaller ratio of surface area to volume in a round-bottomed flask. Cooling is again conducted using an ice bath, but heating is sometimes done on a steam bath for low-boiling liquids. The narrow neck is necessary for connection via a *standard-taper ground glass joint* to a water-cooled *reflux condenser*, where the water flows in a jacket around the central tube.

■ FIG. 1.3
Refluxing solvent in a 5-mL round-bottomed flask fitted with a water-cooled condenser.

Water out

Water in

■ FIG. 1.4
A reflux apparatus for larger reactions. Liquid boils in the flask and condenses on the cold inner surface of the water-cooled condenser.

Central tube

Water out

Water in

Magnetic stirrer

The high heat capacity of water makes it possible to remove a large amount of heat in the larger volume of refluxing vapor (Fig. 1.4).

Heating and Stirring

In modern organic laboratories, electric flask heaters (heating mantles), used alone or as sand baths, are used exclusively for heating. Bunsen burners are almost never used because of the danger of igniting flammable organic vapors. For solvents that boil below 90°C, the most common method for heating macroscale flasks is the *steam bath*.

Reactions are often stirred using a *magnetic stirrer* (Fig. 1.4) to help mix reagents and to promote smooth boiling. A Teflon-coated bar magnet (*stirring bar*) is placed in the reaction flask, and a magnetic stirrer is placed under the flask and flask heater. The stirrer contains a large, horizontally rotating bar magnet that attracts the Teflon-coated stirring bar magnet and causes it to turn. The speed of stirring can be adjusted on the front of the magnetic stirrer.

B. Equipment for the Isolation of Products

Filtration

Online Study Center

Videos: The Reaction Tube in Use, Filtration of Crystals Using the Pasteur Pipette

If the product of a reaction crystallizes from the reaction mixture on cooling, the solid crystals are isolated by *filtration*. This can be done in several ways when using microscale techniques. If the crystals are large enough and in a reaction tube, insert a *Pasteur pipette* to the bottom of the tube while expelling the air and withdrawing the solvent (Fig. 1.5). Highly effective filtration occurs between the square, flat tip of the pipette and the bottom of the tube. This method of filtration has several advantages over the alternatives. The mixture of crystals and solvent can be kept on ice during the entire process. This minimizes the solubility of the crystals in the solvent. There are no transfer losses of material because an external filtration device is not used. This technique allows several recrystallizations to be carried out in the same tube with final drying of the product under vacuum. If you know the *tare* (the weight of the empty tube), the weight of the product can be determined without removing it from the tube. In this manner a compound can be synthesized, purified by crystallization, and dried all in the same reaction tube. After removal of material for analysis, the compound in the tube can then be used for the next reaction. This technique is used in many of this book's microscale experiments. When the crystals are dry, they are easily removed from the reaction tube. When they are wet, it is difficult to scrape them out. If the crystals are in more than about 2 mL of solvent, they can be isolated by filtration with a *Hirsch funnel*. The one that is in the microscale kit of apparatus is particularly easy to use because the funnel fits into the *filter flask* with no adapter and is equipped with a *polyethylene frit* for the capture of the filtered crystals (Fig. 1.6). The Wilfilter is especially good for collecting small quantities of crystals (Fig. 1.7).

■ **FIG. 1.5**
Filtration using a Pasteur pipette and a reaction tube.

Pipette bulb

Pasteur pipette

Reaction tube

Note square, flat tip

■ **FIG. 1.6**
A Hirsch funnel with an integral adapter, a polyethylene frit, and a 25-mL filter flask.

Filter paper, 12 mm dia.

Polyethylene filter disk (frit), 10 mm dia.

Hirsch funnel

To aspirator

25-mL Filter flask

■ **FIG. 1.7**
A Wilfilter is placed upside down in a centrifuge tube and spun in a centrifuge.

Crystals

Wilfilter

Filtrate

Online Study Center

Video: Macroscale Crystallization

Macroscale quantities of material can be recrystallized in conical *Erlenmeyer flasks* of the appropriate size. The crystals are collected in porcelain or plastic *Büchner funnels* fit with pieces of filter paper covering the holes in the bottom of the funnel (Fig. 1.8). A rubber *filter adapter* (*Filtervac*) is used to form a vacuum tight seal between the flask and the funnel.

Extraction

Chapter 7: Extraction

The product of a reaction will often not crystallize. It may be a liquid or a viscous oil, it may be a mixture of compounds, or it may be too soluble in the reaction solvent being used. In this case, an immiscible solvent is added, the two layers are shaken to effect *extraction*, and after the layers separate, one layer is removed. On a microscale, this can be done with a Pasteur pipette. The extraction process is repeated if necessary. A tall, thin column of liquid, such as that produced in a reaction tube, makes it easy to selectively remove one layer by pipette. This is more difficult to do in the usual test tube because the height/diameter ratio is small.

Online Study Center

Photos: Extraction with Ether, Extraction with Dichloromethane; Videos: Extraction with Ether, Extraction with Dichloromethane

On a larger scale, a *separatory funnel* is used for extraction (Fig. 1.9a). The mixture can be shaken in the funnel and then the lower layer removed through the

■ FIG. 1.9
(a) A separatory funnel with a Teflon stopcock. (b) A microscale separatory funnel. Remove the polyethylene frit from the micro Büchner funnel before using.

■ FIG. 1.8
A suction filter assembly.

(a)

(b)

■ **FIG. 1.10**
A small-scale sublimation
apparatus.

15-mL Centrifuge
tube, to be filled
with ice

Rubber
adapter

To
vacuum

25-mL Filter flask

Material to
be sublimed

Sublimate

Heat source

stopcock after the stopper is removed. These funnels are available in sizes from
10 mL to 5000 mL. The chromatography column in the apparatus kit is also a
micro separatory funnel (Fig. 1.9b). Remember to remove the frit at the column
base of the micro Büchner funnel and to close the valve before adding liquid.

C. Equipment for Purification

Many solids can be purified by the process of *sublimation*. The solid is heated, and
the vapor of the solid condenses on a cold surface to form crystals in an apparatus
constructed from a *centrifuge tube* fitted with a rubber adapter and pushed into a
filter flask (Fig. 1.10). Caffeine can be purified in this manner. This is primarily
a microscale technique, although sublimers holding several grams of solid are
available.

Mixtures of solids and, occasionally, of liquids can be separated and purified
by *column chromatography*. The *chromatography column* for both microscale and
macroscale work is very similar (Fig. 1.11).

Some of the compounds to be synthesized in these experiments are liquids.
On a very small scale, the best way to separate and purify a mixture of liquids is
by *gas chromatography*, but this technique is limited to less than 100 mg of material on the usual gas chromatograph. For larger quantities of material, *distillation* is used. For this purpose, small distilling flasks are used. These flasks have a
large surface area to allow sufficient heat input to cause the liquid to vaporize rapidly so that it can be distilled and then condensed for collection in a *receiver*. The
apparatus (Fig. 1.12) consists of a *distilling flask*, a *distilling adapter* (which also
functions as an air condenser on a microscale), a *thermometer adapter*, and a *thermometer*; for macroscale, a water-cooled *condenser* and *distilling adapter* are
added to the apparatus (Fig. 1.13). *Fractional distillation* is carried out using a
small, packed *fractionating column* (Fig. 1.14). The apparatus is very similar for
both microscale and macroscale. On a microscale, 2 mL to 4 mL of a liquid can be

Online Study Center

Photo: Sublimation Apparatus

Online Study Center

Photo: Column Chromatography;
Videos: Extraction with Ether,
Extraction with Dichloromethane

Chapter 9: Column
Chromatography

CAUTION: Use mercury-free
thermometers whenever
possible.

Online Study Center

Photo: Simple Distillation
Apparatus; Video: How to
Assemble Apparatus; Photo:
Fractional Distillation Apparatus

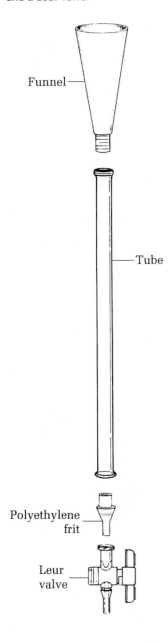

■ FIG. 1.11
A chromatography column consisting of a funnel, a tube, a base fitted with a polyethylene frit, and a Leur valve.

Funnel

Tube

Polyethylene frit

Leur valve

■ FIG. 1.12
A small-scale simple distillation apparatus. Note that the entire thermometer bulb is below the side arm of the distilling adapter.

Thermometer

Thermometer adapter

Distilling adapter and air condenser

Vial (receiver)

30-mL Beaker

Ice (if needed)

Distilling flask

Hot sand bath

Boiling chip

fractionally distilled, and 1 mL or more can be simply distilled. The usual scale in these experiments for macroscale distillation is about 25 mL.

Some liquids with a relatively high vapor pressure can be isolated and purified by *steam distillation*, a process in which the organic compound codistills with water at the boiling point of water. The microscale and macroscale apparatus for this process are shown in Chapter 6.

The collection of typical equipment used for microscale experimentation is shown in Figure 1.15 and for macroscale experimentation in Figure 1.16. Other equipment commonly used in the organic laboratory is shown in Figure 1.17.

Check-in of Lab Equipment

Your first duty will be to check in to your assigned lab desk. The identity of much of the apparatus should already be apparent from the preceding outline of the experimental processes used in the organic laboratory.

Check to see that your thermometer reads about 22°C–25°C (71.6°F–77°F), which is normal room temperature. Examine the fluid column to see that it is

■ **FIG. 1.13**
An apparatus for simple distillation.

- Thermometer
- Thermometer adapter
- Distillation head
- Keck clamp
- Clamp
- Condenser
- Keck clamp
- Distilling flask
- Boiling chip
- Distillation adapter
- Water out
- Water in
- Thermowell
- Receiver (graduated cylinder)

■ **FIG. 1.14**
A microscale fractional distillation apparatus. The thermometer adapter is to be fitted with a thermometer.

- Thermometer adapter (Santoprene)
- Distilling head and air condenser
- Receiver vial (1-dram)
- Fractionating column with copper sponge
- Rod
- Elastomeric connector [Santoprene (white) or Viton (black)]
- 5-mL Round-bottomed flask

■ FIG. 1.15
Microscale apparatus kit.

(a) Pipette (1 mL), graduated in 1/1000ths.
(b) Chromatography column (glass) with polypropylene funnel and 20-μm polyethylene frit in base, which doubles as a micro Büchner funnel. The column, base, and stopcock are also used as a separatory funnel.
(c) Thermometer adapter.
(d) Connector only (Viton).
(e) Magnetic stirring bars (4 × 12 mm) in distillation receiver vial.
(f) Hirsch funnel (polypropylene) with 20-μm fritted polyethylene disk.
(g) Stopcock for chromatography column and separatory funnel.
(h) Claisen adapter/distillation head with air condenser.
(i) Filter flask, 25 mL.
(j) Distillation head, 105° connecting adapter.
(k) Rubber septa/sleeve stoppers, 8 mm.
(l) Syringe (polypropylene).
(m) Connector with support rod.
(n) Centrifuge tube (15 mL)/sublimation receiver, with cap.
(o) Distillation column/air condenser.
(p) Reaction tube, calibrated, 10 × 100 mm.
(q) Erlenmeyer flasks, 10 mL.
(r) Long-necked flask, 5 mL.
(s) Short-necked flask, 5 mL.
(t) Rubber adapter for sublimation apparatus.
(u) Tubing (polyethylene), 1/16-in. diameter.
(v) Spatula (stainless steel) with scoop end.

■ **FIG. 1.16**
Macroscale apparatus kit with 14/20 standard-taper ground-glass joints.

(a) Polyacetal Keck clamps, size 14.
(b) Hex-head glass stopper, 14/20 standard taper.
(c) Hirsch funnel (polypropylene) with 20-μm fritted polyethylene disk.
(d) Filter adapter for sublimation apparatus.
(e) Distilling head with O-ring thermometer adapter.
(f) Vacuum adapter.
(g) Centrifuge tube (15 mL)/sublimation receiver.
(h) Filter flask, 25 mL.
(i) Claisen adapter.
(j) Water-jacketed condenser.
(k) Chromatography column (glass) with polypropylene funnel and 20-μm polyethylene frit in base, which doubles as a micro Büchner funnel.
(l) Stopcock for chromatography column.
(m) Separatory funnel, 125 mL.
(n) Pear-shaped flask, 100 mL.
(o) Pear-shaped flask, 50 mL.
(p) Conical flask (15 mL) with side arm for inlet tube.
(q) Distilling column/air condenser.
(r) Conical reaction vial (5 mL)/distillation receiver.

unbroken and continuous from the bulb up. Replace any flasks that have star-shaped cracks. Remember that apparatus with graduations, stopcocks, or ground glass joints and anything porcelain are expensive. Erlenmeyer flasks, beakers, and test tubes are, by comparison, fairly cheap.

■ FIG. 1.17
Miscellaneous apparatus.
(a) 1.0 ± 0.01 mL graduated
pipette. (b) Septum. (c) 1.0-mL
syringe with blunt needle.
(d) Calibrated Pasteur pipette.
(e) Pipette pump. (f) Glass scorer.
(g) Filtervac. (h) Set of neoprene
filter adapters.

Transfer of Liquids and Solids

Pasteur pipettes (Fig. 1.18) are very useful for transferring small quantities of
liquid, adding reagents dropwise, and carrying out recrystallizations. Discard
used Pasteur pipettes in the special container for waste glass. Surprisingly, the
acetone used to wash out a dirty Pasteur pipette usually costs more than the pipette
itself.

A plastic funnel that fits on the top of the reaction tube is very convenient for
the transfer of solids to reaction tubes or small Erlenmeyer flasks for microscale
experiments (Fig. 1.19). It is also the top of the chromatography column (Fig. 1.11).
A special spatula with a scoop end (Fig. 1.17p) is used to remove solid material

■ **FIG. 1.17** (continued)
(i) Hirsch funnel with perforated plate in place. (j) Rubber thermometer adapter. (k) Powder funnel. (l) Polyethylene wash bottle. (m) Single-pan electronic balance with automatic zeroing and 0.001 g digital readout; 100 g capacity. (n) Electric flask heater. (o) Solid-state control for electric flask heater. (p) Stainless steel spatula. (q) Stirring bar. (r) Keck clamp. (s) Wilfilter.

from the reaction tube. On a large scale, a powder funnel is useful for adding solids to a flask (Fig. 1.17k). A funnel can also be fashioned from a sheet of weighing paper.

Weighing and Measuring

The single-pan electronic balance (Fig. 1.17m), which is capable of weighing to ±0.001 g and having a capacity of at least 100 g, is the single most important instrument making microscale organic experiments possible. Most of the weighing measurements made in microscale experiments will use this type of balance. Weighing is fast and accurate with these balances. There should be one electronic balance for every 12 students. For macroscale experiments, a balance of such

2.0 mL

1.5 mL

1.0 mL

0.75 mL

0.50 mL

0.25 mL

⚠️
Never pipette
by mouth!

0.10 mL

0.05 mL

■ FIG. 1.18
The approximate calibration
of Kimble 9" Pasteur pipette.

high accuracy is not necessary. Here, a balance with ± 0.01 g accuracy would be satisfactory.

A container such as a reaction tube standing in a beaker or flask is placed on the pan. Set the digital readout to register zero and then add the desired quantity of the reagent to the reaction tube as the weight is measured periodically to the nearest milligram. Even liquids are weighed when accuracy is needed. It is much easier to weigh a liquid to 0.001 g than it is to measure it volumetrically to 0.001 mL.

It is often convenient to weigh reagents on glossy weighing paper and then transfer the chemical to the reaction container. The success of an experiment often depends on using just the right amount of starting materials and reagents. Inexperienced workers might think that if 1 mL of a reagent will do the job, then 2 mL will do the job twice as well. Such assumptions are usually erroneous.

Liquids can be measured by either volume or weight according to the following relationship:

$$\text{Volume (mL)} = \frac{\text{weight (g)}}{\text{density (g/mL)}}$$

Modern Erlenmeyer flasks and beakers have approximate volume calibrations fused into the glass, but these are *very* approximate. Better graduations are found on the microscale *reaction tube.* Somewhat more accurate volumetric measurements are made in 10-mL graduated cylinders. For volumes less than 4 mL, use a graduated pipette. **Never** apply suction to a pipette by mouth. The pipette can be fitted with a small plastic syringe using appropriately sized rubber tubing. A Pasteur pipette can be converted into a calibrated pipette with the addition of a plastic syringe (Fig. 1.17d). Figure 1.18 also shows the calibration marks for a 9-in. Pasteur pipette. You will find among your equipment a 1-mL pipette, calibrated in hundredths of a milliliter (Fig. 1.17a). Determine whether it is designed to *deliver* 1 mL or *contain* 1 mL between the top and bottom calibration marks. For our purposes, the latter is the better pipette.

Because the viscosity, surface tension, vapor pressure, and wetting characteristics of organic liquids are different from those of water, the so-called automatic pipette (designed for aqueous solutions) gives poor accuracy in measuring organic liquids. Syringes (Fig. 1.17c and Fig. 1.17d) and pipette pumps (Fig. 1.20), on the other hand, are quite useful, and these will be used frequently. Do not use a syringe that is equipped with a metal needle to measure corrosive reagents because these reagents will dissolve the metal in the needle. Because many reactions are "killed" by traces of moisture, many students' experiments are ruined by damp or wet apparatus. Several reactions that require especially dry or oxygen-free atmospheres will be run in systems sealed with a rubber septum (Fig. 1.17b). Reagents can be added to the system via syringe through this septum to minimize exposure to oxygen or atmospheric moisture.

Careful measurements of weights and volumes take more time than less accurate measurements. Think carefully about which measurements need to be made with accuracy and which do not.

■ **FIG. 1.19**
A funnel for adding solids and
liquids to a reaction tube.

■ **FIG. 1.20**
Using a pipette pump to measure
liquids to ±0.01 mL.

2-mL Pipette
pump

1-mL Pipette
graduated to
± 0.01 mL

Reaction tube

Tares

Tare = weight of empty
container

The tare of a container is its weight when empty. Throughout this laboratory
course, it will be necessary to know the tares of containers so that the weights of
the compounds within can be calculated. If identifying marks can be placed on the
containers (e.g., with a diamond stylus), you may want to record tares for frequently used containers in your laboratory notebook.

To be strictly correct, we should use the word *mass* instead of *weight* because
gravitational acceleration is not constant at all places on earth. But electronic balances record weights, unlike two-pan or triple-beam balances, which record masses.

Washing and Drying
Laboratory Equipment

Washing

Clean apparatus immediately.

Considerable time may be saved by cleaning each piece of equipment soon after use, for you will know at that point which contaminant is present and be
able to select the proper method for its removal. A residue is easier to remove

Both ethanol and acetone are very flammable.

Wash acetone goes in the organic solvents waste container; halogenated solvents go in the halogenated solvents waste container.

■ **FIG. 1.21**
A recrystallization solvent bottle and dispenser.

before it has dried and hardened. A small amount of organic residue can usually be dissolved with a few milliliters of an appropriate organic solvent. Acetone (bp 56.1°C) has great solvent power and is often effective, but it is extremely flammable and somewhat expensive. Because it is miscible with water and vaporizes readily, it is easy to remove from the vessel. Detergent and water can also be used to clean dirty glassware if an appropriate solvent is not found. Cleaning after an operation may often be carried out while another experiment is in process.

A *polyethylene bottle* (Fig. 1.17l) is a convenient wash bottle for acetone. Be careful not to store solvent bottles in the vicinity of the reaction where they can provide additional fuel for an accidental fire. The name, symbol, and formula of a solvent is written on a bottle with a marker or a wax pencil. For macroscale crystallizations, extractions, and quick cleaning of apparatus, it is convenient to have a bottle for each frequently used solvent—95% ethanol, ligroin or hexanes, dichloromethane, ether, and ethyl acetate. A pinhole opposite the spout, which is covered with the finger when in use, will prevent the spout from dribbling the solvent. For microscale work, these solvents are best dispensed from 25-mL or 50-mL bottles with an attached test tube containing a graduated (1-mL) polypropylene pipette (Fig. 1.21). Be aware of any potential hazards stemming from the reactivity of these wash solvents with chemical residues in flasks. Also, be sure to dispose of wash solvents in the proper container. Acetone and most other organic solvents do not contain halogens and can therefore go in the regular organic solvents waste container. However, if dichloromethane or another halogen-containing solvent is used, it must be disposed of in the halogenated solvents waste container.

Sometimes a flask will not be clean after a washing with detergent and acetone. At that point try an abrasive household cleaner. If still no success, try adding dilute acid or base to the dirty glassware, let it soak for a few minutes, and rinse with plenty of water and acetone.

Drying

To dry a piece of apparatus rapidly, rinse with a few milliliters of acetone and invert over a beaker to drain. **Do not use compressed air**, which contains droplets of oil, water, and particles of rust. Instead, draw a slow stream of air through the apparatus using the suction of your water aspirator or house vacuum line.

Miscellaneous Cleanup

If a glass tube or thermometer becomes stuck to a rubber connector, it can be removed by painting on glycerol and forcing the pointed tip of a small spatula between the rubber and the glass. Another method is to select a cork borer that fits snugly over the glass tube, moisten it with glycerol, and slowly work it through the connector. If the stuck object is valuable, such as a thermometer, the best policy is to cut the rubber with a sharp knife. Care should be taken to avoid force that could potentially cause a thermometer to break, causing injury and the release of mercury.

The Laboratory Notebook

The laboratory notebook: What you did. How you did it. What you observed. Your conclusions.

A complete, accurate record is an essential part of all laboratory work. The failure to keep such a record means that laboratory labor is lost. An adequate record includes the procedure (what was done), observations (what happened), and conclusions (what the results mean).

Typically, laboratory personnel use a lined, 8.5 × 11 paperbound notebook and record all data in ink. Never record **anything** on scraps of paper to be recorded later in the notebook. Do not erase, remove, or obliterate notes. The use of whiteout is not good practice either. Simply draw a single line through incorrect entries.

When working in the laboratory, record everything you do and everything you observe **as it happens**. The recorded observations constitute the most important part of the laboratory record; they form the basis for the conclusions you will draw at the end of each experiment. One way to record observations is in a narrative form. Alternatively, the procedure can be written in outline form on the left-hand side of the page, with the observations recorded on the right-hand side.

In some colleges and universities, you will be expected to have all the relevant information about the running of an experiment entered in your notebook *before coming to the laboratory* so that your textbook will not be needed when you are conducting experiments. In industrial laboratories, a notebook may be designed so that carbon copies of all entries are kept. Notebooks are signed and dated by a supervisor, and the carbon copies are removed from the notebook each day and stored in a secure repository. Notebook records become critical legal documents, especially if a discovery turns out to be worth millions of dollars!

Record the physical properties of the product from your experiment, the yield in grams, and the percent yield. Analyze your results. When things did not turn out as expected, explain why. When your record of an experiment is complete, another chemist should be able to understand your account and determine what you did, how you did it, and what conclusions you reached. From the information in your notebook, this person should be able to repeat your work.

The detailed organization and format of your laboratory notebook will depend on your lab instructor's course design and varies from one instructor to another. On the publisher website, you will find an outline for preparing a typical laboratory record and two examples of completed laboratory records.

Online Study Center

General Resources
Laboratory Records

CHAPTER

2

Laboratory Safety, Courtesy, and Waste Disposal

> **PRELAB EXERCISE:** Read this chapter carefully. Locate the emergency eyewash station, the safety shower, the fire extinguisher, and the emergency exits in your laboratory. Check your safety glasses or goggles for size and transparency. Learn which reactions must be carried out in the hood. Learn to use your laboratory fire extinguisher; learn how to summon help and how to put out a clothing fire. Learn first aid procedures for acid and alkali spills on the skin. Learn how to tell if your laboratory hood is working properly. Learn which operations under reduced pressure require special precautions. Check to see that compressed gas cylinders in your lab are firmly fastened to benches or walls. Learn the procedures for properly disposing of solid and liquid waste in your laboratory.

Small-scale (microscale) organic experiments are much safer to conduct than their macroscale counterparts that are run on a scale up to 100 times larger. However, for either microscale or macroscale experiments, the organic chemistry laboratory is an excellent place to learn and practice safety. The commonsense procedures practiced here also apply to other laboratories as well as to the shop, kitchen, and studio.

General laboratory safety information—particularly applicable to this organic chemistry laboratory course—is presented in this chapter. But it is not comprehensive. Throughout this text you will find specific cautions and safety information presented as margin notes printed in red. For a brief and thorough discussion of the topics in this chapter, you should read *Safety in Academic Chemistry Laboratories*.[1] There are also some specific admonitions regarding contact lenses (*see* "Eye Safety").

---

1. American Chemical Society Joint Board-Council Committee on Chemical Safety. *Safety in Academic Chemistry Laboratories, Vol. 1: Accident Prevention for College and University Students,* 7th ed.; American Chemical Society: Washington, DC, 2003.

Important General Rules

- Know the safety rules of your particular laboratory.
- Know the locations of emergency eyewashes, fire extinguishers, safety showers, and emergency exits.
- Never eat, drink, smoke, or apply cosmetics while in the laboratory.
- Wear gloves and aprons when handling corrosive materials.
- Never work alone.

Dress sensibly.

- Perform no unauthorized experiments and do not distract your fellow workers; horseplay has no place in the laboratory.
- Dress properly for lab work. Do not wear open-toed shoes; your feet must be completely covered; wear shoes that have rubber soles and no heels or sneakers. Confine long hair and loose clothes. Do not wear shorts.
- Immediately report any accident to your instructor.
- If the fire extinguisher is used, report this to your instructor.
- Never use mouth suction to fill a pipette.
- Always wash your hands before leaving the laboratory.
- Do not use a solvent to remove a chemical from your skin. This will only hasten the absorption of the chemical through the skin.
- Do not use cell phones or tape, CD, MP3, or similar music players while working in the laboratory.
- Refer to the chemical supplier's hazard warning information or Material Safety Data Sheet (MSDS) when handling a new chemical for the first time.

Eye protection

Eye Safety

Eye protection is extremely important. Safety glasses of some type must be worn at all times. It has been determined "that contact lenses can be worn in most work environments provided the same approved eye protection is worn as required of other workers in the area. Approved eye protection refers to safety glasses or goggles."[2] Chemical splash goggles are the preferred eye protection. One of the most important features of safety glasses/goggles is the brow bar. It is critical to have proper eye protection above the eyes; a brow bar satisfies this requirement for adequate splash protection.

Ordinary prescription eyeglasses do not offer adequate protection. Laboratory safety glasses should be constructed of plastic or tempered glass. If you do not have such glasses, wear goggles that afford protection from splashes and objects coming from the side as well as from the front. If plastic safety glasses are permitted in your laboratory, they should have side shields (Fig. 2.1). Eye safety cannot be overemphasized in the chemistry laboratory.

---

2. Ramsey, H.; and Breazeale, W. H. J. Jr. *Chem. Eng. News* **1998**, *76* (22), 6.

■ **FIG. 2.1**
(a) Chemical splash goggles.
(b) Safety glasses.

Laboratory Courtesy

Please show up on time and be prepared for the day's work. Clean up and leave promptly at the end of the lab period. Clean your desktop and sink before you leave the lab. Be certain that no items such as litmus paper, used filter papers, used cotton, or stir bars collect in the sink. Dispose of all trash properly. Please keep the balances clean. Always replace the caps on reagent bottles after use.

Working with Flammable Substances

Relative flammability of organic solvents.

Flammable substances are the most common hazard in the organic laboratory. Two factors can make today's organic laboratory much safer than its predecessor: (1) making the scale of the experiments as small as possible and (2) not using flames. Diethyl ether (bp 35°C), the most flammable substance you will usually work with in this course, has an ignition temperature of 160°C, which means that a hot plate at that temperature will cause it to burn. For comparison, *n*-hexane (bp 69°C), a constituent of gasoline, has an ignition temperature of 225°C. The flash points of these organic liquids—that is, the temperatures at which they will catch fire if exposed to a flame or spark—are below -20°C. These are very flammable liquids; however, if you are careful to eliminate all possible sources of ignition, they are not difficult to work with. Except for water, almost all of the liquids you will use in the laboratory are flammable.

■ **FIG. 2.2**
Solvent safety can.

Bulk solvents should be stored in and dispensed from safety cans (Fig. 2.2). These and other liquids will burn in the presence of the proper amount of their flammable vapors, oxygen, and a source of ignition (most commonly a flame or spark). It is usually difficult to remove oxygen from a fire, although it is possible to put out a fire in a beaker or a flask by simply covering the vessel with a flat object, thus cutting off the supply of air. Your lab notebook might do in an emergency. The best prevention is to pay close attention to sources of ignition—open flames, sparks, and hot surfaces. Remember, the vapors of flammable liquids are **always** heavier than air and thus will travel along bench tops, down drain troughs, and remain in sinks. For this reason all flames within the vicinity of a flammable liquid must be extinguished. Adequate ventilation is one of the best ways to prevent flammable vapors from accumulating. Work in an exhaust hood when manipulating large quantities of flammable liquids.

Flammable vapors travel along bench tops.

CAUTION: Keep ignition sources away from flammable liquids.

If a person's clothing catches fire and there is a safety shower close at hand, then shove the person under it and turn the shower on. Otherwise, push the person down and roll him or her over to extinguish the flames (stop, drop, and roll!). It is extremely important to prevent the victim from running or standing because the greatest harm comes from breathing the hot vapors that rise past the mouth. The safety shower

Flammable vapors plus air
in a confined space are
explosive.

might then be used to extinguish glowing cloth that is no longer aflame. A so-called fire blanket should not be used because it tends to funnel flames past the victim's mouth, and clothing continues to char beneath it. It is, however, useful for retaining warmth to ward off shock after the flames are extinguished.

An organic chemistry laboratory should be equipped with a carbon dioxide or dry chemical (monoammonium phosphate) *fire extinguisher* (Fig. 2.3). To use this type of extinguisher, lift it from its support, pull the ring to break the seal, raise the horn, aim it at the base of the fire, and squeeze the handle. Do not hold on to the horn because it will become extremely cold. Do not replace the extinguisher; report the incident so the extinguisher can be refilled.

When disposing of certain chemicals, be alert for the possibility of *spontaneous combustion*. This may occur in oily rags; organic materials exposed to strong oxidizing agents such as nitric acid, permanganate ion, and peroxides; alkali metals such as sodium; or very finely divided metals such as zinc dust and platinum catalysts. Fires sometimes start when these chemicals are left in contact with filter paper.

Working with Hazardous Chemicals

If you do not know the properties of a chemical you will be working with, it is wise to regard the chemical as hazardous. The *flammability* of organic substances poses the most serious hazard in the organic laboratory. There is a possibility that storage containers in the laboratory may contribute to a fire. Large quantities of organic solvents should not be stored in glass bottles; they should be stored in solvent safety cans. Do not store chemicals on the floor.

A flammable liquid can often be vaporized to form, with air, a mixture that is explosive in a confined space. The beginning chemist is sometimes surprised to learn that diethyl ether is more likely to cause a laboratory fire or explosion than a worker's accidental anesthesia. The chances of being confined in a laboratory with a concentration of ether high enough to cause a loss of consciousness are extremely small, but a spark in such a room would probably destroy the building.

The probability of forming an explosive mixture of volatile organic liquids with air is far greater than that of producing an explosive solid or liquid. The chief functional groups that render compounds explosive are the *peroxide, acetylide, azide, diazonium, nitroso, nitro*, and *ozonide* groups (Fig. 2.4). Not all members of

■ **FIG. 2.4**
Functional groups that can be
explosive in some compounds.

$$R-O-O-R \qquad R-C\equiv C-\text{Metal}$$

Peroxide   **Acetylide**

$$R-N=N=N \qquad R-NO_2$$

Azide   **Nitro**

$$R-N=O \qquad R-\overset{+}{N}\equiv N$$

Nitroso   **Diazonium salts**   **Ozonide**

these groups are equally sensitive to shock or heat. You would find it difficult to detonate trinitrotoluene (TNT) in the laboratory, but nitroglycerine is treacherously explosive. Peroxides present special problems that are discussed in the next section.

Safety glasses or goggles must be worn at all times.

You will need to contend with the corrosiveness of many of the reagents you will handle. The principal danger here is to the eyes. Proper eye protection is mandatory, and even small-scale experiments can be hazardous to the eyes. It takes only a single drop of a corrosive reagent to do permanent damage. Handling concentrated acids and alkalis, dehydrating agents, and oxidizing agents calls for commonsense care to avoid spills and splashes and to avoid breathing the often corrosive vapors.

Certain organic chemicals present acute toxicity problems from short-duration exposure and chronic toxicity problems from long-term or repeated exposure. Exposure can result from ingestion, contact with the skin, or, most commonly, inhalation. Currently, great attention is being focused on chemicals that are teratogens (chemicals that often have no effect on a pregnant woman but cause abnormalities in a fetus), mutagens (chemicals causing changes in the structure of the DNA, which can lead to mutations in offspring), and carcinogens (cancer-causing chemicals). Small-scale experiments significantly reduce these hazards but do not completely eliminate them.

Working with Explosive Hazards

1. Peroxides

Ethers form explosive peroxides.

Certain functional groups can make an organic molecule become sensitive to heat and shock, such that it will explode. Chemists work with these functional groups only when there are no good alternatives. One of these functional groups, the peroxide group (R—O—O—R), is particularly insidious because it can form spontaneously when oxygen and light are present (Fig. 2.5). Ethers, especially cyclic ethers and those made from primary or secondary alcohols (such as tetrahydrofuran, diethyl ether, and diisopropyl ether), form peroxides. Other compounds that form peroxides are aldehydes, alkenes that have allylic hydrogen atoms (such as cyclohexene), compounds having benzylic hydrogens on a

■ FIG. 2.5
Some compounds that form peroxides.

Tetrahydrofuran   **Diisopropyl ether**   **Dioxane**   **Benzylic compounds**   **Ketones**

Cyclohexene   **Vinyl acetate**   **Allylic compounds**   **Aldehydes**

tertiary carbon atom (such as isopropyl benzene), and vinyl compounds (such as vinyl acetate). Peroxides are low-power explosives but are extremely sensitive to shock, sparks, light, heat, friction, and impact. The greatest danger from peroxide impurities comes when the peroxide-forming compound is distilled. The peroxide has a higher boiling point than the parent compound and remains in the distilling flask as a residue that can become overheated and explode. For this reason, one should never distill a liquid until the distilling flask is completely dry, and the distillation should be run in a hood with the sash down to help contain a possible explosion.

Never distill to dryness.

The Detection of Peroxides	The Removal of Peroxides
To a solution of 0.01 g of sodium iodide in 0.1 mL of glacial acetic acid, add 0.1 mL of the liquid suspected of containing a peroxide. If the mixture turns brown, a high concentration of peroxide is present; if it turns yellow, a low concentration of peroxide is present.	Pouring the solvent through a column of activated alumina will remove peroxides and simultaneously dry the solvent. Do not allow the column to dry out while in use. When the alumina column is no longer effective, wash the column with 5% aqueous ferrous sulfate and discard the column as nonhazardous waste.

Problems with peroxide formation are especially critical for ethers. Ethers (R-O-R′) form peroxides readily. Because ethers are frequently used as solvents, they are often used in quantity and then removed to leave reaction products. Cans of diethyl ether should be dated when opened. If opened cans are not used within one month, they should be treated for peroxides and disposed of.

t-Butyl methyl ether, $(CH_3)_3C-O-CH_3$, with a primary carbon on one side of the oxygen and a tertiary carbon on the other does not form peroxides easily. It is highly desirable to use this in place of diethyl ether for extraction. Refer to the discussion in Chapter 7.

You may have occasion to use *30% hydrogen peroxide*. This material causes severe burns if it contacts the skin and decomposes violently if contaminated with metals or their salts. Be particularly careful not to contaminate the reagent bottle.

2. Closed Systems

A closed system is defined as not being open to the atmosphere. Any sealed system is a closed system. If a closed system is not properly prepared, an explosion may result from the system being under pressure, caused from gas or heat evolution from the reaction or from applied heat to the system. One way to prevent an explosion of a closed system is to use glassware that can withstand the pressure and to evacuate the system under vacuum before it is closed to the atmosphere.

Most reactions are run in open systems; that is, they are run in apparatus that are open to atmosphere, either directly or through a nitrogen line hooked up to a bubbler, which is open to atmosphere.

Working with Corrosive Substances

Handle strong acids, alkalis, dehydrating agents, and oxidizing agents carefully so as to avoid contact with the skin and eyes and to avoid breathing the corrosive vapors that attack the respiratory tract. All strong, concentrated acids attack the skin and eyes. *Concentrated sulfuric acid* is both a dehydrating agent and a strong acid and will cause very severe burns. *Nitric acid* and *chromic acid* (used in cleaning solutions) also cause bad burns. *Hydrofluoric acid* is especially harmful and causes deep, painful, and slow-healing wounds. It should be used only after thorough instruction. You should wear approved safety glasses or goggles, protective gloves, and an apron when handling these materials.

Add H_2SO4, P_2O_5, CaO, and NaOH to water, not the reverse.

Sodium, potassium, and ammonium hydroxides are common bases that you will encounter. Sodium and potassium hydroxides are extremely damaging to the eyes, and ammonium hydroxide is a severe bronchial irritant. Like sulfuric acid, sodium hydroxide, phosphorous pentoxide, and calcium oxide are powerful dehydrating agents. Their great affinity for water will cause burns to the skin. Because they release a great deal of heat when they react with water, to avoid spattering they should always be added to water rather than water being added to them. That is, the heavier substance should always be added to the lighter one so that rapid mixing results as a consequence of the law of gravity.

You will receive special instructions when it comes time to handle metallic sodium, lithium aluminum hydride, and sodium hydride, three substances that can react explosively with water.

Among the strong oxidizing agents, *perchloric acid* ($HClO_4$) is probably the most hazardous. It can form heavy metal and organic *perchlorates* that are *explosive*, and it can react explosively if it comes in contact with organic compounds.

If one of these substances gets on the skin or in the eyes, wash the affected area with very large quantities of water, using the safety shower and/or eyewash station (Fig. 2.6) until medical assistance arrives. Do not attempt to neutralize the reagent chemically. Remove contaminated clothing so that thorough washing can take place. Take care to wash the reagent from under the fingernails.

Wipe up spilled hydroxide pellets *rapidly.*

Take care not to let the reagents, such as sulfuric acid, run down the outside of a bottle or flask and come in contact with your fingers. Wipe up spills immediately with a very damp sponge, especially in the area around the balances. Pellets of sodium and potassium hydroxide are very hygroscopic and will dissolve in the water they pick up from the air; they should therefore be wiped up very quickly. When handling large quantities of corrosive chemicals, wear protective gloves, a face mask, and a neoprene apron. The corrosive vapors can be avoided by carrying out work in a good exhaust hood.

Do not use a plastic syringe with a metal needle to dispense corrosive inorganic reagents, such as concentrated acids or bases.

Working with Toxic Substances

Many chemicals have very specific toxic effects. They interfere with the body's metabolism in a known way. For example, the cyanide ion combines irreversibly with hemoglobin to form cyanometmyoglobin, which can no longer carry oxygen.

■ **FIG. 2.6**
Emergency shower and eyewash station.

Aniline acts in the same way. Carbon tetrachloride and other halogenated compounds can cause liver and kidney failure. Carcinogenic and mutagenic substances deserve special attention because of their long-term insidious effects. The ability of certain carcinogens to cause cancer is very great; for example, special precautions are needed when handling aflatoxin B_1. In other cases, such as with dioxane, the hazard is so low that no special precautions are needed beyond reasonable, normal care in the laboratory.

Women of childbearing age should be careful when handling any substance of unknown properties. Certain substances are highly suspected as teratogens and will cause abnormalities in an embryo or fetus. Among these are benzene, toluene, xylene, aniline, nitrobenzene, phenol, formaldehyde, dimethylformamide (DMF), dimethyl sulfoxide (DMSO), polychlorinated biphenyls (PCBs), estradiol, hydrogen sulfide, carbon disulfide, carbon monoxide, nitrites, nitrous oxide, organolead and mercury compounds, and the notorious sedative thalidomide. Some of these substances will be used in subsequent experiments. Use care when working with these (and all) substances. Of course, the leading known cause of embryotoxic effects is ethyl alcohol in the form of maternal alcoholism. The amount of ethanol vapor inhaled in the laboratory or absorbed through the skin is so minute that it is unlikely to have morbid effects.

It is impossible to avoid handling every known or suspected toxic substance, so it is wise to know what measures should be taken. Because the eating of food or the consumption of beverages in the laboratory is strictly forbidden and because one should never taste material in the laboratory, the possibility of poisoning by mouth is remote. Be more careful than your predecessors—the hallucinogenic properties of LSD and **all** artificial sweeteners were discovered by accident. The two most important measures to be taken, then, are (1) avoiding skin contact by wearing the *proper* type of protective gloves (*see* "Gloves") and (2) avoiding inhalation by working in a good exhaust hood.

Many of the chemicals used in this course will be unfamiliar to you. Their properties can be looked up in reference books, a very useful one being the *Aldrich Handbook of Fine Chemicals*.[3] Note that 1,4-dichlorobenzene is listed as a "toxic irritant" and naphthalene is listed as an "irritant." Both are used as mothballs. Camphor, used in vaporizers, is classified as a "flammable solid irritant." Salicylic acid, which we will use to synthesize aspirin (Chapter 41), is listed as a "moisture-sensitive toxic." Aspirin (acetylsalicylic acid) is classified as an "irritant." Caffeine, which we will isolate from tea or cola syrup (Chapter 7), is classified as "toxic." Substances not so familiar to you, for example, 1-naphthol and benzoic acid, are classified, respectively, as "toxic irritant" and "irritant." To put things in perspective, nicotine is classified as "highly toxic." Pay attention to these health warnings. In laboratory quantities, common chemicals can be hazardous. Wash your hands carefully after coming in contact with laboratory chemicals. Consult the *Hazardous Laboratory Chemicals Disposal Guide*[4] for information on truly hazardous chemicals.

3. Free copies of this catalog can be obtained from http://www.sigmaaldrich.com/Brands/Aldrich.html.

4. Armour, M-A. *Hazardous Laboratory Chemicals Disposal Guide*, 3rd ed.; CRC Press LLC: Boca Raton, FL, 2003.

Because you have not had previous experience working with organic chemicals, most of the experiments you will carry out in this course will not involve the use of known carcinogens, although you will work routinely with flammable, corrosive, and toxic substances. A few experiments involve the use of substances that are suspected of being carcinogenic, such as hydrazine. If you pay proper attention to the rules of safety, you should find working with these substances no more hazardous than working with ammonia or nitric acid. The single, short-duration exposure you might receive from a suspected carcinogen, should an accident occur, would probably have no long-term consequences. The reason for taking the precautions noted in each experiment is to learn, from the beginning, good safety habits.

Gloves

Be aware that protective gloves in the organic laboratory may not offer much protection. Polyethylene and latex rubber gloves are very permeable to many organic liquids. An undetected pinhole may bring with it long-term contact with reagents. Disposable polyvinyl chloride (PVC) gloves offer reasonable protection from contact with aqueous solutions of acids, bases, and dyes, but no one type of glove is useful as a protection against all reagents. It is for this reason that no less than 25 different types of chemically resistant gloves are available from laboratory supply houses. Some gloves are quite expensive and will last for years.

If disposable gloves are available, fresh nitrile gloves can be worn whenever handling a corrosive substance and disposed of once the transfer is complete. When not wearing gloves, it is advised that you wash your hands every 15 min to remove any traces of chemicals that might be on them.

Using the Laboratory Hood

Modern practice dictates that in laboratories where workers spend most of their time working with chemicals, there should be one exhaust hood for every two people. This precaution is often not possible in the beginning organic chemistry laboratory, however. In this course you will find that for some experiments the hood must be used and for others it is advisable; in these instances, it may be necessary to schedule experimental work around access to the hoods. Many experiments formerly carried out in the hood can now be carried out at the lab desk because the concentration of vapors is significantly minimized when working at a microscale.

The hood offers a number of advantages when working with toxic and flammable substances. Not only does it draw off the toxic and flammable fumes, but it also affords an excellent physical barrier on all four sides of a reacting system when the sash is pulled down. If a chemical spill occurs, it may be contained within the hood.

Keep the hood sash closed.

It is your responsibility each time you use a hood to see that it is working properly. You should find some type of indicating device that will give you this information on the hood itself. A simple propeller on a cork works well. The hood is a backup device. Never use it alone to dispose of chemicals by evaporation; use an aspirator tube or carry out a distillation. Toxic and flammable fumes should be trapped or condensed in some way and disposed of in the prescribed manner. The sash should be pulled down unless you are actually carrying out manipulations on the experimental apparatus. The water, gas, and electrical controls should be on the outside of the hood so it is not necessary to open the hood to make adjustments. The ability of the hood to remove vapors is greatly enhanced if the apparatus is kept as close to the back of the hood as possible. Everything should be at least 15 cm back from the hood sash. Chemicals should not be permanently stored in the hood but should be removed to ventilated storage areas. If the hood is cluttered with chemicals, you will not achieve a good, smooth airflow or have adequate room for experiments.

Working at Reduced Pressure

Whenever a vessel or system is evacuated, an implosion could result from atmospheric pressure on the empty vessel. It makes little difference whether the vacuum is perfect or just 10 mm Hg; the pressure difference is almost the same (760 versus 750 mm Hg). An implosion may occur if there is a star crack in the flask or if the flask is scratched or etched. Only with heavy-walled flasks specifically designed for vacuum filtration is the use of a safety shield (Fig. 2.7) ordinarily unnecessary. The chances of implosion of the apparatus used for microscale experiments are remote.

Implosion

Dewar flasks (thermos bottles) are often found in the laboratory without shielding. These should be wrapped with friction tape or covered with a plastic net to prevent the glass from flying about in case of an implosion (Fig. 2.8). Similarly, vacuum desiccators should be wrapped with tape before being evacuated.

■ **FIG. 2.7**
Safety shield.

■ **FIG. 2.8**
Dewar flask with safety net in place.

Working with Compressed Gas Cylinders

Many reactions are carried out under an inert atmosphere so that the reactants and/or products will not react with oxygen or moisture in the air. Nitrogen and argon are the inert gases most frequently used. Oxygen is widely used both as a reactant and to provide a hot flame for glassblowing and welding. It is used in the oxidative coupling of alkynes (Chapter 24). Helium is the carrier gas used in gas chromatography. Other gases commonly used in the laboratory are ammonia, often used as a solvent; chlorine, used for chlorination reactions; acetylene, used in combination with oxygen for welding; and hydrogen, used for high- and low-pressure hydrogenation reactions.

The following rule applies to all compressed gases: Compressed gas cylinders should be firmly secured at all times. For temporary use, a clamp that attaches to the laboratory bench top and has a belt for the cylinder will suffice (Fig. 2.9). Eyebolts and chains should be used to secure cylinders in permanent installations. Flammable gases should be stored 20 ft from oxidizing gases.

A variety of outlet threads are used on gas cylinders to prevent incompatible gases from being mixed because of an interchange of connections. Both right- and left-handed external and internal threads are used. Left-handed nuts are notched to differentiate them from right-handed nuts. Right-handed threads are used on non-fuel and oxidizing gases, and left-handed threads are used on fuel gases, such as hydrogen. Never grease the threads on tank or regulator valves.

Cylinders come equipped with caps that should be left in place during storage and transportation. These caps can be removed by hand. Under these caps is a cylinder valve. It can be opened by turning the valve counterclockwise; however, because most compressed gases in full cylinders are under very high pressure (commonly up to 3000 lb/in.^{2}), a pressure regulator must be attached to the cylinder. This pressure regulator is almost always of the diaphragm type and has two gauges, one indicating the pressure in the cylinder, the other the outlet pressure (Fig. 2.10). On the outlet, low-pressure side of the regulator is a small needle valve and then the outlet connector. After connecting the regulator to the cylinder,

Always clamp gas cylinders.

■ **FIG. 2.9**
Gas cylinder clamp.

Hand-wheel valve

■ **FIG. 2.10**
Gas pressure regulator. Turn two-flanged diaphragm valve clockwise to increase outlet pressure.

Clockwise movement of diaphragm valve handle *increases* pressure.

Outlet pressure gauge

Cylinder pressure gauge

Needle valve

Outlet

Notches indicating left-hand thread

Diaphragm valve

■ **FIG. 2.11**
Gas cylinder cart.

Cap

Never attempt to identify an
unknown organic compound by
smelling it.

Clean up spills rapidly.

Mercury requires special
measures—see your instructor.

unscrew the diaphragm valve (turn it counterclockwise) before opening the cylinder valve on the top of the cylinder. This valve should be opened only as far as necessary. For most gas flow rates in the laboratory, this will be a very small amount. The gas flow or pressure is increased by turning the two-flanged diaphragm valve **clockwise**. When the apparatus is not being used, turn off the cylinder valve (clockwise) on the top of the cylinder (Fig. 2.9). Before removing the regulator from the cylinder, reduce the flow or pressure to zero. Cylinders should never be emptied to zero pressure and left with the valve open because the residual contents will become contaminated with air. Empty cylinders should be labeled "empty." Their valves should be closed and capped, and the cylinders should be returned to the storage area and separated from full cylinders. Gas cylinders should never be dragged or rolled from place to place but should be fastened onto and moved in a cart designed for that purpose (Fig. 2.11). The cap should be in place whenever the cylinder is moved. If you detect even a small leak from any valve or connection, immediately seek the help of an instructor to remedy the problem. If there is a major leak of a corrosive or flammable gas, notify those around you to leave the area and seek help immediately.

Odoriferous Chemicals

Some organic chemicals just smell bad. Among these are the thiols (organic derivatives of hydrogen sulfide), isonitriles, many amines (e.g., cadaverine), and butyric acid. Washing apparatus and, if necessary, hands in a solution of a quaternary ammonium salt may solve the problem. These compounds apparently complex with many odoriferous substances, allowing them to be rinsed away. Commercial products (e.g., Zephiran, Roccal, San-O-Fec, and others) are available at pet and farm supply stores.

Waste Disposal–Cleaning Up

Spilled solids should simply be swept up and placed in the appropriate solid waste container. This should be done promptly because many solids are hygroscopic and become difficult if not impossible to sweep up in a short time. This is particularly true of sodium hydroxide and potassium hydroxide; these strong bases should be dissolved in water and neutralized with sodium bisulfate before disposal.

The method used to clean up spills depends on the type and amount of chemical spilled. If more than 1 or 2 g or mL of any chemical, particularly a corrosive or volatile one, is spilled, you should consult your instructor for the best way to clean up the spill. If a large amount of volatile or noxious liquid is spilled as might happen if a reagent bottle is dropped and broken, advise those in the area to leave the laboratory and contact your instructor immediately. If a spill involves a large amount of flammable liquid, be aware of any potential ignition sources and try to eliminate them. Large amounts of spilled acid can be neutralized with granular limestone or cement; large amounts of bases with solid sodium bisulfate, $NaHSO_4$. Large amounts of volatile liquids can be absorbed into materials such as vermiculite, diatomaceous earth, dry sand, kitty litter, or paper towels and these materials swept up and placed in a separate disposal container.

For spills of amounts less than 2 g of chemical, proceed as follows. Acid spills should be neutralized by dropping solid sodium carbonate onto them, testing the pH, wiping up the neutralized material with a sponge, and rinsing the neutral salt solution down the drain. Bases should be neutralized by sprinkling solid sodium bisulfate onto them, checking the pH, and wiping up with a sponge or towel. Do not use paper towels to wipe up spills of strong oxidizers such as dichromates or nitrates; the towels can ignite. Bits of sodium metal will also cause paper towels to ignite. Sodium metal is best destroyed with *n*-butyl alcohol. Always wear goves when cleaning up a spill.

Cleaning Up

In the not-too-distant past it was common practice to wash all unwanted liquids from the organic laboratory down the drain and to place all solid waste in the trash basket. For environmental reasons, this is never a wise practice and is no longer allowed by law.

Organic reactions usually employ a solvent and often involve the use of a strong acid, a strong base, an oxidant, a reductant, or a catalyst. None of these should be washed down the drain or placed in the wastebasket. Place the material, classified as waste, in containers labeled for nonhazardous solid waste, organic solvents, halogenated organic solvents, or hazardous wastes of various types.

Waste containers:
Nonhazardous solid waste
Organic solvents
Halogenated organic solvents
Hazardous waste (various types)

Nonhazardous waste encompasses such solids as paper, corks, TLC plates, solid chromatographic absorbents such as alumina or silica that are dry and free of residual organic solvents, and solid drying agents such as calcium chloride or sodium sulfate that are also dry and free of residual organic solvents. These will ultimately end up in a sanitary landfill (the local dump). Any chemicals that are leached by rainwater from this landfill must not be harmful to the environment. In the *organic solvents* container are placed the solvents that are used for recrystallization and for running reactions, cleaning apparatus, and so forth. These solvents can contain dissolved, solid, nonhazardous organic solids. This solution will go to an incinerator where it will be burned. If the solvent is halogenated (e.g., dichloromethane) or contains halogenated material, it must go in the *halogenated organic solvents* container. Ultimately, this will go to a special incinerator equipped with a scrubber to remove HCl from the combustion gases. The organic laboratory should also have several other waste disposal containers for special hazardous, reactive, and noncombustible wastes that would be incompatible with waste organic solvents and other materials. For example, it would be dangerous to place oxidants in lysts with many organics. In particular, separate waste containers should be provided for toxic heavy metal wastes containing mercury, chromium, or lead salts, and so forth. The cleaning up sections throughout this text will call your attention to these special hazards.

Hazardous wastes such as sodium hydrosulfite (a reducing agent), platinum catalysts, and Cr^{6+} (an oxidizing agent) cannot be burned and must be shipped to a secure landfill. To dispose of small quantities of a hazardous waste (e.g., solid mercury hydroxide), the material must be carefully packed in bottles and placed in a 55-gal ($\approx$208-L) drum called a lab pack, to which an inert material has been added. The lab pack is carefully documented and hauled off to a site where such waste is disposed of by a bonded, licensed, and heavily regulated waste disposal company. Formerly, many hazardous wastes were disposed of by burial in a secure landfill.

The kinds of hazardous waste that can be thus disposed of have become extremely limited in recent years, and much of the waste undergoes various kinds of treatment at the disposal site (e.g., neutralization, incineration, or reduction) to put it in a form that can be safely buried in a secure landfill or flushed to a sewer. There are relatively few places for approved disposal of hazardous waste. For example, there are none in New England, so most hazardous waste from this area is trucked to South Carolina. The charge to small generators of waste is usually based on the volume of waste. So, 1000 mL of a 2% cyanide solution would cost far more to dispose of than 20 g of solid cyanide, even though the total amount of this poisonous substance is the same. It now costs far more to dispose of most hazardous chemicals than it does to purchase them new.

American law states that a material is not a waste until the laboratory worker declares it a waste. So—for pedagogical and practical reasons—we want you to regard the chemical treatment of the byproducts of each reaction in this text as a part of the experiment.

In the section titled "Cleaning Up" at the end of each experiment, the goal is to reduce the volume of hazardous waste, to convert hazardous waste to less hazardous waste, or to convert it to nonhazardous waste. The simplest example is concentrated sulfuric acid. As a byproduct from a reaction, it is obviously hazardous. But after careful dilution with water and neutralization with sodium carbonate, the sulfuric acid becomes a dilute solution of sodium sulfate, which in almost every locale can be flushed down the drain with a large quantity of water. Anything flushed down the drain must be accompanied by a large excess of water. Similarly, concentrated bases can be neutralized, oxidants such as Cr^{6+} can be reduced, and reductants such as hydrosulfite can be oxidized (by hypochlorite or household bleach). Dilute solutions of heavy metal ions can be precipitated as their insoluble sulfides or hydroxides. The precipitate may still be a hazardous waste, but it will have a much smaller volume.

One type of hazardous waste is unique: a harmless solid that is damp with an organic solvent. Alumina from a chromatography column and calcium chloride used to dry an ether solution are examples. Being solids, they obviously cannot go in the organic solvents container, and being flammable they cannot go in the nonhazardous waste container. A solution to this problem is to spread the solid out in the hood to let the solvent evaporate. You can then place the solid in the nonhazardous waste container. The savings in waste disposal costs by this operation are enormous. However, be aware of the regulations in your area as they may not allow evaporation of small amounts of organic solvents in a hood. If this is the case, special containers should be available for disposal of these wet solids.

Our goal in "Cleaning Up" is to make you more aware of *all* aspects of an experiment. Waste disposal is now an extremely important aspect. Check to be sure the procedure you use is permitted by law in your location. Three sources of information have been used as the basis of the procedures at the end of each experiment: the *Aldrich Catalog Handbook of Fine Chemicals*,[5] which gives brief

---

5. See footnote 3 on page 30.

disposal procedures for every chemical in their catalog; *Prudent Practices in the Laboratory: Handling and Disposal of Chemicals*[6]; and the *Hazardous Laboratory Chemicals Disposal Guide.*[7] The last title listed here should be on the bookshelf of every laboratory. This 464-page book gives detailed information about hundreds of hazardous substances, including their physical properties, hazardous reactions, physiological properties, health hazards, spillage disposal, and waste disposal. Many of the treatment procedures in "Cleaning Up" are adaptations of these procedures. *Destruction of Hazardous Chemicals in the Laboratory*[8] complements this book.

The area of waste disposal is changing rapidly. Many levels of laws apply—local, state, and federal. What may be permissible to wash down the drain or evaporate in the hood in one jurisdiction may be illegal in another, so before carrying out any waste disposal, check with your college or university waste disposal officer.

Biohazards

The use of microbial growth bioassays is becoming common in chemistry laboratories. The use of infectious materials presents new hazards that must be recognized and addressed. The first step in reducing hazards when using these materials is to select infectious materials that are known not to cause illness in humans and are of minimal hazard to the environment. A number of procedures should be followed to make use of these materials safe: Individuals need to wash hands after they handle these materials and before they leave the laboratory; work surfaces need to be decontaminated at the end of each use; and all infectious materials need to be decontaminated before disposal.

QUESTIONS

1. Write a balanced equation for the reaction between the iodide ion, a peroxide, and the hydrogen ion. What causes the orange or brown color?
2. Why does the horn of the carbon dioxide fire extinguisher become cold when the extinguisher is used?
3. Why is water *not* used to extinguish most fires in an organic laboratory?

6. National Research Council. *Prudent Practices in the Laboratory: Handling and Disposal of Chemicals* National Academy Press: Washington, DC, 1995.

7. See footnote 4 on page 30.

8. Lunn, G.; Sansone, E. B. *Destruction of Hazardous Chemicals in the Laboratory*; Wiley: New York, 1994.

Melting Points and Boiling Points

Online Study Center

This icon will direct you to techniques, equipment setups, and online resources at http://college. hmco.com/PIC/ williamsonMMOE5e.

PRELAB EXERCISE: Draw the structure of each of the following organic compounds, identify the intermolecular attractive forces for each, and list them in order of increasing boiling point as predicted by the relative strength of those intermolecular forces: (a) acetaldehyde, (b) sodium formate, (c) ethanol, and (d) propane.

PART 1: Five Concepts for Predicting Physical Properties

In organic chemistry, structure is everything. A molecule's structure determines both its physical properties and its reactivity. Since the dawn of modern chemistry 200 years ago, over 20 million substances, most of them organic compounds, have been isolated, and their properties and reactions have been studied. It became apparent from these studies that certain structural features in organic molecules would affect the observed properties in a predictable way and that these millions of organic compounds could be organized into classes based on molecular size, composition, and the pattern of bonds between atoms. Chemists also saw trends in certain properties based on systematic changes in these structural features. This organized knowledge allows us to look at a compound's structure and to predict the physical properties of that compound.

Physical properties, such as melting point, boiling point, and solubility, are largely determined by *intermolecular attractive forces.* You learned about these properties in previous chemistry courses. Because a solid understanding of these concepts is critical to understanding organic chemistry, we will review the different types of forces in the context of structural organic chemistry. Using five simple concepts, you should be able to look at the structures of a group of different organic molecules and predict which might be liquids, gases, or solids and which might be soluble in water. You can often predict the boiling point, melting point, or solubility of one structure relative to other structures. In fact, as your knowledge grows, you may be able to predict a compound's approximate melting or boiling temperature based on its structure. Your understanding of intermolecular attractive forces will be very useful in this chapter's experiments on melting and boiling points and those in Chapters 5 and 6 that involve distillation and boiling points.

1. London Attractive Forces (Often Called Van der Waals Forces)

Organic molecules that contain only carbon and hydrogen (hydrocarbons) are weakly attracted to each other by London forces. Though weak, these attractive forces increase as molecular size increases. Thus, the larger the molecule, the greater the attractive force for neighboring molecules and the greater the energy required to get two molecules to move apart. This trend can be seen if we compare

CH_4

Methane
mp −182°C
bp −162°C
Gas at room temp.

Hexane, C_6H_{14}
mp −95°C
bp +69°C
Liquid at room temp.

Tetracosane, $C_{24}H_{50}$
mp +51°C
bp +391°C
Solid at room temp.

the melting points and boiling points of three hydrocarbons of different size: methane, hexane, and tetracosane.

We know that methane is called natural gas because methane's physical state at room temperature ($20°C = 68°F$) is a gas. Its London forces are so weak that methane must be cooled to $-162°C$ at 1 atm of pressure before the molecules will stick together enough to form a liquid. Hexane is a very common liquid solvent found on most organic laboratory shelves. The intermolecular forces between its molecules are strong enough to keep them from flying apart, but the molecules are still able to flex and slide by each other to form a fluid. Hexane must be heated above $69°C$, which is $231°C$ hotter than methane, to convert all its molecules to a gas. Tetracosane, a C_{24} solid hydrocarbon, is four times larger than hexane, and its London forces are strong enough to hold the molecules rigidly in place at room temperature. Tetracosane is one of the many long-chain hydrocarbons found in candle wax, which must be heated in order to disrupt the intermolecular forces and melt the wax into a liquid. A lot of energy is required to convert liquid tetracosane to a gas, as evidenced by its extremely high boiling point ($391°C$).

2. Dipole-Dipole Attractive Forces

The attractive forces between molecules increases when functional groups containing electronegative atoms such as chlorine, oxygen, and nitrogen are present because these atoms are more electronegative than carbon. These atoms pull electrons toward themselves, making their end of the bond slightly negatively charged (δ^-) and leaving the carbon slightly positively charged (δ^+), as shown for isopropyl chloride and acetone.

Isobutane
mp $-137°C$
bp $0°C$
Gas at room temp.

Isopropyl chloride
mp $-117°C$
bp $+35°C$
Liquid at room temp.

Acetone
mp $-94°C$
bp $+56°C$
Liquid at room temp.

A bond with a slight charge separation is termed a *polar* bond, and polar bonds often give a molecule a *dipole*: slightly positive and negative ends symbolized by an arrow in the direction of the negative charge ($+\!\!\rightarrow$). Attraction of the positive end of one molecule's dipole to the negative end of another's dipole occurs between polar molecules, which increases the intermolecular attractive force. Dipole-dipole attractive forces are stronger than London forces, as demonstrated in the previous examples that show an increase in melting point and boiling point when a methyl group of isobutane is replaced by chlorine or oxygen.

3. Hydrogen Bonding

Hydrogen bonding is an even stronger intermolecular attractive force, as evidenced by the large increase in the melting point and boiling points of the alcohol methanol (MW = 32) relative to those of the hydrocarbon ethane (MW = 30), both of comparable molecular weight. Hydrogen bonding occurs with organic molecules containing O—H groups (for example, alcohols and carboxylic acids) or N—H groups (for example, amines or amides). The hydrogen in these groups is attracted to the unshared pair of electrons on the O or N of another molecule, forming a hydrogen bond, often symbolized by a dashed line, which is shown for methanol.

CH_3-CH_3

Ethane
mp –172°C
bp –88°C
Gas at room temp.

Methanol
mp –97°C
bp +65°C
Liquid at room temp.

As this example indicates, the hydrogen bonds extend throughout the liquid.

One can think of these hydrogen bonds as molecular Velcro that can be pulled apart if there is sufficient energy. Hydrogen bonding plays a major role in the special physical behavior of water and is a major determinant of the chemistry of proteins and nucleic acids in living systems.

4. Ionic Attractive Forces

Recall that ionic substances, such as table salt (NaCl), are usually solids with high melting points (>300°C) due to the strong attractive forces between positive and negative ions. Most organic molecules contain only covalent bonds and have no ionic attractive forces between them. However, there are three important exceptions involving acidic or basic functional groups that can form ionic structures as the pH is raised or lowered.

1. The hydrogen on the —OH of the carboxyl group in carboxylic acids, such as acetic acid, is acidic (H^+ donating) and reacts with bases such as potassium hydroxide (KOH) and sodium bicarbonate ($NaHCO_3$) to form salts. The process is reversed by lowering the pH by adding an acid.

Potassium acetate   Acetic acid   Sodium acetate
mp 306°C   mp 17°C   mp >300°C

The dry salts are ionic and have very high melting points, which is expected for ionic substances. Note that this acidity is *not* observed for alcohols where the —OH group is attached to a singly bonded (sp^3 or saturated) carbon.

2. The hydrogen on an —OH group that is attached to an aromatic ring is weakly acidic and reacts with strong bases such as sodium hydroxide (NaOH) to form high melting ionic salts, as evidenced by the reaction of phenol to sodium phenolate. Again, the reaction is reversed by the addition of an acid.

Phenol   Sodium phenolate
mp 41°C   mp 382°C

Note again that this acidity is *not* observed for alcohols where the —OH group is attached to a singly bonded (sp^3 or saturated) carbon.

3. Amines (but not amides) are basic (H^+ accepting) and will react with acid to form ionic amine salts with elevated melting points, as shown, for example, for isopropyl amine.

Isopropyl amine   Isopropyl amine hydrochloride
mp –95°C   mp 162°C

Amine salts can be converted back to amines by raising the pH by adding a base.

5. Competing Intermolecular Forces and Solubility

For pure compounds containing identical molecules, the total attractive force between molecules is the sum of all the attractive forces listed previously, both weak and strong. These forces tend to work together to raise melting and boiling points as the size of the molecule's hydrocarbon skeleton increases and as polar, hydrogen bonded, or ionic functional groups are incorporated into the molecule.

However, solubility involves the interaction of two different molecules, which may have different types of attractive forces. When we try to dissolve one substance in another, we have to disrupt the attractive forces in both substances to get the molecules of the two substances to intermingle. For example, to get water (polar with hydrogen bonding) and the hydrocarbons (nonpolar and no hydrogen bonding) in motor oil to mix and dissolve in one another, we would have to disrupt the London attractive forces between the oil molecules and the hydrogen bonds between the water molecules. Because London forces are weak, separating the oil molecules does not require much energy. However, breaking apart the much stronger hydrogen bonds by inserting oil molecules between the water molecules requires considerable energy and is unfavorable. Therefore, oil or even the simplest hydrocarbon, methane, is insoluble in water. This is the molecular basis of the old adage "Oil and water don't mix."

In addition to carbon and hydrogen, the majority of organic molecules contain other elements, such as nitrogen and oxygen, in functional groups that can be polar, exhibit hydrogen bonding, show ionic tendencies, or have any combination thereof. Can we predict the water solubility of these organic substances? Let's look at some examples and see.

Figure 3.1 shows a collection of small organic molecules of about the same size and molecular weight listed in order of increasing boiling point or melting point, which is consistent with the types of intermolecular forces discussed. With the exception of the hydrocarbon butane, all of these substances are very soluble in water—at least 100 g will dissolve in 1 L of water. It appears that the intermolecular attractive forces between these polar, hydrogen bonded, or ionic molecules and water compensates for the disruption of hydrogen bonding between water molecules so the organic molecules can move into and intermingle with the water molecules—in other words, dissolve.

Figure 3.2 shows a collection of larger organic molecules than those in Figure 3.1, again listed in order of increasing melting and boiling point, which is consistent with our knowledge of the strength of intermolecular attractive forces. The important difference for this group is that the hydrocarbon portion of each molecule is four carbons larger than for those in Figure 3.1. We might predict that the larger hydrocarbon portion makes them behave more like the water-insoluble hydrocarbon octane. Indeed, the larger hydrocarbon portion of these molecules greatly reduces their solubility in water to less than 5 g/L of water except for the two ionic compounds. These two, the amine hydrochloride and the sodium carboxylate compounds, have higher solubility—tens of grams per liter of water— proof that ionic charges can interact strongly with water molecules.

This trend in water solubility based on the size of the hydrocarbon portion continues for the set of even larger organic molecules shown in Figure 3.3 containing C_{16} to C_{18} hydrocarbon chains. Most are virtually insoluble in water; even the ionic forms have solubilities of less than 1 g/L of water.

In addition to water, many other liquid solvents are used in the organic laboratory to dissolve substances, including acetone, dichloromethane (CH_2Cl_2), ethanol (CH_3CH_2OH), diethyl ether ($CH_3CH_2OCH_2CH_3$), hexane, methanol, and toluene ($C_6H_5CH_3$). Predicting the solubility of different organic compounds,

■ **FIG. 3.1**

Some small organic molecules containing 4 atoms (carbon, oxygen, and nitrogen) in order of increasing melting or boiling points.

C_4 Hydrocarbon, butane
mp −138°C; bp 0°C
Insoluble in H_2O

C_3 Amine
mp −43°C; bp 48°C
Soluble in H_2O; Soluble in organic solvents

C_3 Ketone, acetone
mp −94°C; bp 56°C
Soluble in H_2O; Soluble in organic solvents

C_3 Alcohol
mp −127°C; bp 97°C
Soluble in H_2O; Soluble in organic solvents

C_2 Carboxylic acid. acetic acid
mp 17°C; bp 117°C
Soluble in H_2O; Soluble in organic solvents

C_3 Amine hydrochloride
mp 161°C
Soluble in H_2O; Insoluble in organic solvents

Sodium salt of C_2 carboxylic acid
mp 324°C
Soluble in H_2O; Insoluble in organic solvents

■ **FIG. 3.2**

Some organic molecules containing 8 atoms (carbon, oxygen, and nitrogen) in order of increasing melting or boiling points.

C_8 Hydrocarbon, octane
mp −57°C; bp 126°C
Insoluble in H_2O

C_7 Amine
mp −18°C; bp 154°C
Insoluble in H_2O; Soluble in organic solvents

C_7 Ketone
mp −35°C; bp 150°C
Insoluble in H_2O; Soluble in organic solvents

C_7 Alcohol
mp −34°C; bp 175°C
Insoluble in H_2O; Soluble in organic solvents

C_6 Carboxylic acid
mp −2°C; bp 200°C
Insoluble in H_2O; Soluble in organic solvents

C_7 Amine hydrochloride
mp 242°C
Soluble in H_2O; Insoluble in organic solvents

Sodium salt of C_6 carboxylic acid
mp 245°C
Soluble in H_2O; Insoluble in organic solvents

such as those shown in Figures 3.1, 3.2, and 3.3, in these solvents can be done using the intermolecular attractive force concepts discussed here. For example, because the molecules in Figure 3.3 have long hydrocarbon skeletons, you would predict that these would probably be soluble in the hydrocarbon hexane. This predictive rule can be summed up as "Like dissolves like." You might also predict

■ FIG. 3.3

Some organic molecules containing 18 atoms (carbon, oxygen, and nitrogen) in order of increasing melting or boiling points.

C₁₈ Hydrocarbon
mp 6°C
Insoluble in H_2O

C₁₇ Ketone
mp 48°C
Insoluble in H_2O; Soluble in organic solvents

C₁₇ Amine
mp 49°C
Insoluble in H_2O; Soluble in organic solvents

C₁₇ Alcohol
mp 53°C
Insoluble in H_2O; Soluble in organic solvents

C₁₆ Carboxylic acid
mp 63°C
Insoluble in H_2O; Soluble in organic solvents

C₁₇ Amine hydrochloride
mp 165°C
Soluble in H_2O; Slightly soluble in organic solvents

Sodium salt of C₁₆ carboxylic acid
mp 270°C
Soluble in H_2O; Slightly soluble in organic solvents

that the two ionic materials would be the least soluble in hexane because of the strong intermolecular forces in these solids, as evidenced by their high melting points, which are so unlike the weak London forces in hexane. The solubility of organic compounds in organic solvents and water at low, neutral, and high pH will be considered in more detail when you learn about recrystallization in Chapter 4 and extraction in Chapter 7.

PART 2: Melting Points
A. Thermometers

There are a few types of thermometers that can be used to read melting point (and boiling point) temperatures: mercury-in-glass thermometers, non-mercury thermometers, and digital thermometers. Mercury-in-glass thermometers provide highly accurate readings and are ideal for use at high temperatures (260ºC–400ºC). Care should be taken not to break the thermometer, which will release the toxic mercury. Teflon-coated mercury thermometers are usable up to 260ºC and are less likely to spill mercury if broken. If breakage does happen, inform your instructor immediately because special equipment is required to clean up mercury spills. A digital thermometer (Fig. 3.4) has a low heat capacity and a fast response time. It is more robust than a glass thermometer and does not, of course, contain mercury. Nonmercury thermometers may be filled with isoamyl benzoate (a biodegradable liquid) or with a custom organic red-spirit liquid instead of mercury. These thermometers give reasonably accurate readings at temperatures up to 150°C, but above this temperature they need to be carefully calibrated. These thermometers should be stored vertically to prevent thread separation.

CAUTION: Mercury is toxic. Immediately report any broken thermometers to your instructor.

B. Melting Points

The melting point of a pure solid organic compound is one of its characteristic physical properties, along with molecular weight, boiling point, refractive index, and density. A pure solid will melt reproducibly over a narrow range of temperatures, typically less than 1°C. The process of determining this melting point is done on a truly micro scale using less than 1 mg of material. The apparatus is simple, consisting of a thermometer, a capillary tube to hold the sample, and a heating bath.

Melting points—a micro technique

Melting points are determined for three reasons: (1) If the compound is a known one, the melting point will help to characterize the sample. (2) If the compound is new, then the melting point is recorded to allow future characterization by others. (3) The range of the melting point is indicative of the purity of the compound; an impure compound will melt over a wide range of temperatures. Recrystallization of the compound will purify it and decrease the melting point range. In addition, the entire range will be displaced upward. For example, an impure sample might melt from 120°C to 124°C and after recrystallization melt at 125°C–125.5°C. A solid is considered pure if the melting point does not rise after recrystallization.

Characterization

An indication of purity

A crystal is an orderly arrangement of molecules in a solid. As heat is added to the solid, the molecules will vibrate and perhaps rotate but still remain a solid. At a characteristic temperature the crystal will suddenly acquire the necessary energy to overcome the forces that attract one molecule to another and will undergo translational motion—in other words, it will become a liquid.

The forces by which one molecule is attracted to another include ionic attractions, London forces, hydrogen bonds, and dipole-dipole attractions. Most, but by no means all, organic molecules are covalent in nature and melt at temperatures below 300°C. Typical inorganic compounds are ionic and have much higher

■ **FIG. 3.4**
A digital thermometer.

Digital thermometer

°C

Surface probe

■ **FIG. 3.5**

A melting point–composition diagram for mixtures of the solids X and Y.

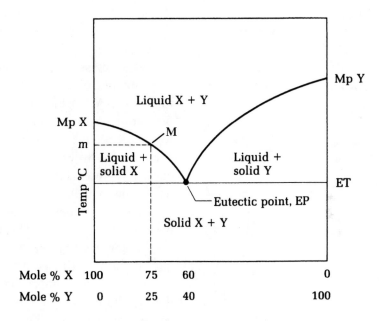

melting points (e.g., sodium chloride melts at 800°C). Ionic organic molecules often decompose before melting, as do compounds having many strong hydrogen bonds, such as sucrose.

Melting point generalizations

Other factors being equal, larger molecules melt at higher temperatures than smaller molecules. Among structural isomers, the more symmetrical isomers will have the higher melting point. Among optical isomers, the R and S enantiomers will have the same melting points; but the racemate (a mixture of equal parts of R and S) will usually possess a different melting point. Diastereomers, another type of stereoisomer, will have different melting points. Molecules that can form hydrogen bonds will usually possess higher melting points than their counterparts of similar molecular weight.

A phase diagram

The melting point behavior of impure compounds is best understood by considering a simple binary mixture of compounds X and Y (Fig. 3.5). This melting point–composition diagram shows melting point behavior as a function of composition. The melting point of a pure compound is the temperature at which the vapor pressures of the solid and liquid are equal. But in dealing with a mixture, the situation is different. Consider the case of a mixture of 75% X and 25% Y. At a temperature below the eutectic temperature (ET), the mixture is solid Y and solid X. At ET, the solid begins to melt. The melt is a solution of Y dissolved in liquid X. The vapor pressure of the solution of X and Y together is less than that of pure X at the melting point; therefore, the temperature at which X will melt is lower when mixed with Y. This is an application of Raoult's law (*see* Chapter 5). As the temperature is increased, more and more of solid X melts until it is all gone at point **M** (temperature *m*). The melting point range is thus from ET to *m*. In practice it is very difficult to detect the ET when a melting point is determined in a capillary because it represents the point at which an infinitesimal amount of the solid mixture has begun to melt.

In this hypothetical example, the liquid solution becomes saturated with Y at the eutectic point (EP). This is the point at which X and Y and their liquid solutions are in equilibrium. A mixture of X and Y containing 60% X will appear to have a sharp melting point at the ET.

The melting point range of a mixture of compounds is generally broad, and the breadth of the range is an indication of purity. The chances of accidentally coming on the eutectic composition are small. Recrystallization will enrich the predominant compound while excluding the impurity and will, therefore, decrease the melting point range.

It should be apparent that the impurity must be soluble in the compound, so an insoluble impurity such as sand or charcoal will not depress the melting point. The impurity does not need to be a solid. It can be a liquid such as water (if it is soluble) or an organic solvent, such as the one used to recrystallize the compound; this advocates the necessity for drying the compound before determining its melting point.

Advantage is taken of the depression of melting points of mixtures to prove whether or not two compounds having the same melting points are identical. If X and Y are identical, then a mixture of the two will have the same melting point; if X and Y are not identical, then a small amount of X in Y or of Y in X will reduce the melting point.

The eutectic point *(marginal note)*

Melting point depression *(marginal note)*

Mixed melting points *(marginal note)*

Apparatus

Melting Point Capillaries

Before using a melting point apparatus, the sample needs to be prepared for analysis. Most melting point determinations require that the sample be placed in a capillary tube. The experiments in this book require capillary tubes for sample preparation. Capillaries may be obtained commercially or may be produced by drawing out 12-mm soft-glass tubing. The tubing is rotated in the hottest part of a Bunsen burner flame until it is very soft and begins to sag. It should not be drawn out during heating; it is removed from the flame and after a slight hesitation drawn steadily and not too rapidly to arm's length. With some practice it is possible to

■ **FIG. 3.6**
Sealing a melting point
capillary tube.

Samples that sublime

A small rubber band can be
made by cutting off a very
short piece of ¼" gum rubber
tubing.

Thomas–Hoover Uni-Melt

produce 10–15 good tubes in a single drawing. The long capillary tube can be cut
into 100-mm lengths with a glass scorer. Each tube is sealed by rotating the end in
the edge of a small flame, as seen in Figure 3.6.

Filling Melting Point Capillaries. The dry sample is ground to a fine powder on a
watch glass or a piece of glassine paper on a hard surface using the flat portion of a
spatula. It is formed into a small pile, and the open end of the melting point capillary
is forced down into the pile. The sample is shaken into the closed end of the capillary
by rapping sharply on a hard surface or by dropping it down a 2-ft length of glass tubing onto a hard surface. The height of the sample should be no more than 2–3 mm.

Sealed Capillaries. Some samples sublime (go from a solid state directly to the
vapor phase without appearing to melt) or undergo rapid air oxidation and decompose at the melting point. These samples should be sealed under vacuum.
This can be accomplished by forcing a capillary through a hole previously made
in a rubber septum and evacuating the capillary using a water aspirator or a me-
chanical vacuum pump (Fig. 3.7). Using the flame from a small micro burner, the
tube is gently heated about 15 mm above the tightly packed sample. This will
cause any material in this region to sublime away. It is then heated more strongly
in the same place to collapse the tube, taking care that the tube is straight when it
cools. It is also possible to seal the end of a Pasteur pipette, add the sample, pack
it down, and seal off a sample under vacuum in the same way.

Melting Point Devices. The apparatus required for determining an accurate melting point need not be elaborate; the same results are obtained on the simplest as
on the most complex devices. The simplest setup involves attaching the sample-
filled, melting point capillary to a thermometer using a rubber band and immersing them into a silicone oil bath (Fig. 3.8). This rubber band must be above the
level of the oil bath; otherwise, it will break in the hot oil. The sample should be
close to and on a level with the center of the thermometer bulb. This method can
analyze compounds whose melting points go up to ~350°C. If determinations are
to be done on two or three samples that differ in melting point by as much as
10°C, two or three capillaries can be secured to the thermometer together; the
melting points can be observed in succession without removing the thermometer
from the bath. As a precaution against the interchange of tubes while they are being attached, use some system of identification, such as one, two, and three dots
made with a marking pencil.

More sophisticated melting point devices, some of which can attain temperatures of 500°C, will now be described.

The Thomas–Hoover Uni-Melt apparatus (Fig. 3.9) will accommodate up to
seven capillaries in a small, magnified, lighted beaker of high-boiling silicone oil
that is stirred and heated electrically. The heating rate is controlled with a variable
transformer that is part of the apparatus. The rising mercury column of the thermometer can be observed with an optional traveling periscope device so the eye
need not move away from the capillary. For industrial, analytical, and control

■ **FIG 3.7**
Evacuation of a melting point
capillary prior to sealing.

To aspirator

Rubber hose

Glass tube

Rubber septum

Melting point
capillary

Mel-Temp

Seal here

Sample

Fisher-Johns

■ **FIG 3.8**
A simple melting point apparatus.

Melting point
capillary

Small rubber band

Heating oil
bath

Sample

■ **FIG. 3.9**
The Thomas–Hoover Uni-Melt
melting point apparatus.

work the Mettler apparatus determines the melting point automatically and displays the result in digital form.

The Mel-Temp apparatus (Fig. 3.10) consists of an electrically heated aluminum block that accommodates three capillaries. The sample is illuminated through the lower port and observed with a six-power lens through the upper port. The heating rate can be controlled and, with a special thermometer, the apparatus can be used up to 500°C—far above the useful limit of silicone oil (which is about 350°C). For this melting point apparatus it is advisable to use a digital thermometer rather than the mercury-in-glass thermometer.

The Fisher-Johns melting point apparatus (Fig. 3.11) is used to determine the melting point of a single sample. Instead of a capillary tube, the sample is placed between two thin glass disks that are placed on an aluminum heating stage. Heating is controlled by a variable transformer, and melting is observed through a magnifier; the melting temperature is read from a mercury-in-glass thermometer. This apparatus can be used for compounds that melt between 20°C and 300°C.

Determining the Melting Point

The accuracy of the melting point depends on the accuracy of the thermometer, so the first exercise in the following experiments will be to calibrate the thermometer. Melting points of pure, known compounds will be determined and deviations recorded so a correction can be applied to future melting points. Be forewarned, however, that thermometers are usually fairly accurate.

■ FIG. 3.10
The Mel-Temp melting point apparatus.

■ FIG 3.11
The Fisher-Johns melting point apparatus.

 The rate of heating is the most important factor in obtaining accurate melting points. Heat no faster than 1°C per minute.

The most critical factor in determining an accurate melting point is the rate of heating. At the melting point the temperature increase should not be greater than 1°C per minute. This may seem extraordinarily slow, but it is necessary in order for heat from the oil bath or the heating block to be transferred equally to the sample and to the glass and mercury of the thermometer.

From your own experience you know the rate at which ice melts. Consider performing a melting point experiment on an ice cube. Because water melts at 0°C, you would need to have a melting point bath a few degrees below zero. To observe the true melting point of the ice cube, you would need to raise the temperature extraordinarily slowly. The ice cube would appear to begin to melt at 0°C and, if you waited for temperature equilibrium to be established, it would all be melted at 0.5°C. If you were impatient and raised the temperature too rapidly, the ice might appear to melt over a range of 0°C to 20°C. Similarly, melting points determined in capillaries will not be accurate if the rate of heating is too fast.

EXPERIMENTS

1. Calibration of the Thermometer

Determine the melting point of standard substances (Table 3.1) over the temperature range of interest. The difference between the values found and those expected constitutes the correction that must be applied to future temperature readings. If the thermometer has been calibrated previously, then determine one or more melting points of known substances to familiarize yourself with the technique. If the

TABLE 3.1 • **Melting Point Standards**

Compound		Structure	Melting Point (°C)
Naphthalene	(a)		80–82
Urea	(b)	O ‖ H₂NCNH₂	132.5–133
Sulfanilamide	(c)	NH₂ / SO₂NH₂	164–165
4-Toluic acid	(d)	COOH / CH₃	180–182
Anthracene	(e)		214–217
Caffeine (evacuated capillary)	(f)		234–236.5

determinations do not agree within 1°C, then repeat the process. Both mercury-in-glass and digital thermometers will need to be calibrated; nonmercury thermometers are not typically used for melting point determination.

2. Melting Points of Pure Urea and Cinnamic Acid

Using a metal spatula, crush the sample to a fine powder on a hard surface such as a watch glass. Push the open end of a melting point capillary into the powder and force the powder down in the capillary by tapping the capillary or by dropping it through a long glass tube held vertically and resting on a hard surface. The column of solid should be no more than 2–3 mm in height and should be tightly packed.

$-CH=CH-COOH$

Cinnamic acid

Heat rapidly to within 20°C of the melting point.

Heat slowly (<1°C/min) near the melting temperature.

If the approximate melting temperature is known, the bath can be heated rapidly until the temperature is about 20°C below this point; the heating during the last 15°C–20°C should slow down considerably so *the rate of heating at the melting point is no more than 1°C per minute* while the sample is melting. As the melting point is approached, the sample may shrink because of crystalline structure changes. However, the melting process begins when the first drops of liquid are seen in the capillary and ends when the last trace of solid disappears. For a pure compound this whole process may occur over a range of only 0.5°C; hence, it is necessary to slowly increase the temperature during the determination.

Determine the melting point (mp) of either urea (mp 132.5°C–133°C) or cinnamic acid (mp 132.5°C–133°C). Repeat the determination; if the two determinations do not check within 1°C, repeat a third time.

3. Melting Points of Urea-Cinnamic Acid Mixtures

IN THIS EXPERIMENT you will see dramatic evidence of the phenomenon of melting point depression, which will allow you to prepare a phase diagram like that shown in Figure 3.5 (on page 47).

Make mixtures of urea and cinnamic acid in the approximate proportions 1:4, 1:1, and 4:1 by putting side by side the correct number of equal-sized small piles of the two substances and then mixing them. Grind the mixture thoroughly for at least a minute on a watch glass using a metal spatula. Note the ranges of melting of the three mixtures and use the temperatures of complete liquefaction to construct a rough diagram of melting point versus composition.

4. Unknowns

Determine the melting point of one or more of the unknowns selected by your instructor and identify the substance based on its melting point (Table 3.2). Prepare two capillaries of each unknown. Run a very fast determination on the first sample to ascertain the approximate melting point. Cool the melting point bath to just below the melting point and make a slow, careful determination using the other capillary.

5. An Investigation: Determination of Molecular Weight Using Melting Point Depression

Before the mass spectrometer came into common usage, the molal freezing point depression of camphor was used to determine molecular weights. Whereas a 1% solid solution of urea in cinnamic acid will cause a relatively small melting point depression, a 1% by weight solid solution in camphor of any organic compound with a molecular weight of 100 will cause a 4.0°C depression in the melting point of the camphor. Quantitative use of this relationship can be used to determine the

TABLE 3.2 • Melting Point Unknowns

Compound	Melting Point (°C)
Benzophenone	49–51
Maleic anhydride	52–54
4-Nitrotoluene	54–56
Naphthalene	80–82
Acetanilide	113.5–114
Benzoic acid	121.5–122
Urea	132.5–133
Salicylic acid	158.5–159
Sulfanilamide	165–166
Succinic acid	184.5–185
3,5-Dinitrobenzoic acid	205–207
p-Terphenyl	210–211

molecular weight of an unknown. You can learn more about the details of this technique in very old editions of *Organic Experiments*[1] or by searching the Web for "colligative properties, molal freezing point depression." Visit this book's website for more information.

PART 3: Boiling Points

The boiling point of a pure organic liquid is one of its characteristic physical properties, just like its density, molecular weight, and refractive index, and the melting point of its solid state. The boiling point is used to characterize a new organic liquid, and knowledge of the boiling point helps to compare one organic liquid to another, as in the process of identifying an unknown organic substance.

A comparison of boiling points with melting points is instructive. The process of determining the boiling point is more complex than that for the melting point: It requires more material, and because it is less affected by impurities, it is not as good an indication of purity. Boiling points can be determined on a few microliters of a liquid, but on a small scale it is difficult to determine the boiling point *range*. This requires enough material to distill—about 1 to 2 mL. Like the melting point, the boiling point of a liquid is affected by the forces that attract one molecule to another—ionic attraction, London forces, dipole-dipole interactions, and hydrogen bonding, as discussed in Part 1 of this chapter.

Structure and Boiling Point

In a homologous series of molecules the boiling point increases in a perfectly regular manner. The normal saturated hydrocarbons have boiling points ranging from $-162°C$ for methane to $330°C$ for $n\text{-}C_{19}H_{40}$, an increase of about $27°C$ for each

1. Fieser L. F. *Organic Experiments*, 2nd ed.; D.C. Heath: Lexington, MA, 1968; 38–42.

CH_2 group. It is convenient to remember that *n*-heptane with a molecular weight of 100 has a boiling point near 100°C (98.4°C). A spherical molecule such as 2,2-dimethylpropane has a lower boiling point than *n*-pentane because it does not have as many points of attraction to adjacent molecules. For molecules of the same molecular weight, those with dipoles, such as carbonyl groups, will have higher boiling points than those without, and molecules that can form hydrogen bonds will boil even higher. The boiling point of such molecules depends on the number of hydrogen bonds that can be formed. An alcohol with one hydroxyl group will boil at a lower temperature than an alcohol with two hydroxyl groups if they both have the same molecular weight. A number of other generalizations can be made about boiling point behavior as a function of structure; you will learn about these throughout your study of organic chemistry.

Boiling Point as a Function of Pressure

Boiling points decrease about 0.5°C for each 10-mm decrease in atmospheric pressure.

Because the boiling point of a pure liquid is defined as the temperature at which the vapor pressure of the liquid exactly equals the pressure exerted on it, the boiling point will be a function of atmospheric pressure. At an altitude of 14,000 ft the boiling point of water is 81°C. At pressures near that of the atmosphere at sea level (760 mm), the boiling point of most liquids decreases about 0.5°C for each 10-mm decrease in atmospheric pressure. This generalization does not hold for greatly reduced pressures because the boiling point decreases as a nonlinear function of pressure (*see* Fig. 5.2 on page 91). Under these conditions a nomograph relating the observed boiling point, the boiling point at 760 mm, and the pressure in millimeters should be consulted (*see* Fig. 6.19 on page 128). This nomograph is not highly accurate; the change in boiling point as a function of pressure also depends on the type of compound (polar, nonpolar, hydrogen bonding, etc.). Consult the *CRC Handbook of Chemistry and Physics*[2] for the correction of boiling points to standard pressure.

CAUTION: Mercury is toxic. Immediately report any broken thermometers to your instructor.

Most mercury-in-glass laboratory thermometers have a mark around the stem that is 3 in. (76 mm) from the bottom of the bulb. This is the immersion line; the thermometer will record accurate temperatures if immersed to this line. If you break a mercury thermometer, immediately inform your instructor, who will use special apparatus to clean up the mercury. Mercury vapor is very toxic.

Calibrating the Thermometer

If you have not previously carried out a calibration, test the 0°C point of your thermometer with a well-stirred mixture of crushed ice and distilled water. To check the 100°C point, put 2 mL of water in a test tube with a boiling chip to prevent bumping and boil the water gently over a hot sand bath with the thermometer in the vapor from the boiling water. Make sure that the thermometer does not touch the side of the test tube. Then immerse the bulb of the thermometer into the liquid and see if you can observe superheating. Check the atmospheric pressure to determine the true boiling point of the water.

2. Lide, D. R., ed. *CRC Handbook of Chemistry and Physics,* 86th ed.; CRC Press: Boca Raton, FL, 2005.

Distillation Considerations

Prevention of Superheating—Boiling Sticks and Boiling Stones

Superheating occurs when a very clean liquid in a very clean vessel is heated to a temperature above its boiling point without ever actually boiling. That is, if a thermometer is placed in the superheated liquid, the thermometer will register a temperature higher than the boiling point of the liquid. If boiling does occur under these conditions, it occurs with explosive violence. To avoid this problem, boiling stones or boiling sticks are always added to liquids before heating them to boiling—whether to determine a boiling point or to carry out a reaction or distillation. These boiling stones or sticks provide the nuclei on which the bubble of vapor indicative of a boiling liquid can form; be careful not to confuse the bubbling for boiling. Some boiling stones, also called boiling chips, are composed of porous unglazed porcelain. This material is filled with air in numerous fine capillaries. With heating, this air expands to form the fine bubbles on which even boiling can take place. Once the liquid cools, it will fill these capillaries and the boiling chip will become ineffectual, so another chip must be added each time the liquid is reheated to boiling. Wooden boiling sticks about 1.5 mm in diameter—often called applicator sticks—also promote even boiling and, unlike stones, are removed easily from the solution. None of these work well for vacuum distillation (*see* Chapter 6).

Closed Systems

Distillations that are run at atmospheric pressure need to be open to the atmosphere to avoid pressure buildup, which could lead to an explosion. Therefore, always make sure that a distillation setup is not a closed system—unless, of course, you are running a vacuum distillation.

Boiling Point Determination: Apparatus and Technique

Boiling Point Determination by Distillation

When enough material is available (at least 3 mL), the best method for determining the boiling point of a liquid is to distill it (*see* Chapter 5). Distillation allows the boiling range to be determined and thus gives an indication of purity. Bear in mind, however, that a constant boiling point is not a guarantee of homogeneity and thus purity. Constant-boiling azeotropes such as 95% ethanol are common.

All procedures involving volatile and/or flammable solvents should be conducted in a fume hood.

Boiling Point Determination Using a Digital Thermometer and a Reaction Tube

Boiling points can be measured rapidly and accurately using an electronic digital thermometer, as depicted in Figure 3.12. Although digital thermometers are currently too expensive for each student to have, several of these in the laboratory can greatly speed up the determination of boiling points. Digital thermometers are

Online Study Center

Photo: Boiling Point Determination with a Digital Thermometer

■ FIG. 3.12
Using a digital thermometer
for determining boiling points.

Digital
thermometer

°C

79

Surface
probe

Refluxing
vapor

Boiling chip   Boiling liquid

much safer to use because there is no danger from toxic mercury vapor if the thermometer is accidentally dropped.

The surface probe of the digital thermometer is the active element. Unlike the bulb of mercury at the end of a thermometer, this element has a very low heat capacity and a very fast response time, so boiling points can be determined very quickly in this apparatus. About 0.2 mL to 0.3 mL of the liquid and a boiling chip are heated on a sand bath until the liquid refluxes about 3 cm up the tube. The probe should not touch the side of the reaction tube but should be placed approximately 5 mm above the liquid. The boiling point is the highest temperature recorded by the thermometer and is maintained for about 1 min. The application

■ FIG. 3.13
A small-scale boiling-point apparatus. Be sure the thermometer does not touch the tube.

Thermometer adapter

Refluxing vapor

Boiling chip

Boiling liquid

Smaller-scale boiling point apparatus

of heat will drive tiny bubbles of air from the boiling chip; do not mistake these tiny bubbles for true boiling; this mistake can readily happen if the unknown has a very high boiling point.

Boiling Point Determination in a Reaction Tube

If a digital thermometer is not available, use the apparatus shown in Figure 3.13. Using a distilling adapter at the top of a reaction tube allows access to the atmosphere. Place 0.3 mL of the liquid along with a boiling stone in a 10 × 100-mm reaction tube, clamp a thermometer so that the bulb is just above the level of the liquid, and then heat the liquid with a sand bath. It is *very important* that no part of the thermometer touch the reaction tube. Heating is regulated so that the boiling liquid refluxes about 3 cm up the thermometer but does not boil out of the apparatus. If you cannot see the refluxing liquid, carefully run your finger down the side of the reaction tube until you feel heat. This indicates where the liquid is refluxing. Droplets of liquid must drip from the thermometer bulb to thoroughly heat the mercury. The boiling point is the highest temperature recorded by the thermometer and is maintained over about a 1-min time interval.

The application of heat will drive out tiny air bubbles from the boiling chip. Do not mistake these tiny bubbles for true boiling. This can occur if the unknown has a very high boiling point. It may take several minutes to heat up the mercury in the thermometer bulb. True boiling is indicated by drops dripping from the thermometer, with a constant temperature recorded on the thermometer. If the temperature is not constant, then you are probably not observing true boiling.

Boiling Point Determination Using a 3-mm to 5-mm Tube

For smaller quantities, a 3-mm to 5-mm diameter tube is attached to the side of the thermometer by a rubber band (Fig. 3.14) and heated with a liquid bath. The tube, which can be made from tubing 3 mm to 5 mm in diameter, contains a small inverted capillary. This is made by cutting a 6-mm piece from the sealed end of a melting point capillary, inverting it, and sealing the closed end to the capillary. A centimeter ruler is printed on the inside back cover of this book.

When the sample is heated in this device, the air in the inverted capillary will expand, and an occasional bubble will escape. At the true boiling point a continuous and rapid stream of bubbles will emerge from the inverted capillary. When this occurs, the heating is stopped, and the bath is allowed to cool. A time will come when bubbling ceases and the liquid just begins to rise in the inverted capillary. The temperature at which this happens is recorded. The liquid is allowed to partially fill the small capillary, and the heat is applied carefully until the first bubble emerges from the capillary. The temperature is recorded at that point. The two temperatures approximate the boiling point range for the liquid.

As the liquid was being heated, the air expanded in the inverted capillary and was replaced by vapor of the liquid. The liquid was actually slightly superheated when rapid bubbles emerged from the capillary, but on cooling a point was reached at which the pressure on the inside of the capillary matched the outside (atmospheric) pressure. This is, by definition, the boiling point.

■ **FIG. 3.14**
A smaller-scale boiling point apparatus.

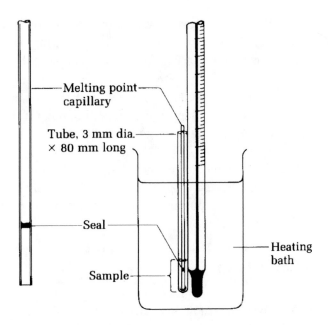

Melting point capillary

Tube, 3 mm dia. × 80 mm long

Seal

Sample

Heating bath

Cleaning Up. Place the boiling point sample in either the halogenated or nonhalogenated waste container. Do not pour it down the sink.

QUESTIONS

1. What effect would poor circulation of the melting point bath liquid have on the observed melting point?
2. What is the effect of an insoluble impurity, such as sodium sulfate, on the observed melting point of a compound?
3. Three test tubes, labeled A, B, and C, contain substances with approximately the same melting points. How could you prove the test tubes contain three different chemical compounds?
4. One of the most common causes of inaccurate melting points is too rapid heating of the melting point bath. Under these circumstances, how will the observed melting point compare to the true melting point?
5. Strictly speaking, why is it incorrect to speak of a melting *point*?
6. What effect would the incomplete drying of a sample (for example, the incomplete removal of a recrystallization solvent) have on the melting point?
7. Why should the melting point sample be finely powdered?
8. You suspect that an unknown is acetanilide (mp 113.5°C–114°C). Give a qualitative estimation of the melting point when the acetanilide is mixed with 10% by weight of naphthalene.
9. You have an unknown with an observed melting point of 90°C–93°C. Is your unknown compound A with a reported melting point of 95.5°C–96°C or compound B with a reported melting point of 90.5°C–91°C? Explain.

10. Why is it important to heat the melting point bath or block slowly and steadily when the temperature gets close to the melting point?

11. Why is it important to pack the sample tightly in the melting point capillary?

12. An unknown compound is suspected to be acetanilide (mp 113.5°C–114°C). What would happen to the melting point if this unknown were mixed with (a) an equal quantity of pure acetanilide? (b) an equal quantity of benzoic acid?

13. Which would be expected to have the higher boiling point, *t*-butyl alcohol (2-methyl-2-propanol) or *n*-butyl alcohol (1-butanol)? Explain.

14. What is the purpose of the side arm of the thermometer adapter in Figure 3.13?

Online Study Center

General Resources
Web Links

REFERENCE

Weissberger, Arnold, and Bryant W. Rossiter (eds.). *Physical Methods of Chemistry*, Vol. 1, Part V. New York: Wiley-Interscience, 1971.

Recrystallization

Recrystallization: the most important purification method for solids, especially for small-scale experiments.

PRELAB EXERCISE: Write an expanded outline for the seven-step process of recrystallization.

Recrystallization is the most important method for purifying solid organic compounds. It is also a very powerful, convenient, and efficient method of purification, and it is an important industrial technique that is still relevant in the chemical world today. For instance, the commercial purification of sugar is done by recrystallization on an enormous scale.

A pure, crystalline organic substance is composed of a three-dimensional array of molecules held together primarily by London forces. These attractive forces are fairly weak; most organic solids melt in the range between 22°C and 250°C. An impure organic solid will not have a well-defined crystal lattice because impurities do not allow the crystalline structure to form. The goal of recrystallization is to remove impurities from a solid to allow a perfect crystal lattice to grow.

There are four important concepts to consider when discussing the process of recrystallization:

1. Solubility
2. Saturation level
3. Exclusion
4. Nucleation

Recrystallization involves dissolving the material to be purified (the solute) in an appropriate hot solvent to yield a solution (*solubility*). As the solvent cools, the solution becomes saturated with respect to the solute (*saturation level*), which then recrystallizes. As the perfectly regular array of a crystal is formed, impurities are excluded (*exclusion*), and the crystal is thus a single pure substance. Soluble impurities remain in solution because they are not concentrated enough to saturate the solution. Recrystallization is initiated at a point of *nucleation*—a seed crystal, a speck of dust, or a scratch on the wall of the test tube if the solution is supersaturated with the solute.

In this chapter you will carry out the recrystallization process, one of the most important laboratory operations of organic chemistry, by following its seven steps. Then you will perform several actual recrystallization experiments.

The Seven Steps of Recrystallization

The process of recrystallization can be broken into seven discrete steps: (1) choosing the solvent and solvent pairs; (2) dissolving the solute; (3) decolorizing the solution with pelletized Norit; (4) filtering suspended solids; (5) recrystallizing the solute; (6) collecting and washing the crystals; and (7) drying the crystals. A detailed description of each of these steps is given in the following sections.

Step 1. Choosing the Solvent and Solvent Pairs

Similia similibus solvuntur.

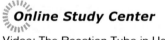

Online Study Center

Video: The Reaction Tube in Use

In choosing the solvent, the chemist is guided by the dictum "like dissolves like." Even the nonchemist knows that oil and water do not mix and that sugar and salt dissolve in water but not in oil. Hydrocarbon solvents such as hexane will dissolve hydrocarbons and other nonpolar compounds, and hydroxylic solvents such as water and ethanol will dissolve polar compounds. It is often difficult to decide, simply by looking at the structure of a molecule, just how polar or nonpolar it is and which solvent would be best. Therefore, the solvent is often chosen by experimentation. If an appropriate single solvent cannot be found for a given substance, a solvent pair system may be used. The requirement for this solvent pair is miscibility; both solvents should dissolve in each other for use as a recrystallization solvent system.

The ideal solvent

The best recrystallization solvent (and none is ideal) will dissolve the solute when the solution is hot but not when the solution is cold; it will either not dissolve the impurities at all or it will dissolve them very well (so they do not recrystallize out along with the solute); it will not react with the solute; and it will be nonflammable, nontoxic, inexpensive, and very volatile (so it can be removed from the crystals).

Miscible: capable of being mixed

Some common solvents and their properties are presented in Table 4.1 in order of decreasing polarity of the solvent. Solvents adjacent to each other in the list will dissolve in each other; that is, they are miscible with each other, and each solvent will, in general, dissolve substances that are similar to it in chemical structure. These solvents are used both for recrystallization and as solvents in which reactions are carried out.

Procedure

Choosing a Solvent

Online Study Center

Video: Picking a Solvent

To choose a solvent for recrystallization, place a few crystals of the impure solute in a small test tube or centrifuge tube and add a very small drop of the solvent. Allow the drop to flow down the side of the tube and onto the crystals. If the crystals

TABLE 4.1 • Recrystallization Solvents

Solvent	Boiling Point (°C)	Remarks
Water (H_2O)	100	It is the solvent of choice because it is cheap, nonflammable, and nontoxic and will dissolve a large variety of polar organic molecules. Its high boiling point and high heat of vaporization make it difficult to remove from crystals.
Acetic acid (CH_3COOH)	118	It will react with alcohols and amines, and it is difficult to remove from crystals. It is not a common solvent for recrystallizations, although it is used as a solvent when carrying out oxidation reactions.
Dimethyl sulfoxide (DMSO; CH_3SOCH_3)	189	It is not a commonly used solvent for recrystallization, but it is used for reactions.
Methanol (CH_3OH)	64	It is a very good solvent that is often used for recrystallization. It will dissolve molecules of higher polarity than other alcohols.
95% Ethanol (CH_3CH_2OH)	78	It is one of the most commonly used recrystallization solvents. Its high boiling point makes it a better solvent for less polar molecules than methanol. It evaporates readily from crystals. Esters may undergo an interchange of alcohol groups on recrystallization.
Acetone (CH_3COCH_3)	56	It is an excellent solvent, but its low boiling point means there is not much difference in the solubility of a compound at its boiling point compared to about 22°C.
2-Butanone; also known as methyl ethyl ketone (MEK; $CH_3COCH_2CH_3$)	80	It is an excellent solvent that has many of the most desirable properties of a good recrystallization solvent.
Ethyl acetate ($CH_3COOC_2H_5$)	78	It is an excellent solvent that has about the right combination of moderately high boiling point and the volatility needed to remove it from crystals.
Dichloromethane; also known as methylene chloride (CH_2Cl_2)	40	Although a common extraction solvent, dichloromethane boils too to make it a good recrystallization solvent. It is useful in a solvent pair with ligroin.
Diethyl ether; also known as ether ($CH_3CH_2OCH_2CH_3$)	35	Its boiling point is too low for recrystallization, although it is an extremely good solvent and fairly inert. It is used in a solvent pair with ligroin.
Methyl *t*-butyl ether ($CH_3OC(CH_3)_3$)	52	It is a relatively new and inexpensive solvent because of its large-scale use as an antiknock agent and oxygenate in gasoline. It does not easily form peroxides; it is less volatile than diethyl ether, but it has the same solvent characteristics. (*See also* Chapter 7.)
Dioxane ($C_4H_8O_2$)	101	It is a very good solvent that is not too difficult to remove from crystals; it is a mild carcinogen, and it forms peroxides.
Toluene ($C_6H_5CH_3$)	111	It is an excellent solvent that has replaced the formerly widely used benzene (a weak carcinogen) for the recrystallization of aryl compounds. Because of its boiling point, it is not easily removed from crystals.

(continued)

TABLE 4.1 • (*continued*)

Solvent	Boiling Point (°C)	Remarks
Pentane (C_5H_{12})	36	It is a widely used solvent for nonpolar substances. It is not often used alone for recrystallization, but it is good in combination with several other solvents as part of a solvent pair.
Hexane (C_6H_{14})	69	It is frequently used to recrystallize nonpolar substances. It is inert and has the correct balance between boiling point and volatility. It is often used as part of a solvent pair. (*See also* ligroin.)
Cyclohexane (C_6H_{12})	81	It is similar in all respects to hexane. (*See also* ligroin.)
Petroleum ether	30–60	It is a mixture of hydrocarbons, of which pentane is the chief component. It is used interchangeably with pentane because it is cheap. Unlike diethyl ether or *t*-butyl methyl ether, it is not an ether in the modern chemical sense.
Ligroin	60–90	It is a mixture of hydrocarbons with the properties of hexane and cyclohexane. It is a very commonly used recrystallization solvent. It is also sold as "hexanes."

Note: The solvents in this table are listed in decreasing order of polarity. Adjacent solvents in the list are, in general, miscible with each other.

dissolve instantly at about 22°C, that solvent cannot be used for recrystallization because too much of the solute will remain in solution at low temperatures. If the crystals do not dissolve at about 22°C, warm the tube on a hot sand bath and observe the crystals. If they do not go into solution, add 1 more drop of solvent. If the crystals go into solution at the boiling point of the solvent and then recrystallize when the tube is cooled, you have found a good recrystallization solvent. If not, remove the solvent by evaporation and try a different solvent. In this trial-and-error process it is easiest to try low-boiling solvents first because they can be easily removed. Occasionally, no single satisfactory solvent can be found, so mixed solvents, or *solvent pairs*, are used.

Solvent Pairs

To use a mixed solvent pair, dissolve the crystals in the better solvent (more solubilizing) and add the poorer solvent (less solubilizing) to the hot solution until it becomes cloudy, and the solution is saturated with the solute. The two solvents must, of course, be miscible with each other. Some useful solvent pairs are given in Table 4.2.

TABLE 4.2 • **Solvent Pairs**

Acetic acid–water	Ethyl acetate–cyclohexane
Ethanol-water	Acetone-ligroin
Acetone-water	Ethyl acetate–ligroin
Dioxane-water	*t*-Butyl methyl ether–ligroin
Acetone-ethanol	Dichloromethane-ligroin
Ethanol–*t*-butyl methyl ether	Toluene-ligroin

Step 2. Dissolving the Solute

Microscale Procedure

Once a recrystallization solvent has been found, the impure crystals are placed in a reaction tube, the solvent is added dropwise, the crystals are stirred with a microspatula or a small glass rod, and the tube is warmed on a steam bath or a sand bath until the crystals dissolve. Care must be exercised to use the minimum amount of solvent at or near boiling. Observe the mixture carefully as solvent is being added. Allow sufficient time for the boiling solvent to dissolve the solute and note the rate at which most of the material dissolves. When you believe most of the material has been dissolved, stop adding solvent. There is a possibility that your sample is contaminated with a small quantity of an insoluble impurity that never will dissolve. To hasten the solution process, crush large crystals with a stirring rod, taking care not to break the reaction tube.

If the solution contains no undissolved impurities and is not colored from impurities, you can simply let it cool, allowing the solute to recrystallize (step 5), and then collect the crystals (step 6). On the other hand, if the solution is colored, it must be treated with activated (decolorizing) charcoal and then filtered before recrystallization (step 3). If it contains solid impurities, it must be filtered before recrystallization takes place (step 4).

On a microscale, there is a tendency to use too much solvent so that on cooling the hot solution little or no material recrystallizes. This is not a hopeless situation. The remedy is to evaporate some of the solvent (by careful boiling) and repeat the cooling process. Inspect the hot solution.

A solution (solute dissolved in solvent) can become *superheated*; that is, heated above its boiling point without actually boiling. When boiling does suddenly occur, it can happen with almost explosive violence, a process called *bumping*. To prevent this from happening, a *wood applicator* stick can be added to the solution (Fig. 4.1). Air trapped in the wood comes out of the stick and forms the nuclei on which even boiling can occur. Porous porcelain *boiling chips* work in the same way. Never add a boiling chip or a boiling stick to a hot solution because the hot solutuion may be superheated and boil over or bump.

Macroscale Procedure

Place the substance to be recrystallized in an Erlenmeyer flask (never use a beaker), add enough solvent to cover the crystals, and then heat the flask on a steam bath (if the solvent boils below 90°C) or a hot plate until the solvent boils. (Note: Adding a boiling stick or a boiling chip to the solution will promote even boiling. It is easy to superheat the solution; that is, heat it above the boiling point with no boiling taking place. Once the solution does boil, it does so with explosive violence; it bumps.) Never add a boiling chip or boiling stick to a hot solution.

Stir the mixture or, better, swirl it (Fig. 4.2) to promote dissolution. Add solvent gradually, keeping it at the boiling point, until all of the solute dissolves. A glass rod with a flattened end can sometimes be useful in crushing large particles of solute to speed up the dissolving process. Be sure no flames are nearby when working with flammable solvents.

Do not use too much solvent.

Online Study Center

Video: Recrystallization

Prevention of bumping

Do not use wood applicator sticks (boiling sticks) in place of boiling chips in a reaction. Use them only for recrystallization.

Online Study Center

Video: Macroscale Crystallization

All procedures involving volatile and/or flammable solvents should be conducted in a fume hood.

■ FIG. 4.1

A reaction tube being used for recrystallization. The wood applicator stick ("boiling stick") promotes even boiling and is easier to remove than a boiling chip. The Thermowell sand is cool on top and hotter deeper down, so it provides a range of temperatures. The reaction tube is long and narrow; it can be held in the hand while the solvent refluxes. Do not use a boiling stick in place of a boiling chip in a reaction.

Wood applicator stick

Cool at this point

Air condenser

Boiling solvent

Temperature controlled by depth in sand

■ FIG. 4.2

Swirling of a solution to mix contents and help dissolve material to be recrystallized.

Be careful not to add too much solvent. Note how rapidly most of the material dissolves; stop adding solvent when you suspect that almost all of the desired material has dissolved. It is best to err on the side of too little solvent rather than too much. Undissolved material noted at this point could be an insoluble impurity that never will dissolve. Allow the solvent to boil, and if no further material dissolves, proceed to step 4 to remove suspended solids from the solution by filtration or if the solution is colored, go to step 3 to carry out the decolorization process. If the solution is clear, proceed to step 5.

Step 3. Decolorizing the Solution with Pelletized Norit

Online Study Center

Video: Decolorization of a Solution with Norit

Activated charcoal = decolorizing carbon = Norit

The vast majority of pure organic chemicals are colorless or a light shade of yellow; consequently, this step is not usually required. Occasionally, a chemical reaction will produce high molecular weight byproducts that are highly colored. The impurities can be adsorbed onto the surface of activated charcoal by simply boiling the solution with charcoal. Activated charcoal has an extremely large surface area per gram (several hundred square meters) and can bind a large number of molecules to this surface. On a commercial scale, the impurities in brown sugar are adsorbed onto charcoal in the process of refining sugar.

Add a small amount (0.1% of the solute weight is sufficient) of pelletized Norit to the colored solution and then boil the solution for a few minutes. Be careful not to add the charcoal pieces to a superheated solution; the charcoal functions like hundreds of boiling chips and will cause the solution to boil over. Remove the Norit by filtration as described in step 4.

Step 4. Filtering Suspended Solids

The filtration of a hot, saturated solution to remove solid impurities or charcoal can be performed in a number of ways. These processes include gravity filtration, pressure filtration, decantation, or removing the solvent with a Pasteur pipette. Vacuum filtration is not used because the hot solvent will cool during the process, and the product will recrystallize in the filter. Filtration can be one of the most vexing operations in the laboratory if the desired compound recrystallizes during filtration. Test the solution or a small portion of it before filtration to ensure that no crystals form at about 22°C. Like decolorization with charcoal, the removal of solid impurities by filtration is usually not necessary.

Microscale Procedure

(A) Removal of Solution with a Pasteur Pipette

Online Study Center

Video: Filtration of Crystals Using the Pasteur Pipette

If the solid impurities are large in size, they can be removed by filtration of the liquid through the small space between the square end of a Pasteur pipette and the bottom of a reaction tube (Fig. 4.3). Expel air from the pipette by squeezing the pipette bulb as the pipette is being pushed to the bottom of the tube. Use a small additional quantity of solvent to rinse the tube and pipette. Anhydrous calcium chloride, a drying agent, is easily removed in this way. The removal of very fine material, such as traces of charcoal, is facilitated by filtration of the solution through a small piece of filter paper (3 mm^2) placed in a reaction tube. This process is even easier if the filter paper is the thick variety, such as that from which Soxhlet extraction thimbles are made.[1]

(B) Filtration in a Pasteur Pipette

Online Study Center

Photo: Preparation of a Filter Pipette

To filter 0.1 mL to 2 mL of a solution, dilute the solution with enough solvent so that the solute will not recrystallize at about 22°C. Prepare a filter pipette by pushing a tiny bit of cotton into a Pasteur pipette, put the solution to be filtered into this filter pipette using another Pasteur pipette, and then force the liquid through the filter using air pressure from a pipette bulb (Fig. 4.4). Fresh solvent should be added to rinse the pipette and cotton. The filtered solution is then concentrated by evaporation. One problem encountered with this method is using too much cotton packed too tightly in the pipette so that the solution cannot be forced through it. To remove very fine impurities, such as traces of decolorizing charcoal, a 3-mm to 4-mm layer of Celite filter aid can be added to the top of the cotton.

(C) Removal of Fine Impurities by Centrifugation

To remove fine solid impurities from up to 4 mL of solution, dilute the solution with enough solvent so that the solute will not recrystallize at about 22°C. Counterbalance the reaction tube and centrifuge for about 2 min at high speed in a laboratory centrifuge. The clear supernatant can be decanted (poured off) from the solid on the bottom of the tube. Alternatively, with care, the solution can be removed with a Pasteur pipette, leaving the solid behind.

---

1. Belletire, J. L.; Mahmoodi, N. O. *J. Chem. Educ.* **1989**, *66*, 964.

■ **FIG. 4.3**
Filtration using a Pasteur
pipette and a reaction tube.

■ **FIG. 4.4**
Filtration of a solution in a
Pasteur pipette.

Pipette bulb

Pasteur pipette

Reaction tube

Note square,
flat tip

Solution
to be filtered

Cotton

Celite
(optional)

Online Study Center

Video: Microscale
Crystallization

Use filter paper on top
of frit.

Using the chromatography
column for pressure filtration

(D) Pressure Filtration with a Micro Büchner Funnel

The technique applicable to volumes from 0.1 mL to 5 mL is to use a micro
Büchner funnel. It is made of polyethylene and is fitted with a porous polyethylene frit that is 6 mm in diameter. This funnel fits in the bottom of an inexpensive
disposable polyethylene pipette in which a hole is cut (Fig. 4.5). The solution to
be filtered is placed in the pipette using a Pasteur pipette. The thumb covers the
hole in the plastic pipette and pressure is applied to filter the solution. It is good
practice to place a 6-mm-diameter piece of filter paper over the frit, which would
otherwise become clogged with insoluble material.

   The glass chromatography column can be used in the same way. A piece of
filter paper is placed over the frit. The solution to be filtered is placed in the chromatography column, and pressure is applied to the solution using a pipette bulb.
In both procedures, dilute the solution to be filtered so that it does not recrystallize in the apparatus and use a small amount of clean solvent to rinse the apparatus. The filtered solution is then concentrated by evaporation.

■ **FIG. 4.5**
A pressure filtration apparatus.
The solution to be filtered is
added through the aperture, which
is closed by a finger as pressure
is applied.

Filling
aperture

Polyethylene
transfer pipette

Polyethylene
frit

Büchner
funnel

■ **FIG. 4.6**
Gravity filtration of hot solution
through fluted filter paper.

 ## *Macroscale Procedure*

(A) Decantation

Decant: to pour off. A fast, easy
separation procedure

On a large scale, it is often possible to pour off (decant) the hot solution, leaving
the insoluble material behind. This is especially easy if the solid is granular like
sodium sulfate. The solid remaining in the flask and the inside of the flask should
be rinsed with a few milliliters of the solvent in order to recover as much of the
product as possible.

(B) Gravity Filtration

The most common method for the removal of insoluble solid material is gravity
filtration through fluted filter paper (Fig. 4.6). This is the method of choice for removing finely divided charcoal, dust, lint, and so on. The following equipment is
needed for this process: three labeled Erlenmeyer flasks on a steam bath or a hot
plate (flask A contains the solution to be filtered, flask B contains a few milliliters
of solvent and a stemless funnel, and flask C contains several milliliters of the
crystallizing solvent to be used for rinsing purposes), a fluted piece of filter paper,
a towel for holding the hot flask and drying out the stemless funnel, and boiling
chips for all solutions.

A piece of filter paper is fluted as shown in Figure 4.7 and is then placed in a
stemless funnel. Appropriate sizes of Erlenmeyer flasks, stemless funnels, and

■ **FIG. 4.7**
Fluting a piece of filter paper.

⚠
Be aware that the vapors of
low-boiling solvents can ignite
on an electric hot plate.

■ **FIG. 4.8**
Assemblies for gravity
filtration. Stemless funnels
have diameters of 2.5, 4.2,
5.0, and 6.0 cm.

filter paper are shown in Figure 4.8. The funnel is stemless so that the saturated solution being filtered will not have a chance to cool and clog the stem with crystals. The filter paper should fit entirely inside the rim of the funnel; it is fluted to allow rapid filtration. Test to see that the funnel is stable in the neck of flask B. If not, support it with a ring attached to a ring stand. A few milliliters of solvent and a boiling chip should be placed in flask B into which the solution is to be filtered. This solvent is brought to a boil on the steam bath or hot plate along with the solution to be filtered.

The solution to be filtered (in flask A) should be saturated with the solute at the boiling point. Note the volume and then add 10% more solvent (from flask C). The resulting slightly dilute solution is not as likely to recrystallize in the funnel during filtration. Bring the solution to be filtered to a boil, grasp flask A in a towel, and pour the solution into the filter paper in the stemless funnel equipped in flask B (Fig. 4.6). The funnel should be warm to prevent recrystallization from occurring in the funnel. This can be accomplished in two ways: (1) Invert the funnel over a steam bath for a few seconds, pick up the funnel with a towel, wipe it perfectly dry, place it on top of flask B, and then add the fluted filter paper; or (2) place the stemless funnel in the neck of flask B and allow the solvent to reflux into the funnel, thereby warming it.

Pour the solution to be filtered (in flask A) at a steady rate into the fluted filter paper (equipped in flask B). Check to see whether recrystallization is occurring in the filter. If it does, add boiling solvent (from flask C heated on a steam bath or a hot plate) until the crystals dissolve, dilute the solution being filtered, and carry on. Rinse flask A with a few milliliters of boiling solvent (from flask C) and rinse the fluted filter paper with this same solvent.

Because the filtrate has been diluted to prevent it from recrystallizing during the filtration process, the excess solvent must now be removed by boiling the solution. This process can be speeded up somewhat by blowing a slow current of air into the flask in the hood or using an aspirator tube to pull vapors into the aspirator (Fig. 4.9 and Fig. 4.10). However, the fastest method is to heat the solvent in the filter flask on a sand bath while the flask is connected to the water aspirator.

■ FIG. 4.9

An aspirator tube in use. A boiling stick may be necessary to promote boiling.

Aspirator tube
To water aspirator
Clamp here
Tared flask
Boiling stick
Steam in
Outlet to sink
Steam bath

■ FIG. 4.10

A tube being used to remove solvent vapors.

To water aspirator or to nitrogen or air supply

Pasteur pipette

Boiling stick

Hot sand bath

■ FIG. 4.11

Evaporation of a solvent under a vacuum.

Hirsch funnel

25-mL Filter flask

To water aspirator

Be sure that you are wearing gloves when doing this step!

The vacuum is controlled with the thumb (Fig. 4.11).[2] Be sure that you are wearing gloves when doing this step! If your thumb is not large enough, put a one-holed rubber stopper into the Hirsch funnel or the filter flask and again control the vacuum with your thumb. If the vacuum is not controlled, the solution may boil over and go out the vacuum hose.

Step 5. Recrystallizing the Solute

On both a macroscale and a microscale, the recrystallization process should normally start from a solution that is saturated with the solute at the boiling point. If it has been necessary to remove impurities or charcoal by filtration, the solution

2. See also Mayo, D. W.; Pike, R. M.; Butcher, S. M. *Microscale Organic Laboratory*; Wiley: New York, 1986; 97.

has been diluted. To concentrate the solution, simply boil off the solvent under an aspirator tube as shown in Figure 4.9 (macroscale) or blow off solvent using a gentle stream of air or, better, nitrogen in the hood as shown in Figure 4.10 (microscale). Be sure to have a boiling chip (macroscale) or a boiling stick (microscale) in the solution during this process but make sure you remove it before initiating recrystallization.

Once it has been ascertained that the hot solution is saturated with the compound just below the boiling point of the solvent, allow it to cool slowly to about 22°C. Slow cooling is a critical step in recrystallization. If the solution is not allowed to cool slowly, precipitation will occur, resulting in impurities "crashing out" of solution along with the desired solute; thus, no exclusion will occur. On a microscale, it is best to allow the reaction tube to cool in a beaker filled with cotton or paper towels, which acts as insulation, so cooling takes place slowly. Even insulated in this manner, the small reaction tube will cool to about 22°C within a few minutes. Slow cooling will guarantee the formation of large crystals, which are easily separated by filtration and easily washed free of adhering impure solvent. On a small scale, it is difficult to obtain crystals that are too large and occlude impurities. Once the tube has cooled to about 22°C without disturbance, it can be cooled in ice to maximize the amount of product that comes out of solution. On a macroscale, the Erlenmeyer flask is set atop a cork ring or other insulator and allowed to cool gradually to about 22°C. If the flask is moved during recrystallization, many nuclei will form, and the crystals will be small and have a large surface area. They will not be easy to filter and wash clean of the mother liquor. Once recrystallization ceases at about 22°C, the flask should be placed in ice to cool further. Make sure to clamp the flask in the ice bath so that it does not tip over.

With slow cooling, recrystallization should begin immediately. If not, add a seed crystal or scratch the inside of the tube with a glass rod at the liquid-air interface. Recrystallization must start on some nucleation center. A minute crystal of the desired compound saved from the crude material will suffice. If a seed crystal is not available, recrystallization can be started on the rough surface of a fresh scratch on the inside of the container.

Step 6. Collecting and Washing the Crystals

Once recrystallization is complete, the crystals must be separated from the ice-cold mother liquor, washed with ice-cold solvent, and dried.

Microscale Procedure

(A) Filtration Using a Pasteur Pipette

The most important filtration technique used in microscale organic experiments employs a Pasteur pipette (Fig. 4.12). About 70% of the crystalline products from the experiments in this text can be isolated in this way. The others will be isolated by filtration on a Hirsch funnel.

The ice-cold crystalline mixture is stirred with a Pasteur pipette and, while air is being expelled from the pipette, forced to the bottom of the reaction tube. The

A saturated solution

Slow cooling is important.

Online Study Center
Videos: Recrystallization, Microscale Crystallization

Add a seed crystal or scratch the tube.

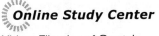
Online Study Center
Video: Filtration of Crystals Using the Pasteur Pipette

■ FIG. 4.12
Filtration using a Pasteur pipette
and a reaction tube.

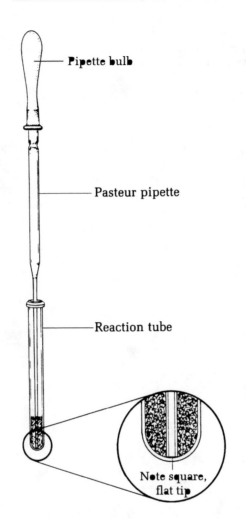

Pipette bulb

Pasteur pipette

Reaction tube

Note square,
flat tip

■ FIG. 4.13
Drying crystals under reduced pressure
in a reaction tube.

To aspirator

Glass tube

Thermometer
adapter

Reaction tube

Beaker
of warm
water

Crystals to
be dried

bulb is released, and the solvent is drawn into the pipette through the very small
space between the square tip of the pipette and the curved bottom of the reaction
tube. When all the solvent has been withdrawn, it is expelled into another reaction
tube. It is sometimes useful to rap the tube containing the wet crystals against a
hard surface to pack them so that more solvent can be removed. The tube is returned to the ice bath, and a few drops of cold solvent are added to the crystals.
The mixture is stirred to wash the crystals, and the solvent is again removed. This
process can be repeated as many times as necessary. Volatile solvents can be removed from the damp crystals under vacuum (Fig. 4.13). Alternatively, the last
traces of solvent can be removed by centrifugation using a Wilfilter (Fig. 4.14).

(B) Filtration Using a Hirsch Funnel

When the volume of material to be filtered is greater than 1.5 mL, collect the material on a Hirsch funnel. The Hirsch funnel in the Williamson/Kontes kit[3] is unique.
It is composed of polypropylene and has an integral molded stopper that fits the
25-mL filter flask. It comes fitted with a 20-μm polyethylene fritted disk, which is
not meant to be disposable, although it costs only about twice as much as an 11-cm

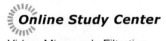

Online Study Center

Video: Microscale Filtration
on the Hirsch Funnel

_____

3. The microscale kit is available through Kontes (www.kontes.com).

■ **FIG. 4.14**

The Wilfilter filtration apparatus. Filtration occurs between the flat face of the polypropylene Wilfilter and the top of the reaction tube.

(a)   (b)

■ **FIG. 4.15**

The Hirsch funnel being used for vacuum filtration. This unique design has a removable and replaceable 20-μm polyethylene frit. No adapter is needed because there is a vacuum-tight fit to the filter flask. Always use a piece of filter paper.

piece of filter paper (Fig. 4.15). Although products can be collected directly on this disk, it is good practice to place an 11- or 12-mm-diameter piece of no. 1 filter paper on the disk. In this way the frit will not become clogged with insoluble impurities. The disk of filter paper can be cut with a cork borer or leather punch. A piece of filter paper *must* be used on the old-style porcelain Hirsch funnels.

Clamp the clean, dry 25-mL filter flask in an ice bath to prevent it from falling over and place the Hirsch funnel with filter paper in the flask. (The reason for cooling the filter flask is to keep the mother liquor cold so it will not dissolve the crystals on the Hirsch funnel when fresh cold solvent is used to wash crystals from the container onto the funnel.) In a separate flask, cool ~10 mL of solvent in an ice bath; this solvent is used for washing the recrystallization flask and for washing the crystals. Wet the filter paper with the solvent used in the recrystallization, turn on the water aspirator (see "The Water Aspirator and the Trap"), and ascertain that the filter paper is pulled down onto the frit. Pour and scrape the crystals and mother liquor onto the Hirsch funnel and, as soon as the liquid is gone from the crystals, break the vacuum at the filter flask by removing the rubber hose.

Rinse the recrystallization flask with ice-cold fresh solvent. Pour this rinse through the Hirsch funnel and reapply vacuum to the filter flask. As soon as all the liquid has disappeared from the crystals, wash the crystals with a few drops of ice-cold solvent. Repeat this washing process as many times as necessary to remove colored material or other impurities from the crystals. In some cases, only one very small wash will be needed. After the crystals have been washed with ice-cold solvent, the vacuum can be left on to dry the crystals. Sometimes it is useful to press solvent from the crystals by using a cork.

(C) Filtration with a Wilfilter (Replacing a Craig Tube)

The isolation of less than 100 mg of recrystallized material from a reaction tube (or any other container) is not easy. If the amount of solvent is large enough (1 mL or more), the material can be recovered by filtration on a Hirsch funnel. But when the volume of liquid is less than 1 mL, much product is left in the tube during transfer to a Hirsch funnel. The solvent can be removed with a Pasteur pipette pressed against the bottom of the tube, a very effective filtration technique, but scraping the damp crystals from the reaction tube results in major losses. If the solvent is relatively low boiling, it can be evaporated by connecting the tube to a water aspirator (*see* Fig. 4.13 on page 73). Once the crystals are dry, they are easily scraped from the tube with little or no loss. Some solvents—and water is the principal culprit—are not easily removed by evaporation. And even though removal of the solvent under vacuum is not terribly difficult, it takes time.

We have invented a filtration device that circumvents these problems: the Wilfilter. After recrystallization has ceased, most of the solvent is removed from the crystals using a Pasteur pipette in the usual way (*see* Fig. 4.12 on page 73). Then the polypropylene Wilfilter is placed on the top of the reaction tube followed by a 15-mL polypropylene centrifuge tube (*see* Fig. 4.14 on page 74). The assembly is inverted and placed in a centrifuge such as the International Clinical Centrifuge that holds twelve 15-mL tubes. The assembly, properly counterbalanced, is centrifuged for about 1 min at top speed. The centrifuge tube is removed from the centrifuge, and the reaction tube is then removed from the centrifuge tube. The three fingers on the Wilfilter keep it attached to the reaction tube. The filtrate is left in the centrifuge tube.

Filtration with the Wilfilter occurs between the top surface of the reaction tube and the flat surface of the Wilfilter. Liquid will pass through that space during centrifugation; crystals will not. The crystals will be found on top of the Wilfilter and inside the reaction tube. The very large centrifugal forces remove all the liquid, so the crystals will be virtually dry and thus easily removed from the reaction tube by shaking or scraping with the metal spatula.

The Wilfilter replaces an older device known as a Craig tube (Fig. 4.16), which consists of an outer tube of 1-, 2-, or 3-mL capacity with an inner plunger made of Teflon (expensive) or glass (fragile). The material to be recrystallized is transferred to the outer tube and recrystallized in the usual way. The inner plunger

Break the vacuum, add a very small quantity of ice-cold wash solvent, and reapply vacuum.

■ **FIG. 4.16**
The Craig tube filtration apparatus. Filtration occurs between the rough ground glass surfaces when the apparatus is centrifuged.

Rough ground glass surfaces

Crystals and solvent

Crystals

Centrifuge tube

Solvent

Online Study Center

Photo: Vacuum Filtration into Reaction Tube through Hirsch Funnel

Online Study Center

Video: Microscale Crystallization

is added, and a wire hanger is fashioned so that the assembly can be removed from the centrifuge tube without the plunger falling off. Filtration in this device occurs through the rough surface that has been ground into the shoulder of the outer tube.

The Wilfilter possesses several advantages: a special recrystallization device is not needed, no transfers of material are needed, it is not as limited in capacity (which is 4.5 mL), and its cost is one-fifth that of a Craig tube assembly.

(D) Filtration into a Reaction Tube on a Hirsch Funnel

If it is desired to have the filtrate in a reaction tube instead of spread on the bottom of the 25-mL filter flask, then the process described in the previous section can be carried out in the apparatus shown in Figure 4.17. The vacuum hose is connected to the side arm using the thermometer adapter and a short length of glass tubing. Evaporate the filtrate in the reaction tube to collect a second crop of crystals.

(E) Filtration into a Reaction Tube on a Micro Büchner Funnel

If the quantity of material being collected is very small, the bottom of the chromatography column is a micro Büchner funnel, which can be fitted into the top of the thermometer adapter, as shown in Figure 4.18. Again, it is good practice to cover the frit with a piece of 6-mm filter paper (cut with a cork borer).

(F) The Micro Büchner Funnel in an Enclosed Filtration Apparatus

In the apparatus shown in Figure 4.19, recrystallization is carried out in the upper reaction tube in the normal way. The apparatus is then turned upside down, the crystals are shaken down onto a micro Büchner funnel, and a vacuum is applied

■ FIG. 4.17

A microscale Hirsch filtration assembly. The Hirsch funnel gives a vacuum-tight seal to the 105° adapter.

Hirsch funnel with fritted disk

To aspirator

■ FIG. 4.18

Filtration using a microscale Büchner funnel.

Micro Büchner funnel with fritted disk (base of chromatography column)

Thermometer adapter

To aspirator

Vacuum-tight connector also serves as clamp for apparatus

Reaction tube with filtrate

■ FIG. 4.19

The Schlenk-type filtration apparatus. The apparatus is inverted to carry out the filtration.

Micro Büchner funnel with fritted disk

To aspirator

■ FIG. 4.20

Matching filter assemblies. The 6.0-cm polypropylene Büchner funnel (right) resists breakage and can be disassembled for cleaning.

Büchner funnels

No. 2 7.5 cm

No. 0 4.2 cm

No. 000 5 cm

Hirsch funnel

Neoprene adapter

250 mL

125 mL

50 mL

6 cm

7 cm

4.25 cm

3.3 cm

5.5 cm

through the side arm. In this apparatus, crystals can be collected in an oxygen-free atmosphere (Schlenk conditions).

Macroscale Apparatus

Filtration on a Hirsch Funnel and a Büchner Funnel

If the quantity of material is small (<2 g), a Hirsch funnel can be used in exactly the way described in a previous section. For larger quantities, a Büchner funnel is used. Properly matched Büchner funnels, filter paper, and flasks are shown in Figure 4.20. The Hirsch funnel shown in the figure has a 5-cm bottom plate to accept 3.3-cm paper.

Clamp the filter flask.

Place a piece of filter paper in the bottom of the Büchner funnel. Wet it with solvent and be sure it lies flat so that crystals cannot escape around the edge and under the filter paper. Then, with the vacuum off, pour the cold slurry of crystals into the center of the filter paper. Apply the vacuum; as soon as the liquid disappears from the crystals, break the vacuum to the flask by disconnecting the hose. Rinse the Erlenmeyer flask with cold solvent. Add this to the crystals and reapply the vacuum just until the liquid disappears from the crystals. Repeat this process as many times as necessary and then leave the vacuum on to dry the crystals.

The Water Aspirator and Trap

The most common way to produce a vacuum for filtration in the organic laboratory is by employing a *water aspirator*. Air is entrained efficiently in the water rushing through the aspirator to produce a vacuum roughly equal to the vapor pressure of the water going through it (17 torr at 20°C, 5 torr at 4°C). A check valve is built into the aspirator, but when the water is turned off, it will often back up into the evacuated system. For this reason a *trap* is always installed in the line (Fig. 4.21). *The water passing through the aspirator should always be turned on full force.*

Opening the screw clamp on the trap can open the system to the atmosphere as well as removing the hose from the small filter flask. Open the system and then turn

■ **FIG. 4.21**
An aspirator, a filter trap, and a funnel. Clamp the small filter flask to prevent it from turning over.

Clamp

Thin-walled tubing

Two-hole rubber stopper

Splashgon

Heavy-walled tubing

500-mL Filter flask

25-mL
Filter flask

off the water to avoid having water sucked back into the filter trap. Thin rubber tubing on the top of the trap will collapse and bend over when a good vacuum is established. You will, in time, learn to hear the differences in the sound of an aspirator when it is pulling a vacuum and when it is working on an open system.

Collecting a Second Crop of Crystals

Regardless of the method used to collect crystals on either a macroscale or a microscale, the filtrate and washings can be combined and evaporated to the point of saturation to obtain a second crop of crystals—hence this advocates having a clean receptacle for the filtrate. This second crop will increase the overall yield, but the crystals will not usually be as pure as the first crop.

Step 7. Drying the Product

Microscale Procedure

Online Study Center
Video: Recrystallization

If possible, dry the product in the reaction tube after removing the solvent with a Pasteur pipette. Simply connecting the tube to the water aspirator can do this. If the tube is clamped in a beaker of hot water, the solvent will evaporate more rapidly under vacuum but make sure not to melt the product (*see* Fig. 4.13 on page 73). Water, which has a high heat of vaporization, is difficult to remove in this way. Scrape the product onto a watch glass and allow it to dry to constant weight, which will indicate that all the solvent has been removed. If the product is collected on a Hirsch funnel or a Wilfilter, the last traces of solvent can be removed by squeezing the crystals between sheets of filter paper before drying them on the watch glass.

Macroscale Procedure

Once the crystals have been washed on a Hirsch funnel or a Büchner funnel, press them down with a clean cork or other flat object and allow air to pass through them until they are substantially dry. Final drying can be done under reduced pressure (Fig. 4.22). The crystals can then be turned out of the funnel and squeezed between sheets of filter paper to remove the last traces of solvent before final drying on a watch glass.

■ FIG. 4.22
Drying a solid by reduced air pressure.

Experiments
1. Solubility Tests

To test the solubility of a solid, transfer an amount roughly estimated to be about 10 mg (the amount that forms a symmetrical mound on the end of a stainless steel spatula) into a reaction tube and add about 0.25 mL of solvent from a calibrated dropper or pipette. Stir with a fire-polished stirring rod that is 4 mm in diameter, break up any lumps, and determine if the solid is readily soluble at room temperature (about 22°C). If the substance is readily soluble at about 22°C in methanol, ethanol, acetone, or acetic acid, add a few drops of water from a wash bottle to see if a solid precipitates. If so, heat the mixture, adjust the composition of the solvent pair to

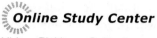

Test Compounds:

OH
OH

Resorcinol

Anthracene

O   OH
C

Benzoic acid

SO₃⁻ Na⁺

NH₂

4-Amino-1-naphthalenesulfonic acid, sodium salt

produce a hot solution saturated at the boiling point, let the solution stand undisturbed, and note the character of the crystals that form.

If the substance fails to dissolve in a given solvent at about 22°C, heat the suspension and observe if a solution occurs. If the solvent is flammable, heat the test tube on a steam bath or in a small beaker of water kept warm on a steam bath or a hot plate. If the solid dissolves completely, it can be declared readily soluble in the hot solvent; if some but not all dissolves, it is said to be moderately soluble, and further small amounts of solvent should then be added until solution is complete.

When a substance has been dissolved in hot solvent, cool the solution by holding the flask under the tap and, if necessary, induce recrystallization by rubbing the walls of the tube with a stirring rod to make sure that the concentration permits recrystallization. Then reheat to dissolve the solid, let the solution stand undisturbed, and inspect the character of the ultimate crystals.

Perform solubility tests on the test compounds shown in the margin in each of the the following solvents: water (hydroxylic and ionic), toluene (an aromatic hydrocarbon), and ligroin (a mixture of aliphatic hydrocarbons). Note the degree of solubility in the solvents—cold and hot—and suggest suitable solvents, solvent pairs, or other expedients for the recrystallization of each substance. Record the crystal form, at least to the extent of distinguishing between needles (pointed crystals), plates (flat and thin), and prisms. How do your observations conform to the generalization that like dissolves like?

Cleaning Up. Place organic solvents and solutions of the compounds in the organic solvents container. Dilute the aqueous solutions with water and flush down the drain. (For this and all other "Cleaning Up" sections, refer to the complete discussion of waste disposal procedures in Chapter 2.)

2. Recrystallization of Pure Phthalic Acid, Naphthalene, and Anthracene

COOH
COOH

Phthalic acid

Naphthalene

Anthracene

The process of recrystallization can be readily observed using phthalic acid. In the *CRC Handbook of Chemistry and Physics*, in the table "Physical Constants of Organic Compounds," the entry for phthalic acid gives the following solubility data (in grams of solute per 100 mL of solvent). The superscripts refer to temperature in degrees Celsius:

Water	Alcohol	Ether, etc.
0.54[14]	11.71[18]	0.69[15] eth., i. chl.
18[99]		

The large difference in solubility in water as a function of temperature suggests that water is the solvent of choice. The solubility in alcohol is high at about 22°C. Ether is difficult to use because it is so volatile; the compound is insoluble in chloroform (i. chl.).

Microscale Procedure for Phthalic Acid

Online Study Center

Video: Recrystallization

Set the heater control to about 20% of the maximum.

Recrystallize 60 mg (0.060 g) of phthalic acid from the minimum volume of water, using the previous data to calculate the required volume. First, turn on an electrically heated sand bath. Add the solid to a 10 × 100 mm reaction tube and add water dropwise with a Pasteur pipette. Use the calibration marks found in Chapter 1 (*see* Fig. 1.18 on page 19) to measure the volume of water in the pipette and the reaction tube. Add a boiling stick (a wood applicator stick) to facilitate even boiling and prevent bumping. After a portion of the water has been added, gently heat the solution to boiling on a hot sand bath in the electric heater. The deeper the tube is placed in the sand, the hotter it will be. As soon as boiling begins, continue to add water dropwise until the entire solid just dissolves. Cork the tube, clamp it as it cools, and observe the phenomenon of recrystallization.

Alternate procedure: Dry the crystals under vacuum in a steam bath in the reaction tube.

After the tube reaches about 22°C, cool it in ice, stir the crystals with a Pasteur pipette, and expel the air from the pipette as the tip is pushed to the bottom of the tube. When the tip is firmly and squarely seated in the bottom of the tube, release the bulb and withdraw the water. Rap the tube sharply on a wood surface to compress the crystals and remove as much of the water as possible with the pipette. Then cool the tube in ice and add a few drops of ice-cold ethanol to the tube to remove water from the crystals. Connect the tube to a water aspirator and warm it in a beaker of hot water (*see* Fig. 4.13 on page 73). Once all the solvent is removed, using the stainless steel spatula, scrape the crystals onto a piece of filter paper, fold the paper over the crystals, and squeeze out excess water before allowing the crystals to dry to constant weight. Weigh the dry crystals and calculate the percent recovery of product.

Microscale Procedure for Naphthalene and Anthracene

These compounds can also be isolated using a Wilfilter.

Following the previous procedure, recrystallize 40 mg of naphthalene from 80% aqueous methanol or 10 mg of anthracene from ethanol. You may find it more convenient to use a hot water bath to heat these low-boiling alcohols. These are more typical of compounds to be recrystallized in later experiments because they are soluble in organic solvents. It will be much easier to remove these solvents from the crystals under vacuum than it is to remove water from phthalic acid. You will seldom encounter the need to recrystallize less than 30 mg of a solid in these experiments.

Cleaning Up. Dilute the aqueous filtrate with water and flush the solution down the drain. Phthalic acid is not considered toxic to the environment and can be recycled for future recrystallization experiments. Methanol and ethanol filtrates go into the organic solvents container.

Macroscale Procedure

Using the solubility data for phthalic acid to calculate the required volume, recrystallize 1.0 g of phthalic acid from the minimum volume of water. Add the solid to the smallest practical Erlenmeyer flask and then, using a Pasteur pipette, add water dropwise from a full 10-mL graduated cylinder. A boiling stick (a wood applicator stick) facilitates even boiling and will prevent bumping. After a portion of the water has been added, gently heat the solution to boiling on a hot plate. As soon as boiling begins, continue to add water dropwise until the entire solid dissolves. Place the flask on a cork ring or other insulator and allow it to cool undisturbed to about 22°C, during which time the recrystallization process can be observed. Slow cooling favors large crystals. Then cool the flask in an ice bath, decant (pour off) the mother liquor (the liquid remaining with the crystals), and remove the last traces of liquid with a Pasteur pipette. Scrape the crystals onto a filter paper using a stainless steel spatula, squeeze the crystals between sheets of filter paper to remove traces of moisture, and allow the crystals to dry. Alternatively, the crystals can be collected on a Hirsch funnel. Compare the calculated volume of water to the volume of water actually used to dissolve the acid. Calculate the percent recovery of dry, recrystallized phthalic acid.

Cleaning Up. Dilute the filtrate with water and flush the solution down the drain. Phthalic acid is not considered toxic to the environment and can be recycled for future recrystallization experiments.

3. Decolorizing a Solution with Decolorizing Charcoal

Into a reaction tube place 1.0 mL of a solution of methylene blue dye that has a concentration of 10 mg per 100 mL of water. Add to the tube about 10 or 12 pieces of decolorizing charcoal, shake, and observe the color over a period of 1–2 min. Heat the contents of the tube to boiling (reflux) and observe the color by holding the tube in front of a piece of white paper from time to time. How rapidly is the color removed? If the color is not removed in a minute or so, add more charcoal pellets.

Cleaning Up. Place the Norit in the nonhazardous solid waste container.

4. Decolorization of Brown Sugar (Sucrose, $C_{12}H_{22}O_{11}$)

Raw sugar is refined commercially with the aid of decolorizing charcoal. The clarified solution is seeded generously with small sugar crystals, and excess water is removed under vacuum to facilitate recrystallization. The pure white crystalline product is collected by centrifugation. Brown sugar is partially refined sugar and can be easily decolorized using charcoal.

In a 50-mL Erlenmeyer flask, dissolve 15 g of dark brown sugar in 30 mL of water by heating and stirring. Pour half the solution into another 50-mL flask. Heat one of the solutions nearly to its boiling point, allow it to cool slightly, and add 250 mg (0.25 g) of decolorizing charcoal (Norit pellets) to it. Bring the solution back to near the boiling point for 2 min; then filter the hot solution into an Erlenmeyer flask through a fluted filter paper held in a previously heated funnel. Treat the other half of the sugar solution in exactly the same way but use only 50 mg of decolorizing charcoal. In collaboration with a fellow student, try heating the solutions for only 15 s after adding the charcoal. Compare your results.

Cleaning Up. Decant (pour off) the aqueous layer. Place the Norit in the nonhazardous solid waste container. The sugar solution can be flushed down the drain.

5. Recrystallization of Benzoic Acid from Water and a Solvent Pair

COOH

Benzoic acid

Recrystallize 50 mg of benzoic acid from water in the same way phthalic acid was recrystallized. Then in a dry reaction tube dissolve another 50-mg sample of benzoic acid in the minimum volume of hot methanol and add water to the hot solution dropwise. When the hot solution becomes cloudy and recrystallization has begun, allow the tube to cool slowly to about 22°C; then cool it in ice and collect the crystals. Compare recrystallization in water to that in the solvent pair.

Cleaning Up. The methanol-water solution can be disposed in the organic solvents waste container or, if regulations permit, diluted with water and flushed down the drain.

6. Recrystallization of Naphthalene from a Mixed Solvent

Naphthalene

Do not try to grasp Erlenmeyer flasks with a test tube holder.

Support the funnel in a ring stand.

Add 2.0 g of impure naphthalene (a mixture of 100 g of naphthalene, 0.3 g of a dye such as Congo Red, and another substance such as magnesium sulfate, or dust) to a 50-mL Erlenmeyer flask along with 3 mL of methanol and a boiling stick to promote even boiling. Heat the mixture to boiling over a steam bath or a hot plate and then add methanol dropwise until the naphthalene just dissolves when the solvent is boiling. The total volume of methanol should be 4 mL. Remove the flask from the heat and cool it rapidly in an ice bath. Note that the contents of the flask set to a solid mass, which would be impossible to handle. Add enough methanol to bring the total volume to 25 mL, heat the solution to its boiling point, remove the flask from the heat, allow it to cool slightly, and add 30 mg of decolorizing charcoal pellets to remove the colored impurity in the solution. Heat the solution to its boiling point for 2 min; if the color is not gone, add more Norit and boil again, and then filter through a fluted filter paper in a previously warmed stemless funnel into a 50-mL Erlenmeyer flask. Sometimes filtration is slow because the funnel fits so snugly into the mouth of the flask that a back pressure develops. If you note that raising the funnel increases the flow of filtrate, fold a small strip of paper two or three times and insert it between the funnel and flask. Wash the used flask with 2 mL of hot methanol and use this liquid to wash the filter paper, transferring the solvent with a Pasteur pipette in a succession of drops around the upper rim of the filter paper. When the filtration is complete, the volume of methanol should be 15 mL. If it is not, evaporate the excess methanol.

Because the filtrate is far from being saturated with naphthalene at this point, it will not yield crystals on cooling; however, the solubility of naphthalene in methanol can be greatly reduced by the addition of water. Heat the solution to its boiling point and add water dropwise from a 10-mL graduated cylinder using a Pasteur pipette (or a precalibrated pipette). After each addition of water, the solution will become cloudy for an instant. Swirl the contents of the flask and heat to redissolve any precipitated naphthalene. After the addition of 3.5 mL of water, the solution will almost be saturated with naphthalene at the boiling point of the solvent. Remove the flask from the heat and place it on a cork ring or other insulating surface to cool, without being disturbed, to about 22°C.

Immerse the flask in an ice bath along with another flask containing a 30:7 mixture of methanol and water. This cold solvent will be used for washing the crystals. The cold recrystallization mixture is collected by vacuum filtration on a small 50-mm Büchner funnel (Fig. 4.23). The water flowing through the aspirator should always be turned on full force. In collecting the product by suction filtration, use a spatula to dislodge crystals and ease them out of the flask. If crystals still remain in the flask, some filtrate can be poured back into the recrystallization flask as a rinse for washing as often as desired because it is saturated with solute. To free the crystals from contaminating the mother liquor, break the suction, pour a few milliliters of the fresh cold solvent mixture into the Büchner funnel, and immediately reapply suction. Repeat this process until the crystals and the filtrate are free of color. Press the crystals with a clean cork to eliminate excess solvent, pull air through the filter cake for a few minutes, and then put the large, flat, platelike crystals out on a filter paper to dry. The yield of pure white crystalline naphthalene

■ **FIG. 4.23**
A suction filter assembly clamped to provide firm support. The funnel must be pressed down on the Filtervac to establish reduced pressure in the flask.

Filtervac

should be about 1.6 g. The mother liquor contains about 0.25 g, and about 0.15 g is retained in the charcoal and on the filter paper.

Cleaning Up. Place the Norit in the nonhazardous solid waste container. The methanol filtrate and washings are placed in the organic solvents container.

7. Purification of an Unknown

Recall the seven-step recrystallization procedure:

1. Choose the solvent.
2. Dissolve the solute.
3. Decolorize the solution (if necessary).
4. Filter suspended solids (if necessary).
5. Recrystallize the solute.
6. Collect and wash the crystals.
7. Dry the product.

You will purify an unknown provided by your instructor, 2.0 g if working on a macroscale and 100 mg if working on a microscale. Conduct tests for solubility and the ability to recrystallize in several organic solvents, solvent pairs, and water. Conserve your unknown by using very small quantities for the solubility tests. If only a drop or two of solvent is used, heating the test tube on a steam bath or a sand bath can evaporate the solvent, and the residue can be used for another test. If decolorization is necessary, dilute the solution before filtration. It is very difficult to filter a hot, saturated solution from decolorizing carbon without recrystallization occurring in the filtration apparatus. Evaporate the decolorized solution to the point of saturation and proceed with the recrystallization. Submit as much pure product as possible with evidence of its purity (i.e., the melting point). From the posted list identify the unknown. If an authentic sample is available, your identification can be verified by a mixed melting point determination (*see* Chapter 3).

Cleaning Up. Place decolorizing charcoal, if used, and filter paper in the nonhazardous solid waste container. Put organic solvents in the organic solvents container and flush aqueous solutions down the drain.

Recrystallization Problems and Their Solutions

Induction of Crystallization

Occasionally, a sample will not crystallize from solution on cooling, even though the solution is saturated with the solute at elevated temperature. The easiest method for inducing crystallization is to add to the supersaturated solution Seeding a seed crystal that has been saved from the crude material (if it was crystalline before crystallization was attempted). In a probably apocryphal tale, the great sugar chemist Emil Fischer merely had to wave his beard over a recalcitrant solution, and the appropriate seed crystals would drop out, causing recrystallization to occur. In the absence of seed crystals, scratching the inside of the flask with a stirring rod at the liquid-air interface can often induce recrystallization. One theory holds that part of the freshly scratched glass surface has angles and planes corresponding to the crystal structure, and crystals start growing on these spots. Recrystallization is often very slow to begin. Placing the sample in a refrigerator overnight will bring success. Other expedients are to change the solvent (usually to a less soluble one) and to place the sample in an open container where slow evaporation and dust from the air may help induce recrystallization.

Scratching

Oils and "Oiling Out"

When cooled, some saturated solutions—especially those containing water—deposit not crystals but small droplets referred to as oils. "Oiling out" occurs when the temperature of the solution is above the melting point of the crystals. If these droplets solidify and are collected, they will be found to be quite impure. Similarly, the melting point of the desired compound may be depressed to a point such that a low-melting eutectic mixture of the solute and the solvent comes out of solution. The simplest remedy for this problem is to lower the temperature at which the solution becomes saturated with the solute by simply adding more solvent. In extreme cases it may be necessary to lower this temperature well below 22°C by cooling the solution with dry ice. If oiling out persists, use another solvent.

Online Study Center

Video: Formation of an Oil Instead of Crystals

Crystallize at a lower temperature

Recrystallization Summary

Online Study Center

Video: Picking a Solvent

Video: Recrystallization

Video: Decolorization of a Solution with Norit

Photo: Preparation of a Filter Pipette; Video: Microscale Crystallization

1. **Choosing the solvent.** "Like dissolves like." Some common solvents are water, methanol, ethanol, ligroin, and toluene. When you use a solvent pair, dissolve the solute in the better solvent and add the poorer solvent to the hot solution until saturation occurs. Some common solvent pairs are ethanol-water, ether-ligroin, and toluene-ligroin.
2. **Dissolving the solute.** In an Erlenmeyer flask or reaction tube, add solvent to the crushed or ground solute and heat the mixture to boiling. Add more solvent as necessary to obtain a hot, saturated solution.
3. **Decolorizing the solution.** If it is necessary to remove colored impurities, cool the solution to about 22°C and add more solvent to prevent recrystallization from occurring. Add decolorizing charcoal in the form of pelletized Norit to the cooled solution and then heat it to boiling for a few minutes, making sure to swirl the solution to prevent bumping. Remove the Norit by filtration and then concentrate the filtrate.
4. **Filtering suspended solids.** If it is necessary to remove suspended solids, dilute the hot solution slightly to prevent recrystallization from occurring during filtration. Filter the hot solution. Add solvent if recrystallization begins in the funnel. Concentrate the filtrate to obtain a saturated solution.

Photo: Recrystallization; Video: Recrystallization

5. Recrystallizing the solute.   Let the hot saturated solution cool to about 22°C spontaneously. Do not disturb the solution. Then cool it in ice. If recrystallization does not occur, scratch the inside of the container or add seed crystals.

Photos: Use of the Wilfilter, Filtration Using a Pasteur Pipette; Videos: Microscale Filtration on the Hirsch Funnel, Filtration of Crystals Using the Pasteur Pipette

6. Collecting and washing the crystals.   Collect the crystals using the Pasteur pipette method, the Wilfilter, or by vacuum filtration on a Hirsch funnel or a Büchner funnel. If the latter technique is employed, wet the filter paper with solvent, apply vacuum, break vacuum, add crystals and liquid, apply vacuum until solvent just disappears, break vacuum, add cold wash solvent, apply vacuum, and repeat until crystals are clean and filtrate comes through clear.

Photo: Drying Crystals Under Vacuum; Video: Recrystallization

7. Drying the product.   Press the product on the filter to remove solvent. Then remove it from the filter, squeeze it between sheets of filter paper to remove more solvent, and spread it on a watch glass to dry.

QUESTIONS

1. A sample of naphthalene, which should be pure white, was found to have a grayish color after the usual purification procedure. The melting point was correct, and the melting point range was small. Explain the gray color.
2. How many milliliters of boiling water are required to dissolve 25 g of phthalic acid? If the solution were cooled to 14°C, how many grams of phthalic acid would recrystallize out?
3. Why should activated carbon be used during a recrystallization?
4. If a little activated charcoal does a good job removing impurities in a recrystallization, why not use a larger quantity?
5. Under which circumstances is it wise to use a mixture of solvents to carry out a recrystallization?
6. Why is gravity filtration rather than suction filtration used to remove suspended impurities and charcoal from a hot solution?
7. Why is a fluted filter paper used in gravity filtration?
8. Why are stemless funnels used instead of long-stem funnels to filter hot solutions through fluted filter paper?
9. Why is the final product from the recrystallization process isolated by vacuum filtration rather than gravity filtration?

CHAPTER
5

Distillation

Online Study Center

This icon will direct you to techniques, equipment setups, and online resources at http://college.hmco.com/PIC/williamsonMMOE5e.

Distillation is a common method for purifying liquids and can be used to determine their boiling points.

PRELAB EXERCISE: Predict what a plot of temperature versus the volume of distillate will look like for the simple distillation and the fractional distillation of (a) a cyclohexane-toluene mixture and (b) an ethanol-water mixture.

The origins of distillation are lost in antiquity, when humans in their thirst for more potent beverages found that dilute solutions of fermented alcohol could be separated into alcohol-rich and water-rich portions by heating the solution to boiling and condensing the vapors above the boiling liquid—the process of distillation.

Because ethyl alcohol (ethanol) boils at 78°C and water boils at 100°C, one might naively assume that heating a 50:50 mixture of ethanol and water to 78°C would cause the ethanol molecules to leave the solution as a vapor that could be condensed as pure ethanol. However, in such a mixture of ethanol and water, the water boils at about 87°C, and the vapor above the mixture is not 100% ethanol.

A liquid contains closely packed but mobile molecules of varying energy. When a molecule of the liquid approaches the vapor-liquid boundary and possesses sufficient energy, it may pass from the liquid phase into the gas phase. Some of the molecules present in the vapor phase above the liquid may, as they approach the surface of the liquid, reenter the liquid phase and thus become part of the condensed phase. In so doing, the molecules relinquish some of their kinetic energy (i.e., their motion is slowed). Heating the liquid causes more molecules to enter the vapor phase; cooling the vapor reverses this process.

When a closed system is at equilibrium, many molecules are escaping into the vapor phase from the liquid phase, and an equal number are returning from the vapor phase to the liquid phase. The extent of this equilibrium is measured as the vapor pressure. Even when energy is increased and more molecules in the liquid phase have sufficient energy to escape into the vapor phase, equilibrium is maintained because the number moving from the vapor phase into the liquid phase also increases. However, the number of molecules in the vapor phase increases, which increases the vapor pressure. The number of molecules in the vapor phase depends primarily on the volume of the system, the temperature, the combined pressure of all the gaseous components, and the strength of the intermolecular forces exerted in the liquid phase. Review the introduction to Chapter 3 about the types of intermolecular forces.

Simple Distillation

Simple distillation involves boiling a liquid in a vessel (a distilling flask) and directing the resulting vapors through a condenser, in which the vapors are cooled and converted to a liquid that flows back into a collection vessel (a receiving flask). (*See* Fig. 5.5 on page 95.) Simple distillation is used to purify liquid mixtures by separating one liquid component either from nonvolatile substances or from another liquid that differs in boiling point by at least 75°C. The initial condensate will have essentially the same mole ratio of liquids as the vapor just above the boiling liquid. The closer the boiling points of the components of a liquid mixture, the more difficult they are to completely separate by simple distillation.

Fractional Distillation

Fractional distillation differs from simple distillation in that a fractionating column is placed between the distilling flask and the condenser. This fractionating column allows for successive condensations and distillations and produces a much better separation between liquids with boiling points closer than 75°C. The column is packed with material that provides a large surface area for heat exchange between the ascending vapor and the descending liquid. As a result, multiple condensations and vaporizations occur as the vapors ascend the column. Condensing of the higher-boiling vapor releases heat, which causes vaporization of the lower-boiling liquid on the packing so that the lower-boiling component moves up while the higher-boiling component moves down. Some of the lower-boiling component will run back into the distilling flask. Each successive condensation-vaporization cycle, also called a *theoretical plate*, produces a vapor that is richer in the more volatile fraction. As the temperature of the liquid mixture is increased, the lower-boiling fractions become enriched in the vapor.

Heat exchange between ascending vapor and descending liquid

A large surface area for the packing material is desirable, but the packing cannot be so dense that pressure changes take place within the column to cause nonequilibrium conditions. Also, if the column packing has a very large surface area, it will absorb (hold up) much of the material being distilled. Several different packings for distilling columns have been tried, including glass beads, glass helices, and carborundum chips. One of the best packings in our experience is a copper or steel sponge (Chore Boy). It is easy to insert into the column; it does not come out of the column as beads do; and it has a large surface area, good heat transfer characteristics, and low holdup. It can be used in both microscale and macroscale apparatus.

Column packing

Holdup: unrecoverable distillate that wets the column packing

The ability of different column packings to separate two materials of differing boiling points is evaluated by calculating the number of theoretical plates. Each theoretical plate corresponds to one condensation-vaporization cycle. Other things being equal, the number of theoretical plates is proportional to the height of

Height equivalent to a theoretical plate (HETP)

Equilibration is slow.

Good fractional distillation takes a long time.

■ FIG. 5.1
A bubble plate distilling column.

Overflow pipe

Plate

Riser for vapor

the column, so various packings are evaluated according to the *height equivalent to a theoretical plate (HETP)*; the smaller the HETP, the more plates the column will have and the more efficient it will be. The calculation is made by analyzing the proportion of lower- to higher-boiling material at the top of the column and in the distillation pot.[1]

Although not obvious, the most important variable that contributes to good fractional distillation is the rate at which the distillation is carried out. A series of simple distillations take place within a fractionating column, and it is important that complete equilibrium be attained between the ascending vapors and the descending liquid. This process is not instantaneous. It should be an adiabatic process; that is, heat should be transferred from the ascending vapor to the descending liquid with no gain of heat or net heat loss to the surroundings. Advanced distillation systems use thermally insulated, vacuum-jacketed fractionating columns. They also allow the adjustment of the ratio between the amount of condensate that is directed to the receiving flask and the amount returned to the distillation column. A reflux ratio of 30:1 or 50:1 is not uncommon for a 40-plate column. Although a distillation of this type takes several hours, this is far less time than if one to had to do 40 distillations, one after the other, and yields much better separated compounds.

Perhaps it is easiest to understand the series of redistillations that occur in fractional distillation by examining the bubble plate column used to fractionally distill crude oil (Fig. 5.1). These columns dominate the skyline at oil refineries, with some being 150 ft high and capable of distilling 200,000 barrels of crude oil per day. The crude oil enters the column as a hot vapor. Some of this vapor with high-boiling components condenses on one of the plates. The more volatile substances travel through the bubble cap to the next higher plate, where some of the less-volatile components condense. As high-boiling liquid material accumulates on a plate, it descends through the overflow pipe to the next lower plate, and vapor rises through the bubble cap to the next higher plate. The temperature of the vapor that is rising through a cap is above the boiling point of the liquid on that plate. As bubbling takes place, heat is exchanged, and the less volatile components on that plate vaporize and go on to the next plate. The composition of the liquid on a plate is the same as that of the vapor coming from the plate below. So, on each plate a simple distillation takes place. At equilibrium, vapor containing low-boiling material is ascending through the column, and high-boiling liquid is descending.

As a purification method, distillation, particularly fractional distillation, requires larger amounts of material than recrystallization, liquid/liquid extraction, or chromatography. Performing a fractional distillation on less than 1 g of material is virtually impossible. Fractional distillation can be carried out on a scale of about 3–4 g. As will be seen in Chapters 8, 9, and 10, various types of chromatography are employed for separations of milligram quantities of liquids.

1. Weissberger, A., ed. *Techniques of Organic Chemistry*, Vol. IV; Wiley-Interscience: New York, 1951.

Liquid Mixtures

If two different liquid compounds are mixed, the vapor above the mixture will contain some molecules of each component. Let us consider a mixture of cyclohexane and toluene. The vapor pressures, as a function of temperature, are plotted in Figure 5.2. When the vapor pressure of the liquid equals the applied pressure, the liquid boils. Figure 5.2 shows that, at 760 mm Hg (standard atmospheric pressure), these pure liquids boil at about 81°C and 111°C, respectively. If one of these pure liquids were to be distilled, we would find that the boiling point of the liquid would equal the temperature of the vapor and that the temperature of the vapor would remain constant throughout the distillation.

Figure 5.3 is a boiling point–composition diagram for the cyclohexane-toluene system. If a mixture of 75 mole percent toluene and 25 mole percent cyclohexane is heated, we find that it boils at 100°C (point A). Above a binary mixture of cyclohexane and toluene, the vapor pressure has contributions from each component. Raoult's law states that the vapor pressure of the cyclohexane is equal to the product of the vapor pressure of pure cyclohexane and the mole fraction of cyclohexane in the liquid mixture:

Raoult's law of partial pressures

$$P_c = P_c^\circ N_c$$

where P_c is the partial pressure of cyclohexane, P_c° is the vapor pressure of pure cyclohexane at the given temperature, and N_c is the mole fraction of cyclohexane in the mixture. For toluene,

The mole fraction of cyclohexane is equal to the moles of cyclohexane in the mixture divided by the total number of moles (cyclohexane plus toluene) in the mixture.

$$P_t = P_t^\circ N_t$$

FIG. 5.2

Vapor pressure versus temperature plots for cyclohexane and toluene.

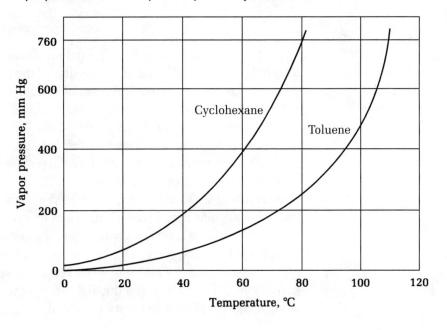

■ FIG. 5.3
Boiling point–composition curves
for a mixture of cyclohexane and
toluene.

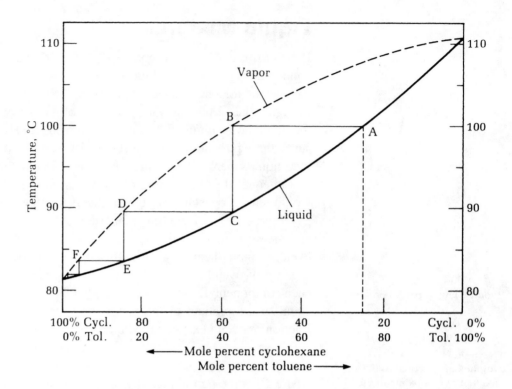

The total vapor pressure above the solution (P_{Tot}) is given by the sum of the partial pressures due to cyclohexane and toluene:

$$P_{Tot} = P_c + P_t$$

Dalton's law states that the mole fraction of cyclohexane (X_c) in the vapor at a given temperature is equal to the partial pressure of the cyclohexane at that temperature divided by the total pressure:

$$X_c = \frac{P_c}{\text{total vapor pressure}}$$

At 100°C cyclohexane has a partial pressure of 433 mm Hg, and toluene has a partial pressure of 327 mm Hg; the sum of the partial pressures is 760 mm Hg, so the liquid boils. If some of the liquid in equilibrium with this boiling mixture were condensed and analyzed, it would be found to be 433/760, or 57 mole percent cyclohexane (point B, Fig. 5.3). This is the best separation that can be achieved on a simple distillation of this mixture. As the simple distillation proceeds, the boiling point of the mixture moves toward 111°C along the line from point A, and the vapor composition becomes richer in toluene as it moves from point B to 110°C. To obtain pure cyclohexane, it would be necessary to condense the liquid at point B and redistill it. When this is done, it is found that the liquid boils at 90°C (point C), and the vapor equilibrium with this liquid is about 85 mole percent cyclohexane (point D). Therefore, to separate a mixture of cyclohexane and toluene, a series of fractions would be collected, and each of these would be partially redistilled. If this fractional distillation were done enough times, the two components could be completely separated.

Azeotropes

Not all liquids form ideal solutions and conform to Raoult's law. Ethanol and water are two such liquids. Because of molecular interaction, a mixture of 95.5% (by weight) of ethanol and 4.5% of water boils *below* the boiling point of pure ethanol (78.15°C versus 78.3°C). Thus, no matter how efficient the distilling apparatus, 100% ethanol cannot be obtained by distillation of a mixture of, say, 75% water and 25% ethanol. A mixture of liquids of a certain definite composition that distills at a constant temperature without a change in composition is called an *azeotrope*; 95% ethanol is such an azeotrope. The boiling point–composition curve for the ethanol-water mixture is seen in Figure 5.4. To prepare 100% ethanol, the water can be removed chemically (by reaction with calcium oxide) or it can be removed as an azeotrope with still another liquid. An azeotropic mixture of 32.4% ethanol and 67.6% benzene (bp 80.1°C) boils at 68.2°C. A ternary azeotrope containing 74.1% benzene, 18.5% ethanol, and 7.4% water boils at 64.9°C. Absolute alcohol (100% ethanol) is made by adding benzene to 95% ethanol followed by removing the water in the volatile ternary azeotrope of benzene, ethanol, and water.

Ethanol and water form a minimum boiling azeotrope. Substances such as formic acid (bp 100.7°C) and water (bp 100°C) form maximum boiling azeotropes. The boiling point of a formic acid–water azeotrope is 107.3°C.

The ethanol-water azeotrope

■ **FIG. 5.4**
Boiling point–composition curves for a mixture of ethanol and water.

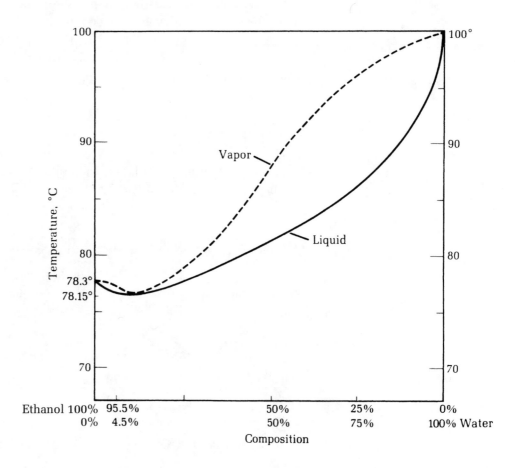

Boiling Points and Distillation

A constant boiling point on distillation does not guarantee that the distillate is a single pure compound.

A pure liquid has a constant boiling point. A change in boiling point during distillation is an indication of impurity. The converse proposition, however, is not always true; that is, constancy of a boiling point does not necessarily mean that the liquid consists of only one compound. For instance, two miscible liquids of similar chemical structure that boil at the same temperature individually will have nearly the same boiling point as a mixture. And, as noted previously, azeotropes have constant boiling points that can be either above or below the boiling points of the individual components.

Distilling a mixture of sugar and water

When a solution of sugar in water is distilled, the boiling point recorded on a thermometer located in the vapor phase is 100°C (at 760 torr) throughout the distillation, whereas the temperature of the boiling sugar solution itself is initially somewhat above 100°C and continues to rise as the concentration of sugar in the remaining solution increases. The vapor pressure of the solution is dependent on the number of water molecules present in a given volume; hence, with increasing concentration of nonvolatile sugar molecules and decreasing concentration of water, the vapor pressure at a given temperature decreases, and a higher temperature is required for boiling. However, sugar molecules do not leave the solution, and the drop clinging to the thermometer is pure water in equilibrium with pure water vapor.

Boiling point changes with pressure.

When a distillation is carried out in a system open to the air (the boiling point is thus dependent on existing air pressure), the prevailing barometric pressure should be noted and allowance made for appreciable deviations from the accepted boiling point temperature (Table 5.1). Distillation can also be done at the lower pressures that can be achieved using an oil pump or an aspirator, which produces a substantial reduction in the boiling point.

EXPERIMENTS

Before beginning any distillation, calibrate the thermometer to ensure accurate readings are made; refer to Part 3 of Chapter 3 for calibration instructions.

TABLE 5.1 • **Variation in Boiling Point with Pressure**

Pressure (mm Hg)	Boiling Point	
	Water (°C)	Benzene (°C)
780	100.7	81.2
770	100.4	80.8
760	100.0	80.3
750	99.6	79.9
740	99.2	79.5
584*	92.8	71.2

*Instituto de Quimica, Mexico City, altitude 7700 ft (2310 m).

1. Simple Distillation

Apparatus for simple distillation

IN THIS EXPERIMENT the two liquids to be separated are placed in a 5-mL round-bottomed, long-necked flask that is fitted to a distilling head (Fig. 5.5). The flask has a larger surface area exposed to heat than does the reaction tube, so the necessary thermal energy can be put into the system to cause the materials to distill. The hot vapor rises and completely envelops the bulb of the thermometer before passing over it and down toward the receiver. The downward-sloping portion of the distilling head functions as an air condenser. The objective is to observe how the boiling point of the mixture changes during the course of its distillation. (Another simple distillation apparatus is shown in Figure 5.6. Here, the long air condenser will condense even low-boiling liquids, and the receiver is far from the heat.)

■ FIG. 5.6
A simple distillation apparatus.

Distillation head

Air condenser

Boiling chip

Short-necked 5-mL flask

■ FIG. 5.5
A small-scale simple distillation apparatus. This apparatus can be adapted for fractional distillation by packing the long neck with a copper sponge. The temperature is regulated by either scraping sand away from or piling sand up around the flask.

Distillation head with air condenser

Receiver vial

Long-necked 5-mL flask

Boiling chip

The rate of distillation is determined by the heat input to the apparatus. This is most easily and effectively controlled by using a spatula to pile up or scrape away hot sand from around the flask.

(A) Simple Distillation of a Cyclohexane-Toluene Mixture

Online Study Center

Photo: Simple Distillation Apparatus

Viton is resistant to hot aromatic vapors.

The thermometer bulb must be *completely below* the side arm.

Cyclohexane	Toluene
bp 81°C	bp 111°C
MW 84.16	MW 92.14
n_D^{20} 1.4260	n_D^{20} 1.4960

Throughout this text information regarding the physical properties of substances has been placed with each various structures in the margin. MW is molecular weight, bp is boiling point, den. is density in g/mL, and n_D^{20} is the refractive index.

There are 21 ± 3 drops per milliliter.

To a 5-mL long-necked, round-bottomed flask, add 2.0 mL of dry cyclohexane, 2.0 mL of dry toluene, and a boiling chip (*see* Fig. 5.5). This flask is joined by means of a Viton (black) connector to a distilling head fitted with a thermometer using a rubber connector. The thermometer bulb should be completely below the side arm of the Claisen head so that the mercury reaches the same temperature as the vapor that distills. The end of the distilling head dips well down into a receiving vial, which rests on the bottom of a 30-mL beaker filled with ice. The distillation is started by piling up hot sand to heat the flask. As soon as boiling begins, the vapors can be seen to rise up the neck of the flask. Adjust the rate of heating by piling up or scraping away sand from the flask so that it takes *several minutes* for the vapor to rise to the thermometer. **The rate of distillation should be no faster than 2 drops per minute.**

Record the temperature versus the number of drops during the entire distillation process. If the rate of distillation is as slow as it should be, there will be sufficient time between drops to read and record the temperature. Continue the distillation until only about 0.4 mL remains in the distilling flask. **Never distill to dryness.** On a larger scale explosive peroxides can sometimes accumulate. At the end of the distillation, measure as accurately as possible, perhaps with a syringe, the volume of the distillate and, after it cools, the volume left in the pot; the difference is the holdup of the column if none has been lost by evaporation. Note the barometric pressure, make any thermometer corrections necessary, and make a plot of milliliters (drop number) versus temperature for the distillation.

Cleaning Up. The pot residue should be placed in the organic solvents container. The distillate can also be placed there or recycled.

(B) Simple Distillation of an Ethanol-Water Mixture

In a 5-mL round-bottomed, long-necked flask place 4 mL of a 10% to 20% ethanol-water mixture. Assemble the apparatus as described previously and carry out the distillation until you believe a representative sample of ethanol has collected in the receiver. In the hood place 3 drops of this sample on a Pyrex watch glass and try to ignite it with the blue cone of a microburner flame. Does it burn? Is any unburned residue observed? There was a time when alcohol-water mixtures were mixed with gunpowder and ignited to give proof that the alcohol had not been diluted. One hundred proof alcohol is 50% ethanol by volume.

Cleaning Up. The distillate and pot residue can be disposed in the organic solvents waste container or, if regulations permit, diluted with water and flushed down the drain.

2. Fractional Distillation

> **IN THIS EXPERIMENT**, just as in the last one, you will distill a mixture of two liquids and again record the boiling points as a function of the volume of distillate (drops). The necessity for a very slow rate of distillation cannot be overemphasized.

Apparatus

Online Study Center

Photos: Column Packing with Chore Boy for Fractional Distillation, Fractional Distillation Apparatus

Assemble the apparatus shown in Figure 5.7. The 10-cm column is packed with 1.5 g of copper sponge and connected to the 5-mL short-necked flask using a black (Viton) connector. The column should be vertical and care should be taken to ensure that the bulb of the thermometer does not touch the side of the distilling head. The column, but not the distilling head, will be insulated with glass wool or cotton at the appropriate time to ensure that the process is adiabatic. Alternatively, the column can be insulated with a cut-off 15-mL polyethylene centrifuge tube.

■ **FIG. 5.7**
A small-scale fractional distillation apparatus. The 10-cm column is packed with 1.5 g of copper sponge (Chore Boy).

Receiver vial

Distilling column packed with copper sponge

Temperature regulated by moving sand

Boiling chip

(A) Fractional Distillation of a Cyclohexane-Toluene Mixture

Never distill in an airtight system.

To a short-necked flask add 2.0 mL of cyclohexane, 2.0 mL of toluene, and a boiling chip. The distilling column is packed with 1.5 g of copper sponge (Fig. 5.7). The mixture is brought to a boil over a hot sand bath. Observe the ring of condensate that should rise slowly through the column; if you cannot at first see this ring, locate it by touching the column with your fingers. It will be cool above the ring and hot below. Reduce the heat by scraping sand away from the flask and wrap the column, but not the distilling head, with glass wool or cotton if it is not already insulated.

Adjust the heat input to the flask by piling up or scraping away sand around the flask.

Insulate the distilling column but not the Claisen head.

21 ± 3 drops = 1 mL

The distilling head and the thermometer function as a small reflux condenser. Again, apply the heat, and as soon as the vapor reaches the thermometer bulb, reduce the heat by scraping away sand. **Distill the mixture at a rate no faster than 2 drops per minute** and record the temperature as a function of the number of drops. If the heat input has been *very* carefully adjusted, the distillation will cease, and the temperature reading will drop after the cyclohexane has distilled. Increase the heat input by piling up the sand around the flask to cause the toluene to distill. Stop the distillation when only about 0.4 mL remains in the flask and measure the volume of distillate and the pot residue as before. Make a plot of the boiling point versus the milliliters of distillate (drops) and compare it to the simple distillation carried out in the same apparatus. Compare your results with those in Figure 5.8.

Cleaning Up. The pot residue should be placed in the organic solvents container. The distillate can also be placed there or recycled.

(B) Fractional Distillation of an Ethanol-Water Mixture

Distill 4 mL of the same ethanol-water mixture used in the simple distillation experiment, following the procedure used for the cyclohexane-toluene mixture

■ **FIG. 5.8**
Simple and fractional distillation curves for cyclohexane and toluene.

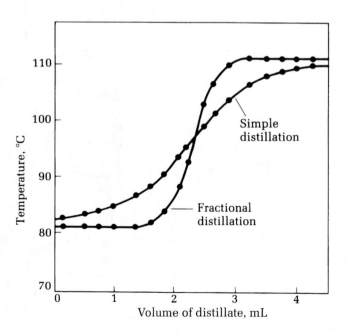

with either the short or the long distilling column. Remove what you regard to be the ethanol fraction and repeat the ignition test. Is any difference noted?

Cleaning Up. The pot residue and distillate can be disposed in the organic solvents waste container or, if regulations permit, diluted with water and flushed down the drain.

3. Instant Microscale Distillation

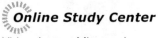

Online Study Center

Video: Instant Microscale Distillation

Frequently, a very small quantity of freshly distilled material is needed in an experiment. For example, two compounds that need to be distilled freshly are aniline, which turns black because of the formation of oxidation products, and benzaldehyde, a liquid that easily oxides to solid benzoic acid. The impurities that arise in both of these compounds have much higher boiling points than the pure compounds, so a very simple distillation suffices to separate them. This can be accomplished as follows.

Place a few drops of the impure liquid in a reaction tube along with a boiling chip. Clamp the tube in a hot sand bath and adjust the heat so that the liquid refluxes about halfway up the tube. Expel the air from a Pasteur pipette, thrust it down into the hot vapor, and then pull the hot vapor into the cold upper portion of the pipette. The vapor will immediately condense and can then be expelled into another reaction tube that is held adjacent to the hot one (Fig. 5.9). In this way enough pure material can be distilled to determine a boiling point, run a spectrum, make a derivative, or carry out a reaction. Sometimes the first drop or two will be cloudy, which indicates the presence of water. This fraction should be discarded in order to obtain pure dry material.

4. Simple Distillation

Apparatus

In any distillation, the flask should be no more than two-thirds full at the start. Great care should be taken not to distill to dryness because, in some cases, high-boiling explosive peroxides can become concentrated.

Assemble the apparatus for macroscale simple distillation, as shown in Figure 5.10, starting with the support ring followed by the electric flask heater and then the flask. One or two boiling stones are put in the flask to promote even boiling. Each ground joint is greased by putting three or four stripes of grease lengthwise around the male joint and pressing the joint firmly into the other without twisting. The air is thus eliminated, and the joint will appear almost transparent. (Do not use excess grease because it will contaminate the product.) Water enters the condenser at the tublature nearest the receiver. Because of the large heat capacity of water, only a very small stream (3 mm diameter) is needed; too much water pressure will cause the tubing to pop off. A heavy rubber band, or better a Keck clamp, can be used to hold the condenser to the distillation head. Note that the bulb of the thermometer is below the opening into the side arm of the distillation head.

■ FIG. 5.9
An apparatus for instant microscale distillation.

■ FIG. 5.10
An apparatus for macroscale simple distillation.

Distillation head

Keck clamp

Clamp

Condenser

Keck clamp

Adapter

Water out

Water in

Graduated cylinder

Refluxing vapor

Boiling liquid

Boiling chip

 CAUTION: Cyclohexane and toluene are flammable; make sure the distilling apparatus is tight.

Do not add a boiling chip to a hot liquid. It may boil over.

(A) Simple Distillation of a Cyclohexane-Toluene Mixture

Place a mixture of 30 mL cyclohexane and 30 mL toluene and a boiling chip in a dry 100-mL round-bottomed flask and assemble the apparatus for simple distillation. After assuring that all connections are tight, heat the flask strongly until boiling begins. Then adjust the heat until the distillate drops at a regular rate of about 1 drop per second. Record both the temperature and the volume of distillate at regular intervals. After 50 mL of distillate is collected, discontinue the distillation. Record the barometric pressure, make any thermometer correction necessary, and plot the boiling point versus the volume of distillate. Save the distillate for fractional distillation.

Cleaning Up. The pot residue should be placed in the organic solvents container. The distillate can also be placed there or recycled.

Dispose of cyclohexane and toluene in the container provided. Do not pour them down the drain.

(B) Simple Distillation of an Ethanol-Water Mixture

In a 500-mL round-bottomed flask place 200 mL of a 20% aqueous solution of ethanol. Follow the previous procedure for the distillation of a cyclohexane-toluene mixture. Discontinue the distillation after 50 mL of distillate has been collected. Working in the hood, place 3 drops of distillate on a Pyrex watch glass and try to ignite it with the blue cone of a microburner flame. Does it burn? Is any unburned residue observed?

Cleaning Up. The pot residue and distillate can be disposed in the organic solvents container or, if regulations permit, diluted with water and flushed down the drain.

5. Fractional Distillation

Apparatus

Assemble the apparatus shown in Figures 5.11 and 5.12. The fractionating column is packed with one-fourth to one-third of a metal sponge. The column should be perfectly vertical and be insulated with glass wool covered with aluminum foil (shiny side in). However, insulation is omitted for this experiment so that you can observe what is taking place in the column.

(A) Fractional Distillation of a Cyclohexane-Toluene Mixture

After the flask from the simple macroscale distillation experiment has cooled, pour the 50 mL of distillate back into the distilling flask, add one or two new boiling chips, and assemble the apparatus for fractional distillation. The stillhead delivers into a short condenser fitted with a bent adapter leading into a 10-mL graduated cylinder. Gradually turn up the heat to the electric flask heater until the mixture of cyclohexane and toluene just begins to boil. As soon as boiling starts, turn down the power. Heat slowly at first. A ring of condensate will rise slowly through the column; if you cannot at first see this ring, locate it by cautiously touching the column with your fingers. The rise should be very gradual so that the column can acquire a uniform temperature gradient. Do not apply more heat until you are sure that the ring of condensate has stopped rising; then increase the heat gradually. In a properly conducted operation, the vapor-condensate mixture reaches the top of the column only after several minutes. Once distillation has commenced, it should continue steadily without any drop in temperature at a rate no greater than 1 mL in 1.5–2 min. Observe the flow and keep it steady by slight increases in heat as required. Protect the column from drafts by wrapping it with

■ FIG. 5.11
An apparatus for macroscale fractional distillation.
The position of the thermometer bulb is critical.

■ FIG. 5.12
A fractionating column and its
packing. Use one-third of a copper
sponge (Chore Boy).

Keck clamp

Rubber tubing

Keck clamp

Fractionating
column

Water out

Stainless steel
sponge
packing

Water in

aluminum foil, glass wool, or even a towel. This insulation will help prevent
flooding of the column, as will slow and steady distillation.

Record the temperature as each milliliter of distillate collects and take more
frequent readings when the temperature starts to rise abruptly. Each time the graduated cylinder fills, quickly empty it into a series of labeled 25-mL Erlenmeyer
flasks. Stop the distillation when a second constant temperature is reached. Plot a
distillation curve and record what you observed inside the column in the course of
the fractionation. Combine the fractions that you think are pure and turn in the

product in a bottle labeled with your name, desk number, the name of the product, the boiling point range, and the weight.

Cleaning Up. The pot residue should be placed in the organic solvents container. The cyclohexane and toluene fractions can also be placed there or recycled.

(B) Fractional Distillation of Ethanol-Water Mixture

Place the 50 mL of distillate from the simple distillation experiment in a 100-mL round-bottomed flask, add one or two boiling chips, and assemble the apparatus for fractional distillation. Follow the previous procedure for the fractional distillation of a cyclohexane-toluene mixture. Repeat the ignition test. Is any difference noted? Alternatively, distill 60 mL of the 10%–20% ethanol-water mixture that results from the fermentation of sucrose (*see* Chapter 64).

Cleaning Up. The pot residue and distillate can be disposed in the organic solvents container or, if regulations permit, diluted with water and flushed down the drain.

6. Fractional Distillation of Unknowns

You will be supplied with an unknown, prepared by your instructor, that is a mixture of two solvents listed in Table 5.2, only two of which form azeotropes. The solvents in the mixture will be mutually soluble and differ in boiling point by more than 20°C. The composition of the mixture (in percentages of the two components) will be either 20:80, 30:70, 40:60, 50:50, 60:40, 70:30, or 80:20. Identify the two compounds and determine the percent composition of each. Perform a fractional distillation on 4 mL of the unknown for microscale; use at least 50 mL of unknown for macroscale. Fractionate the unknown and identify the components from the boiling points. Prepare a distillation curve. You may be directed to analyze your distillate by gas chromatography (*see* Chapter 10) or refractive index (*see* Chapter 14).

TABLE 5.2 • Some Properties of Common Solvents	
Solvent	**Boiling Point (°C)**
Acetone	56.5
Methanol	64.7
Hexane	68.8
1-Butanol	117.2
2-Methyl-2-propanol	82.2
Water	100.0
Toluene*	110.6

*Methanol and toluene form an azeotrope with a boiling point of 63.8°C (69% methanol).

Cleaning Up. Organic material goes in the organic solvents container. Water and aqueous solutions can be flushed down the drain.

QUESTIONS

1. In either of the simple distillation experiments, can you account for the boiling point of your product in terms of the known boiling points of the pure components of your mixture? If so, how? If not, why not?

2. From the plots of the boiling point versus the volume of distillate in the simple distillation experiments, what can you conclude about the purity of your product?

3. From the plots of the boiling point versus the volume of distillate in either of the fractional distillations of the cyclohexane-toluene mixture, what conclusion can you draw about the homogeneity of the distillate?

4. From the plots of the boiling point versus the volume of distillate in either of the fractional distillations of the ethanol-water mixture, what conclusion can you draw about the homogeneity of the distillate? Does it have a constant boiling point? If constant, is it a pure substance?

5. What is the effect on the boiling point of a solution (e.g., water) produced by a soluble nonvolatile substance (e.g., sodium chloride)? What is the effect of an insoluble substance such as sand or charcoal? What is the temperature of the vapor above these two boiling solutions?

6. In the distillation of a pure substance (e.g., water), why does all of the water not vaporize at once when the boiling point is reached?

7. In fractional distillation, liquid can be seen running from the bottom of the distillation column back into the distilling flask. What effect does this returning condensate have on the fractional distillation?

8. Why is it extremely dangerous to attempt to carry out a distillation in a completely closed apparatus (one with no vent to the atmosphere)?

9. Why is better separation of two liquids achieved by slow rather than fast distillation?

10. Explain why a packed fractionating column is more efficient than an unpacked one.

11. In the distillation of the cyclohexane-toluene mixture, the first few drops of distillate may be cloudy. Explain this occurrence.

12. What effect does the reduction of atmospheric pressure have on the boiling point? Can cyclohexane and toluene be separated if the external pressure is 350 mm Hg instead of 760 mm Hg?

13. When water-cooled condensers are used for distillation or for refluxing a liquid, the water enters the condenser at the lowest point and leaves at the highest. Why?

Online Study Center

General Resources
Web Links

CHAPTER

7

Extraction

PRELAB EXERCISE: Describe how to separate a mixture of 3-toluic acid and 4'-aminoacetophenone using acid-base liquid/liquid extraction. What species will end up in the aqueous layer if you mix a solution of benzoic acid and aniline in ether with a solution of $NaHCO_3$ (aq)? Draw the structure of this species.

Extraction is one of the oldest chemical operations known to humankind. The preparation of a cup of coffee or tea involves the extraction of flavor and odor components from dried vegetable matter with hot water. Aqueous extracts of bay leaves, stick cinnamon, peppercorns, and cloves, along with alcoholic extracts of vanilla and almond, are used as food flavorings. For the past 150 years or so, organic chemists have extracted, isolated, purified, and characterized the myriad compounds produced by plants that for centuries have been used as drugs and perfumes—substances such as quinine from cinchona bark, morphine from the opium poppy, cocaine from coca leaves, and menthol from peppermint oil. The extraction of compounds from these natural products is an example of solid/liquid extraction—the solid being the natural product and the liquid being the solvent into which the compounds are extracted. In research, a Soxhlet extractor (Fig. 7.1) is often used for solid/liquid extraction.

Although solid/liquid extraction is the most common technique for brewing beverages and isolating compounds from natural products, liquid/liquid extraction is a very common method used in the organic laboratory, specifically when isolating reaction products. Reactions are typically homogeneous liquid mixtures and can therefore be extracted with either an organic or aqueous solvent. Organic reactions often yield a number of byproducts—some inorganic and some organic. Also, because some organic reactions do not go to 100% completion, a small amount of starting material is present at the end of the reaction. When a reaction is complete, it is necessary to do a *workup*, that is, separate and purify the desired product from the mixture of byproducts and residual starting material. Liquid/liquid extraction is a common separation step in this workup, which is then followed by

■ **FIG. 7.1**
The Soxhlet extractor for the
extraction of solids such as dried
leaves or seeds. The solid is put in
a filter paper thimble. Solvent
vapor rises in the tube on the right;
condensate drops onto the solid in
the thimble, leaches out soluble
material, and, after initiating an
automatic siphon, carries it to the
flask where nonvolatile extracted
material accumulates. Substances
of low solubility can be extracted
by prolonged operation.

Condenser

Paper thimble

Soxhlet

purification of the product. There are two types of liquid/liquid extraction: neutral and acid/base. The experiments in this chapter demonstrate solid/liquid extraction and the two types of liquid/liquid extraction.

Organic products are often separated from inorganic substances in a reaction mixture by liquid/liquid extraction with an organic solvent. For example, in the synthesis of 1-bromobutane (*see* Chapter 16), 1-butanol, also a liquid, is heated with an aqueous solution of sodium bromide and sulfuric acid to produce the product and sodium sulfate.

$$2\ CH_3CH_2CH_2CH_2OH\ +\ 2\ NaBr\ +\ H_2SO_4\ \rightarrow$$
$$2\ CH_3CH_2CH_2CH_2Br\ +\ 2\ H_2O\ +\ Na_2SO_4$$

The 1-bromobutane is isolated from the reaction mixture by extraction with *t*-butyl methyl ether, an organic solvent in which 1-bromobutane is soluble and in which water and sodium sulfate are insoluble. The extraction is accomplished by simply adding *t*-butyl methyl ether to the aqueous mixture and shaking it. Two layers will result: an organic layer and an aqueous layer. The *t*-butyl methyl ether is less dense than water and floats on top; it is easily removed/drained away from the water layer and evaporated to leave the bromo product free of inorganic substances, which reside in the aqueous layer.

Partition Coefficient

The extraction of a compound such as 1-butanol, which is slightly soluble in water as well as very soluble in ether, is an equilibrium process governed by the solubilities of the alcohol in the two solvents. The ratio of the solubilities is known as the *distribution coefficient*, also called the *partition coefficient* (k), and is an equilibrium constant with a certain value for a given substance, pair of solvents, and temperature.

The *concentration* of the solute in each solvent can be well correlated with the *solubility* of the solute in the pure solvent, a figure that is readily found in solubility tables in reference books. For substance C

$$k = \frac{\text{concentration of C in } t\text{-butyl methyl ether}}{\text{concentration of C in water}}$$

$$> \frac{\text{solubility of C in } t\text{-butyl methyl ether (g/100 mL)}}{\text{solubility of C in water (g/100 mL)}}$$

Consider compound A that dissolves in *t*-butyl methyl ether to the extent of 12 g/100 mL and dissolves in water to the extent of 6 g/100 mL.

$$k = \frac{12\text{ g/100 mL } t\text{-butyl methyl ether}}{6\text{ g/100 mL water}} = 2$$

If a solution of 6 g of A in 100 mL of water is shaken with 100 mL of t-butyl methyl ether, then

$$k = \frac{x \text{ g of A}/100 \text{ mL } t\text{-butyl methyl ether}}{6 - x \text{ g of A}/100 \text{ mL water}}$$

from which

$$x = 4.0 \text{ g of A in the ether layer}$$
$$6 - x = 2.0 \text{ g of A left in the water layer}$$

It is, however, more efficient to extract the 100 mL of aqueous solution twice with 50-mL portions of t-butyl methyl ether rather than once with a 100-mL portion.

$$k = \frac{x \text{ g of A}/50 \text{ mL}}{6 - x \text{ g of A}/100 \text{ mL}} = 2$$

from which

$$x = 3.0 \text{ g of A in the } t\text{-butyl methyl ether layer}$$
$$6 - x = 3.0 \text{ g of A in the water layer}$$

If this 3.0 g/100 mL of water is extracted again with 50 mL of t-butyl methyl ether, we can calculate that 1.5 g of A will be in the ether layer, leaving 1.5 g in the water layer. So two extractions with 50-mL portions of ether will extract 3.0 g + 1.5 g = 4.5 g of A, whereas one extraction with a 100-mL portion of t-butyl methyl ether removes only 4.0 g of A. Three extractions with 33-mL portions of t-butyl methyl ether would extract 4.7 g. Obviously, there is a point at which the increased amount of A extracted does not repay the effort of multiple extractions, but remember that several small-scale extractions are more effective than one large-scale extraction.

Properties of Extraction Solvents

Liquid/liquid extraction involves two layers: the organic layer and the aqueous layer. The solvent used for extraction should possess many properties, including the following:

- It should readily dissolve the substance to be extracted at room temperature.
- It should have a low boiling point so that it can be removed readily.
- It should not react with the solute or the other solvent.
- It should not be highly flammable or toxic.
- It should be relatively inexpensive.

In addition, it should not be miscible with water (the usual second phase). No solvent meets every criterion, but several come close. Some common liquid/liquid

TABLE 7.1 • Common Solvents Listed by Density	
Solvent	**Density (g/mL)**
Hexane	0.695
Diethyl ether	0.708
t-Butyl methyl ether	0.740
Toluene	0.867
Water	1.000
Dichloromethane	1.325
Chloroform	1.492

extraction solvent pairs are water-ether, water-dichloromethane, and water-hexane. Notice that each combination includes water because most organic compounds are immiscible in water and therefore can be separated from inorganic compounds. Organic solvents such as methanol and ethanol are not good extraction solvents because they are soluble in water.

Identifying the Layers

One common mistake when performing an extraction is to misidentify the layers and discard the wrong one. It is good practice to save all layers until the desired product is in hand. The densities of the solvents will predict the identities of the top and bottom layers. In general, the densities of nonhalogenated organic solvents are less than 1.0 g/mL and those of halogenated solvents are greater than 1.0 g/mL. Table 7.1 lists the densities of common solvents used in extraction.

Although density is the physical property that determines which layer is on top or on bottom, a very concentrated amount of solute dissolved in either layer can reverse the order. The best method to avoid a misidentification is to perform a drop test. Add a few drops of water to the layer in question and watch the drop carefully. If the layer is water, then the drop will mix with the solution. If the solvent is the organic layer, then the water drop will create a second layer.

Identify layers by a drop test.

Ethereal Extraction Solvents

$$CH_3CH_2—O—CH_2CH_3$$

**Diethyl ether
"Ether"**
MW 74.12, den. 0.708
bp 34.6°C, n_D^{20} 1.3530

In the past, diethyl ether was the most common solvent for extraction in the laboratory. It has high solvent power for hydrocarbons and oxygen-containing compounds. It is highly volatile (bp 34.6°C) and is therefore easily removed from an extract. However, diethyl ether has two big disadvantages: it is highly flammable and poses a great fire threat, and it easily forms peroxides. The reaction of diethyl ether with air is catalyzed by light. The resulting peroxides are higher boiling than the ether and are left as a residue when the ether evaporates. If the residue is heated, it will explode because ether peroxides are treacherously high explosives. In recent years, a new solvent has come on the scene—*tert*-butyl methyl ether.

CH₃
|
H₃C—C—O—CH₃
|
CH₃

tert-Butyl methyl ether
MW 88.14, den. 0.741
bp 55.2°C, n_D^{20} 1.369

■ FIG. 7.2
A separatory funnel with Teflon stopcock.

tert-Butyl methyl ether, called methyl *tert*-butyl ether (MTBE) in industry, has many advantages over diethyl ether as an extraction solvent. Most important, it does not easily form peroxides, so it can be stored for much longer periods than diethyl ether. And, in the United States, it is less than two-thirds the price of diethyl ether. It is slightly less volatile (bp 55°C), so it does not pose the same fire threat as diethyl ether, although one must be as careful in handling this solvent as in handling any other highly volatile, flammable substance. The explosion limits for *t*-butyl methyl ether mixed with air are much narrower than for diethyl ether, the toxicity is less (it is not a carcinogen), the solvent power is the same, and the ignition temperature is higher (224°C versus 180°C).

The weight percent solubility of diethyl ether dissolved in water is 7.2%, whereas that of *t*-butyl methyl ether is 4.8%. The solubility of water in diethyl ether is 1.2%, while in *t*-butyl methyl ether it is 1.5%. Unlike diethyl ether, *t*-butyl methyl ether forms an azeotrope with water (4% water) that boils at 52.6°C. This means that evaporation of any *t*-butyl methyl ether solution that is saturated with water should leave no water residue, unlike diethyl ether.

The low price and ready availability of *t*-butyl methyl ether came about because it replaced tetraethyl lead as the antiknock additive for high-octane gasoline and as a fuel oxygenate, which helps reduce air pollution, but its water solubility has allowed it to contaminate drinking water supplies in states where leaking underground fuel storage tanks are not well regulated. Consequently, it is being replaced with the much more expensive ethanol. In this text, *t*-butyl methyl ether is *strongly* suggested wherever diethyl ether formerly would have been used in an extraction. It will not, however, work as the only solvent in the Grignard reaction, probably because of steric hindrance. So whenever the word *ether* appears in this text as an extraction solvent, it is suggested that *t*-butyl methyl ether be used and not diethyl ether.

Mixing and Separating the Layers

For microscale separations, mixing and separating the layers with a pipette normally incurs very little product loss. Because the two solvents are typically in a reaction tube for microscale extraction, the two layers can be mixed by drawing up and rapidly expelling them with a pipette. Then the layers are allowed to separate, and the bottom layer is separated by drawing it up into a pipette and transferring it to a different container.

For macroscale separations, a separatory funnel (Fig. 7.2) is used to mix and separate the organic and aqueous layers. In macroscale experiments, a frequently used method of working up a reaction mixture is to dilute the mixture with water and extract it with an organic solvent, such as ether, in a separatory funnel. When the stoppered funnel is shaken to distribute the components between the immiscible solvents *t*-butyl methyl ether and water, pressure always develops through volatilization of ether from the heat of the hands, and liberation of a gas (CO_2) (in acid/base extractions) can increase the pressure. Consequently, the funnel is grasped so that the stopper is held in place by one hand

■ **FIG. 7.3**
The correct position for holding a
separatory funnel when shaking.
Point outlet away from yourself
and your neighbors.

and the stopcock by the other, as illustrated in Figure 7.3. After a brief shake or two, the funnel is held in the inverted position shown, and the stopcock is opened cautiously (with the funnel stem pointed away from nearby persons) to release pressure. The mixture can then be shaken more vigorously, with pressure released as necessary. When equilibration is judged to be complete, the slight, constant terminal pressure due to ether is released, the stopper is rinsed with a few drops of ether delivered by a Pasteur pipette, and the layers are allowed to separate. The organic reaction product is distributed wholly or largely into the upper ether layer, whereas inorganic salts, acids, and bases pass into the water layer, which can be drawn off. If the reaction was conducted in alcohol or some other water-soluble solvent, the bulk of the solvent is removed in the water layer, and the remainder can be eliminated in two or three washings with 1–2 volumes of water conducted with the techniques used in the first equilibration. The separatory funnel should be supported in a ring stand, as shown in Figure 7.2.

Before adding a liquid to the separatory funnel, check the stopcock. If it is glass, see that it is properly greased, bearing in mind that too much grease will clog the hole in the stopcock and also contaminate the extract. If the stopcock is Teflon, see that it is adjusted to a tight fit in the bore. Store the separatory funnel with the Teflon stopcock loosened to prevent sticking. Because Teflon has a much larger temperature coefficient of expansion than glass, a stuck stopcock can be loosened by cooling the stopcock in ice or dry ice. Do not store liquids in the separatory funnel; they often leak or cause the stopper or stopcock to freeze. To have sufficient room for mixing the layers, fill the separatory funnel no more than three-fourths full. Withdraw the lower layer from the separatory funnel through the stopcock and pour the upper layer out through the neck.

All too often the inexperienced chemist discards the wrong layer when using a separatory funnel. Through incomplete neutralization, a desired component may still remain in the aqueous layer, or the densities of the layers may change. Cautious workers save all layers until the desired product has been isolated. The organic layer is not always the top layer. If in doubt, perform a drop test by adding a few drops of each to water in a test tube.

Practical Considerations When Mixing Layers

Pressure Buildup

The heat of one's hand or heat from acid/base reactions will cause pressure buildup in an extraction mixture that contains a very volatile solvent such as dichloromethane. The extraction container—whether a test tube or a separatory funnel—must be opened carefully to vent this pressure.

Sodium bicarbonate solution is often used to neutralize acids when carrying out acid/base extractions. The result is the formation of carbon dioxide, which can cause foaming and high pressure buildup. Whenever bicarbonate is used, add it very gradually with thorough mixing and frequent venting of the extraction device. If a large amount of acid is to be neutralized with bicarbonate, the process should be carried out in a beaker.

Emulsions

Imagine trying to extract a soap solution (e.g., a nonfoaming dishwashing detergent) into an organic solvent. After a few shakes with an organic solvent, you would have an absolutely intractable emulsion. An emulsion is a suspension of one liquid as droplets in another. Detergents stabilize emulsions, and so any time a detergent-like molecule is in the material being extracted, there is the danger that emulsions will form. Substances of this type are commonly found in nature, so one must be particularly wary of emulsion formation when creating organic extracts of aqueous plant material, such as caffeine from tea. Emulsions, once formed, can be quite stable. You would be quite surprised to open your refrigerator one morning and see a layer of clarified butter floating on the top of a perfectly clear aqueous solution that had once been milk, but milk is the classic example of an emulsion.

Prevention is the best cure for emulsions. This means shaking the solution to be extracted *very gently* until you see that the two layers will separate readily. If a bit of emulsion forms, it may break simply on standing for a sufficient length of time. Making the aqueous layer highly ionic will help. Add as much sodium chloride as will dissolve and shake the mixture gently. Vacuum filtration sometimes works and, when the organic layer is the lower layer, filtration through silicone-impregnated filter paper is helpful. Centrifugation works very well for breaking emulsions. This is easy on a small scale, but often the equipment is not available for large-scale centrifugation of organic liquids.

Shake gently to avoid emulsions.

Drying Agents

The organic solvents used for extraction dissolve not only the compound being extracted but also water. Evaporation of the solvent then leaves the desired compound contaminated with water. At room temperature water dissolves 4.8% of *t*-butyl methyl ether by weight, and the ether dissolves 1.5% of water. But ether is virtually insoluble in water saturated with sodium chloride (36.7 g/100 mL). If ether that contains dissolved water is shaken with a saturated aqueous solution of sodium chloride, water will be transferred from the *t*-butyl methyl ether to the aqueous layer. So, strange as it may seem, ethereal extracts are routinely dried by shaking them with an aqueous saturated sodium chloride solution.

Solvents such as dichloromethane do not dissolve nearly as much water and are therefore dried over a chemical drying agent. Many choices of chemical drying agents are available for this purpose, and the choice of which one to use is governed by four factors: (1) the possibility of reaction with the substance being extracted, (2) the speed with which it removes water from the solvent, (3) the efficiency of the process, and (4) the ease of recovery from the drying agent.

Some very good but specialized and reactive drying agents are potassium hydroxide, anhydrous potassium carbonate, sodium metal, calcium hydride, lithium aluminum hydride, and phosphorus pentoxide. Substances that are essentially neutral and unreactive and are widely used as drying agents include anhydrous calcium sulfate (Drierite), magnesium sulfate, molecular sieves, calcium chloride, and sodium sulfate.

Drierite, a specially prepared form of calcium sulfate, is a fast and effective drying agent. However, it is difficult to ascertain whether enough has been used.

Drierite, $CaSO_4$

Magnesium sulfate, MgSO$_4$

Molecular sieves, zeolites

Calcium chloride (CaCl$_2$) pellets are the drying agent of choice for small-scale experiments.

Sodium sulfate, Na$_2$SO$_4$

An indicating type of Drierite is impregnated with cobalt chloride, which turns from blue to red when it is saturated with water. This works well when gases are being dried, but it should not be used for liquid extractions because the cobalt chloride dissolves in many protic solvents.

Magnesium sulfate is also a fast and fairly effective drying agent, but it is so finely powdered that it always requires careful filtration for removal.

Molecular sieves are sodium alumino-silicates (zeolites) that have well-defined pore sizes. The 4 Å size adsorbs water to the exclusion of almost all organic substances, making them a fast and effective drying agent. Like Drierite, however, it is impossible to ascertain by appearance whether enough has been used. Molecular sieves in the form of 1/16-in. pellets are often used to dry solvents by simply adding them to the container.

Calcium chloride, recently available in the preferred form of pellets (4 to 80 mesh[1]), is a very fast and effective drying agent. It has the advantage that it clumps together when excess water is present, which makes it possible to know how much to add by observing its behavior. Unlike the older granular form, the pellets do not disintegrate into a fine powder. These pellets are admirably suited to microscale experiments where the solvent is removed from the drying agent with a Pasteur pipette. Calcium chloride is much faster and far more effective than anhydrous sodium sulfate; after much experimentation, we have decided that this is the agent of choice, particularly for microscale experiments. These pellets are used for most of the drying operations in this text. Note, however, that calcium chloride reacts with some alcohols, phenols, amides, and some carbonyl-containing compounds. Advantage is sometimes taken of this property to remove not only water from a solvent but also, for example, a contaminating alcohol (*see* Chapter 16—the synthesis of 1-bromobutane from 1-butanol). Because *t*-butyl methyl ether forms an azeotrope with water, its solutions should, theoretically, not need to be dried; evaporation carries away the water. Drying these ether solutions with calcium chloride pellets removes water droplets that get carried into the ether solution.

Sodium sulfate is a very poor drying agent. It has a very high capacity for water but is slow and not very efficient in the removal of water. Like calcium chloride pellets, it clumps together when wet, and solutions are easily removed from it using a Pasteur pipette. Sodium sulfate has been used extensively in the past and should still be used for compounds that react with calcium chloride.

PART 1: The Technique of Neutral Liquid/Liquid Extraction

The workup technique of liquid/liquid extraction has four steps: (1) mixing the layers, (2) separating the layers, (3) drying the organic layer, and (4) removing the solvent. The microscale neutral liquid/liquid extraction technique is described in the following sections.

---

1. These pellets are available from Fisher Scientific, Cat. No. C614–3.

Step 1. Mixing the Layers

Once the organic and aqueous layers are in contact with one another, mixing is required to ensure that the desired compound(s) get extracted into the desired layer. First, place 1–2 mL of an aqueous solution of the compound to be extracted in a reaction tube. Add about 1 mL of extraction solvent, for example, dichloromethane. Note, as you add the dichloromethane, whether it is the top or the bottom layer. (Since dichloromethane is more dense than water, predict what layer it will be.) An effective way to mix the two layers is to flick the tube with a finger. Grasp the tube firmly at the very top between the thumb and forefinger and flick it vigorously at the bottom (Fig. 7.4). You will find that this violent motion mixes the two layers well, but nothing comes out the top. Another good mixing technique is to pull the contents of the reaction tube into a Pasteur pipette and then expel the mixture back into the tube with force. Doing this several times will effect good mixing of the two layers. A stopper can be placed in the top of the tube, and the contents can be mixed by shaking the tube, but the problem with this technique is that the high vapor pressure of the solvent will often force liquid out around the cork or stopper.

Step 2. Separating the Layers

Always draw out the lower layer and place it in another container.

After thoroughly mixing the two layers, allow them to separate. Tap the tube if droplets of one layer are in the other layer or on the side of the tube. After the layers separate completely, draw up the lower dichloromethane layer into a Pasteur pipette. Leave behind any middle emulsion layer. The easiest way to do this is to attach the pipette to a pipette pump (Fig. 7.5). This allows very precise control of the liquid being removed. It takes more skill and practice to remove the lower layer cleanly with a 2-mL rubber bulb attached to a pipette because the high vapor pressure of the solvent tends to make it dribble out. To avoid losing any of the solution, it is best to hold a clean, dry, empty tube in the same hand as the full tube to receive the organic layer (Fig. 7.6).

From the discussion of the partition coefficient, you know that several small extractions are better than one large one, so repeat the extraction process with two further 1-mL portions of dichloromethane. An experienced chemist might summarize all the preceding with the following notebook entry, "Aqueous layer extracted 3 × 1-mL portions CH_2Cl_2," and in a formal report would write, "The aqueous layer was extracted three times with 1-mL portions of dichloromethane."

If you are working on a larger microscale, a microscale separatory funnel (Fig. 7.7) should be used. A separatory funnel, regardless of size, should be filled to only about two-thirds of its capacity so the layers can be mixed by shaking. The microscale separatory funnel has a capacity of 8.5 mL when full, so it is useful for an extraction with a total volume of about 6 mL.

Use a wood boiling stick to poke out the polyethylene frit from the bottom part of the separatory funnel. Store it for later replacement. Close the valve, add up to 5 mL of the solution to be extracted to the separatory funnel, then add the extraction solvent so that the total volume does not exceed 6 mL.

■ FIG. 7.4

Mixing the contents of a reaction tube by flicking it. Grasp the tube firmly at the very top and flick it vigorously at the bottom. The contents will mix without coming out of the tube.

■ FIG. 7.5

The removal of a solvent from a reaction tube with a pipette and pipette pump.

2-mL Pipette pump

1-mL Pipette graduated to ± 0.01 mL

Reaction tube

■ FIG. 7.6

Grasp both reaction tubes in one hand when transferring material from one tube to another with a Pasteur pipette.

Cap the separatory funnel and mix the contents by inverting the funnel several times. If the two layers separate fairly easily, then the contents can be shaken more thoroughly. If the layers do not separate easily, be careful not to shake the funnel too vigorously because intractable emulsions could form.

Remove the stopper from the funnel, clamp it, and then, grasping the valve with two hands, empty the bottom layer into an Erlenmeyer flask or other container. If the top layer is desired, pour it out through the top of the separatory funnel—don't drain it through the valve, which may have a drop of the lower layer remaining in it.

Step 3. Drying the Organic Layer

Dichloromethane dissolves a very small quantity of water, and microscopic droplets of water are suspended in the organic layer, often making it cloudy. To remove the water, a drying agent, for example, anhydrous calcium chloride pellets, is added to the dichloromethane solution.

■ FIG. 7.7
A microscale separatory funnel.
Remove the polyethylene frit from
the micro Büchner funnel before
using.

Polyethylene cap

Glass column

Micro Büchner funnel

Record the tare of the final container.

How Much Drying Agent Should Be Used?

When a small quantity of the drying agent is added, the crystals or pellets become sticky with water, clump together, and fall rapidly as a lump to the bottom of the reaction tube. There will come a point when a new small quantity of drying agent no longer clumps together, but the individual particles settle slowly throughout the solution. As they say in Scandinavia, "Add drying agent until it begins to snow." The drying process takes about 10–15 min, during which time the tube contents should be mixed occasionally by flicking the tube. The solution should no longer be cloudy but clear (although it may be colored).

Once drying is judged complete, the solvent is removed by forcing a Pasteur pipette to the bottom of the reaction tube and pulling the solvent in. Air is expelled from the pipette as it is being pushed through the crystals or pellets so that no drying agent will enter the pipette. It is very important to wash the drying agent left in the reaction tube with several small quantities of pure solvent to transfer all the extract.

Step 4. Removing the Solvent

If the quantity of extract is relatively small, say 3 mL or less, then the easiest way to remove the solvent is to blow a stream of air (or nitrogen) onto the surface of the solution from a Pasteur pipette (Fig. 7.8). Be sure that the stream of air is very gentle before inserting it into the reaction tube. The heat of vaporization of the solvent will cause the tube to become rather cold during the evaporation and, of course, slow down the process. The easiest way to add heat is to hold the tube in your hand.

Another way to remove the solvent is to attach the Pasteur pipette to an aspirator and pull air over the surface of the liquid. This is not quite as fast as blowing air onto the surface of the liquid and runs the danger of sucking up the liquid into the aspirator.

If the volume of liquid is more than about 3 mL, put it into a 25-mL filter flask, put a plastic Hirsch funnel in place, and attach the flask to the aspirator. By placing your thumb in the Hirsch funnel, the vacuum can be controlled, and heat can be applied by holding the flask in the other hand while swirling the contents (Fig. 7.9).

The reaction tube or filter flask in which the solvent is evaporated should be tared (weighed empty), and this weight recorded in your notebook. In this way, the weight of material extracted can be determined by again weighing the container.

EXPERIMENT

Partition Coefficient of Benzoic Acid

IN THIS EXPERIMENT you will shake a solution of benzoic acid in water with the immiscible solvent dichloromethane. The benzoic acid will distribute (partition) itself between the two layers. By removing the organic layer, drying, and evaporating it, the weight of benzoic acid in the dichloromethane can be determined and thus the ratio in the two layers. This ratio is a constant known as the partition coefficient.

■ **FIG. 7.8**
An aspirator tube being used to
remove solvent vapors.

To water aspirator or
to nitrogen or air supply

Pasteur pipette

■ **FIG. 7.9**
The apparatus for removing a solvent
under vacuum.

To
aspirator

In a reaction tube, place about 100 mg of benzoic acid (weighed to the nearest milligram) and add exactly equal volumes of water followed by dichloromethane (about 1.6 mL each). While making this addition, note which layer is organic and which is aqueous. Put a septum on the tube and shake the contents vigorously for at least 2 min. Allow the tube to stand undisturbed until the layers separate and then carefully draw off, using a Pasteur pipette, *all* of the aqueous layer without removing any of the organic layer. It may be helpful to draw out the tip of the pipette to a fine point in a flame and, using this, to tilt the reaction tube on its side to make this separation as clean as possible.

Add anhydrous calcium chloride pellets to the dichloromethane in very small quantities until it no longer clumps together. Mix the contents of the tube by flicking it and allow it to stand for about 5 min to complete the drying process. Using a dry Pasteur pipette, transfer the dichloromethane to a tared dry reaction tube or a 10-mL Erlenmeyer flask containing a boiling chip. Complete the transfer by washing the drying agent with two more portions of solvent that are added to the original solution and then evaporate the solvent. This can be done by boiling off the solvent while removing solvent vapors with an aspirator tube or by blowing a stream of air or nitrogen into the container while warming it in one's hand (*see* Fig. 7.8). This operation should be performed in a hood.

From the weight of the benzoic acid in the dichloromethane layer, the weight in the water layer can be obtained by difference. The ratio of the weight in dichloromethane to the weight in water is the distribution coefficient because the volumes of the two solvents were equal. Report the value of the distribution coefficient in your notebook.

Cleaning Up. The aqueous layer can be flushed down the drain. Dichloromethane goes into the halogenated organic solvents container. After allowing the solvent to evaporate from the sodium sulfate in the hood, place the sodium sulfate in the non-hazardous solid waste container. If local regulations do not allow for the evaporation of solvents in a hood, dispose of the wet sodium sulfate in a special container.

Part 2: Acid/Base Liquid/Liquid Extraction

Acid/base liquid/liquid extraction involves carrying out simple acid/base reactions to separate strong organic acids, weak organic acids, neutral organic compounds, and basic organic substances. The chemistry involved is given in the following equations, using benzoic acid, phenol, naphthalene, and aniline as examples of the four types of compounds.

Here is the strategy (refer to the flow sheet in Fig. 7.10): The four organic compounds are dissolved in *t*-butyl methyl ether. The ether solution is shaken with a saturated aqueous solution of sodium bicarbonate, a weak base. This will react only with the strong acid, benzoic acid (**1**), to form the ionic salt, sodium benzoate (**5**), which dissolves in the aqueous layer and is removed. The ether solution now contains just phenol (**2**), naphthalene (**4**), and aniline (**3**). A 3 *M* aqueous solution of sodium hydroxide is added, and the mixture is shaken. The hydroxide, a strong base, will react only with the phenol (**2**), a weak acid, to form sodium phenoxide (**6**), an ionic compound that dissolves in the aqueous layer and is removed. The ether now contains only naphthalene (**4**) and aniline (**3**). Shaking it with dilute hydrochloric acid removes the aniline, a base, as the ionic anilinium chloride (**7**). The aqueous layer is removed. Evaporation of the *t*-butyl methyl ether now leaves naphthalene (**4**), the neutral compound. The other three compounds are recovered by adding acid to the sodium benzoate (**5**) and sodium phenoxide (**6**) and base to the anilinium chloride (**7**) to regenerate the covalent compounds benzoic acid (**1**), phenol (**2**), and aniline (**3**).

The ability to separate strong acids from weak acids depends on the acidity constants of the acids and the basicity constants of the bases. In the first equation consider the ionization of benzoic acid, which has an equilibrium constant (K_a) of 6.8×10^{25}. The conversion of benzoic acid to the benzoate anion in equation 4 is governed by the equilibrium constant, K (equation 5), obtained by combining equations 3 and 4.

The pK_a of carbonic acid, H_2CO_3, is 6.35.

$$C_6H_5COOH + H_2O \rightleftharpoons C_6H_5COO^- + H_3O^+ \qquad (1)$$

$$K_a = \frac{[C_6H_5COO^-][H_3O^+]}{[C_6H_5COOH]} = 6.8 \times 10^{-5}, \mathrm{p}K_a = 4.17 \qquad (2)$$

■ **FIG. 7.10**

A flow sheet for the separation of a strong acid, a weak acid, a neutral compound, and a base: benzoic acid, phenol, naphthalene, and aniline (this page). Acid/base reactions of the acidic and basic compounds (opposite page).

In reaction tube A,
1) Dissolve all four compounds in *t*-butyl methyl ether.
2) Mix with HCO₃⁻, remove lower aqueous layer, and place it in tube B.

1) Add OH⁻, mix, remove lower aqueous layer, and place it in tube C.

1) Add HCl, mix, remove lower aqueous layer, and place it in tube D.

1) Dry solution over anhydrous calcium chloride pellets, remove solvent, and evaporate it to dryness in a clean, dry, tared reaction tube.

Naphthalene

Benzoic acid
Forms a white, crystalline precipitate that can be removed by filtration

Phenol

Aniline

Phenol and aniline each form oily layers on top of the aqueous layer. Extract each with *t*-butyl methyl ether: Add ether to the tube, mix, separate layers, dry the ether layer over anhydrous calcium chloride pellets, remove solution from drying agent, and evaporate the solvent.

1
Benzoic acid
$pK_a = 4.17$
Covalent, sol. in org. solvents

5
Sodium benzoate
Ionic, sol. in water

2
Phenol
$pK_a = 10$
Covalent, sol. in org. solvents

6
Sodium phenoxide
Ionic, sol. in water

3
Aniline
$pK_b = 9.30$
Covalent, sol. in org. solvents

7
Anilinium chloride
Ionic, sol. in water

$$K_w = [H_3O^+][OH^-] = 10^{-14} \tag{3}$$

$$C_6H_5COOH + OH^- \rightleftharpoons C_6H_5COO^- + H_2O \tag{4}$$

$$K = \frac{[C_6H_5COO^-]}{[C_6H_5COOH][OH^-]} = \frac{K_a}{K_w} = \frac{6.8 \times 10^{-5}}{10^{-14}} = 3.2 \times 10^8 \tag{5}$$

If 99% of the benzoic acid is converted to $C_6H_5COO^-$,

$$\frac{[C_6H_5COO^-]}{[C_6H_5COOH]} = \frac{99}{1} \tag{6}$$

then from equation 5 the hydroxide ion concentration would need to be 6.8×10^{-7} M. Because saturated $NaHCO_3$ has $[OH^- = 3 \times 10^{-4}$ M, the hydroxide ion concentration is high enough to convert benzoic acid completely to sodium benzoate.

For phenol, with a K_a of 10^{-10}, the minimum hydroxide ion concentration that will produce the phenoxide anion in 99% conversion is 10^{-2} M. The concentration of hydroxide in 10% sodium hydroxide solution is 10^{-1} M, and so phenol in strong base is entirely converted to the water-soluble salt.

General Considerations

If acetic acid was used as the reaction solvent, it would also be distributed largely into the aqueous phase; if the reaction product is a neutral substance, however, the residual acetic acid in the ether can be removed by one washing with excess 5% sodium bicarbonate solution. If the reaction product is a higher molecular weight acid, for example, benzoic acid (C_6H_5COOH), it will stay in the ether layer, while acetic acid is being removed by repeated washing with water; the benzoic acid can then be separated from neutral byproducts by extraction with sodium bicarbonate or sodium hydroxide solution and acidification of the extract. Acids of high molecular weight are extracted only slowly by sodium bicarbonate, so sodium carbonate is used in its place; however, carbonate is more prone than bicarbonate to produce emulsions. Sometimes an emulsion in the lower layer can be settled by twirling the separatory funnel by its stem. An emulsion in the upper layer can be broken by grasping the funnel by the neck and swirling it. Because the tendency to emulsify increases with the removal of electrolytes and solvents, a little sodium chloride solution is added with each portion of wash water. If the layers are largely clear but an emulsion persists at the interface, the clear part of the water layer can be drawn off, and the emulsion run into a second funnel and shaken with fresh ether.

Liquid/liquid extraction and acid/base extraction are employed in the majority of organic reactions because it is unusual to have the product crystallize from the reaction mixture or to be able to distill the reaction product directly from the reaction mixture. In the research literature, one will often see the statement "the reaction mixture was worked up in the usual way," which implies an extraction process of the type described here. Good laboratory practice dictates, however, that the details of the process be written out.

Benzoic acid
mp 123°C, pK_a 4.17

OCH₃ ... OCH₃

1,4-Dimethoxybenzene
(Hydroquinone dimethyl ether)
mp 57°C

Online Study Center

Photo: Extraction with Ether;
Video: Extraction with Ether

OH

H₃C—C—CH₃
       |
      CH₃

4-*tert*-Butylphenol
mp 101°C, pK_a 10.17

EXPERIMENTS

1. Separation of a Carboxylic Acid, a Phenol, and a Neutral Substance

A mixture of equal parts of a carboxylic acid, a phenol, and a neutral substance is to be separated by extraction from an ether solvent. Note carefully the procedure for this extraction. In the next experiment you are to work out your own extraction procedure. Your unknown will consist of either benzoic acid or 2-chlorobenzoic acid (the carboxylic acid), 4-*t*-butyl phenol or 4-bromophenol, and biphenyl or 1,4-dimethoxybenzene (the neutral substance). The object of this experiment is to identify the three substances in the mixture and to determine the percent recovery of each from the mixture.

Procedure

> **IN THIS EXPERIMENT** three organic solids are separated by reaction with base followed by extraction. Bicarbonate converts carboxylic acids (but not phenols) to ions. Hydroxide ion converts phenols (as well as carboxylic acids) to ions. Ionic substances are soluble in water. The addition of hydrochloric acid to the aqueous ionic solutions regenerates nonionic substances. At each step you should ask yourself, "Have I converted a nonionic substance to an ionic one?" (or vice versa). The ionic substances will be in the aqueous layer; the nonionic ones will be in the organic layer.

Dissolve about 0.18 g of the mixture (record the exact weight) in 2 mL of *t*-butyl methyl ether or diethyl ether in a reaction tube (tube 1). Then add 1 mL of a saturated aqueous solution of sodium bicarbonate to the tube. Use the graduations on the side of the tube to measure the amounts because they do not need to be exact. Mix the contents of the tube thoroughly by pulling the two layers into a Pasteur pipette and expelling them forcefully into the reaction tube. Do this for about 3 min. Allow the layers to separate completely and then draw off the lower layer into another reaction tube (tube 2). Add another 0.15 mL of sodium bicarbonate solution to the tube, mix the contents as before, and add the lower layer to tube 2. Exactly which chemical species is in tube 2? Add 0.2 mL of ether to tube 2, mix it thoroughly, remove the ether layer, and discard it. This is called *backwashing* and serves to remove any organic material that might contaminate the contents of tube 2.

Add 1.0 mL of 3 *M* aqueous sodium hydroxide to tube 1, shake the mixture thoroughly, allow the layers to separate, draw off the lower layer using a clean Pasteur pipette, and place it in tube 3. Extract tube 1 with two 0.15-mL portions of water, and add these to tube 3. Backwash the contents of tube 3 with 0.15 mL of ether and discard the ether wash just as was done for tube 2. Exactly which chemical species is in tube 3?

To tube 1 add saturated sodium chloride solution, mix, remove the aqueous layer, and then add to the ether anhydrous calcium chloride pellets until the drying

Online Study Center

Videos: Filtration of Crystals
Using the Pasteur Pipette,
Microscale Filtration on the
Hirsch Funnel

OH

Br

4-Bromophenol
mp 66°C, pK_a 10.2

Biphenyl
mp 71°C

COOH

Cl

2-Chlorobenzoic acid
mp 141°C, pK_a 2.92

The best way to remove the
solvent: under a gentle stream of
air or nitrogen.

agent no longer clumps together. Wash it off with ether after the drying process is
finished. Allow 5–10 min for the drying of the ether solution.

Using the concentration information given in the inside back cover of this
book, calculate exactly how much concentrated hydrochloric acid is needed to neutralize the contents of tube 2. Then, by dropwise addition of concentrated hydrochloric acid, carry out this neutralization while testing the solution with litmus
paper. An excess of hydrochloric acid does no harm. This reaction must be carried
out with *extreme care* because much carbon dioxide is released in the neutralization. Add a boiling stick to the tube and very cautiously heat the tube to bring most
of the solid carboxylic acid into solution. Allow the tube to cool slowly to room
temperature and then cool it in ice. Remove the solvent with a Pasteur pipette and
recrystallize the residue from boiling water. Again, allow the tube to cool slowly to
room temperature and then cool it in ice. At the appropriate time, stir the crystals
and collect them on a Hirsch funnel using the procedures detailed in Chapter 4. The
crystals can be transferred and washed on the funnel using a small quantity of ice
water. The solubility of benzoic acid in water is 1.9 g/L at 0°C and 68 g/L at 95°C.
The solubility of chlorobenzoic acid is similar. Turn the crystals out onto a tared
piece of paper, allow them to dry thoroughly, and determine the percent recovery
of the acid. Assess the purity of the product by checking its melting point.

In exactly the same way, neutralize the contents of tube 3 with concentrated
hydrochloric acid. This time, of course, there will be no carbon dioxide evolution.
Again, heat the tube to bring most of the material into solution, allow it to cool
slowly, remove the solvent, and recrystallize the phenol from boiling water. At the
appropriate time, after the product has cooled slowly to room temperature and
then in ice, it is also collected on a Hirsch funnel, washed with a very small quantity of ice water, and allowed to dry. The percent recovery and melting point are
determined.

The neutral compound is recovered using the Pasteur pipette to remove the
ether from the drying agent and to transfer it to a tared reaction tube. The drying
agent is washed two or three times with additional ether to ensure complete transfer of the product.

Evaporate the solvent by placing the tube in a warm water bath and directing
a stream of nitrogen or air onto the surface of the ether in the hood (*see* Fig. 7.8 on
page 146). An aspirator tube can also be used for this purpose. Determine the
weight of the crude product and then recrystallize it from methanol-water if it is
the low-melting compound. Reread Chapter 4 for detailed instructions on carrying out the process of recrystallization from a mixed solvent. The product is dissolved in about 0.5–1 mL of methanol, and water is added until the solution gets
cloudy, which indicates that the solution is saturated. This process is best carried
out while heating the tube in a hot water bath at 50°C. Allow the tube to cool
slowly to room temperature and then cool it thoroughly in ice. If you have the
high-melting compound, recrystallize it from ethanol (8 mL/g).

The products are best isolated by collection on a Hirsch funnel using an ice-
cold alcohol–water mixture to transfer and wash the compounds. Determine the
percent recovery and the melting point. Turn in the products in neatly labeled
1½-in. × 1½-in. (4 cm × 4 cm) ziplock plastic bags attached to the laboratory

report. If the yield on recrystallization is low, concentrate the filtrate (the mother liquor) and obtain a second crop of crystals.

2. Separation of Neutral and Basic Substances

IN THIS EXPERIMENT remember that hydrochloric acid will convert a nonionic amine to an ionic substance and that base will regenerate the nonionic substance from the ionic form. The nonionic and neutral substances are ether soluble, and the ionic substances will be found in the aqueous layer.

Ether vapors are heavier than air and can travel along bench tops, run down drain troughs, and collect in sinks. Be extremely careful to avoid flames when working with volatile ethers.

A mixture of equal parts of a neutral substance (naphthalene or 1,4-dichlorobenzene) and a basic substance (4-chloroaniline or ethyl 4-aminobenzoate) is to be separated by extraction from an ether solution. Naphthalene and 1,4-dichlorobenzene are completely insoluble in water. The bases will dissolve in hydrochloric acid, while the neutral compounds will remain in ether solution. The bases are insoluble in cold water but will dissolve to some extent in hot water and are soluble in ethanol. Naphthalene and 1,4-dichlorobenzene can be purified as described in Chapter 4. They also sublime very easily. Keep the samples covered.

Naphthalene
mp 82°C

1,4-Dichlorobenzene
mp 56°C

4-Chloroaniline
mp 68–71°C, pK_b 4.15

Ethyl 4-aminobenzoate
mp 90°C, pK_b 4.92

Plan a step-by-step procedure for separating 200 mg of the mixture into its components and have the plan checked by your instructor before proceeding. A flow sheet is a convenient way to present the plan. Select the correct solvent or mixture of solvents for the recrystallization of the bases on the basis of solubility tests. Determine the weights and melting points of the isolated and purified products and calculate the percent recovery of each. Turn in the products in neatly labeled vials or 1 1/2-in. × 1 1/2-in. ziplock plastic bags attached to the report.

Cleaning Up. Combine all aqueous filtrates and solutions, neutralize them, and flush the resulting solution down the drain. Used ether should be placed in the organic solvents container, and the drying agent, once the solvent has evaporated from it, can be placed in the nonhazardous solid waste container. If local regulations do not allow for the evaporation of solvents in a hood, dispose of the wet sodium sulfate in a special container. Any 4-chloroaniline or 1,4-dichlorobenzene should be placed in the halogenated waste container.

3. Separation of Acidic and Neutral Substances

$pH = -\log [H^+]$
pK_a = acidity constant
pK_b = basicity constant

A mixture of equal proportions of benzoic acid, 4-*t*-butylphenol, and 1,4-dimethoxybenzene is to be separated by extraction from *t*-butyl methyl ether. Note the detailed directions for extraction carefully. Prepare a flow sheet (*see* Fig. 7.10 on page 148) for this sequence of operations. In the next experiment you will work out your own extraction procedure.

Procedure

Extinguish all flames when working with *t*-butyl methyl ether! The best method for removing the ether is by simple distillation. Dispose of waste ether in the container provided.

Dissolve 3 g of the mixture in 30 mL of *t*-butyl methyl ether and transfer the mixture to a 125-mL separatory funnel (*see* Fig. 7.2 on page 139) using a little *t*-butyl methyl ether to complete the transfer. Add 10 mL of water and note which layer is organic and which is aqueous. Add 10 mL of a 3 *M* aqueous solution of sodium bicarbonate to the funnel. Swirl or stir the mixture to allow carbon dioxide to escape. Stopper the funnel and cautiously mix the contents. Vent the liberated carbon dioxide and then shake the mixture thoroughly with frequent venting of the funnel. Repeat the process with another 10 mL of bicarbonate solution. Allow the layers to separate completely and then draw off the lower layer into a 50-mL Erlenmeyer flask (labeled flask 1). What does this layer contain?

Benzoic acid
mp 123°C, pK_a 4.17

Add 10 mL of 1.5 *M* aqueous sodium hydroxide to the separatory funnel, shake the mixture thoroughly, allow the layers to separate, and draw off the lower layer into a 50-mL Erlenmeyer flask (labeled flask 2). Repeat the process with another 10 mL of base. Then add an additional 5 mL of water to the separatory funnel, shake the mixture as before, and add this to flask 2. What does flask 2 contain?

Add 15 mL of a saturated aqueous solution of sodium chloride to the separatory funnel, shake the mixture thoroughly, allow the layers to separate, and draw off the lower layer, which can be discarded. What is the purpose of adding saturated sodium chloride solution? Carefully pour the ether layer into a 50-mL Erlenmeyer flask (labeled flask 3) from the top of the separatory funnel, taking great care not to allow any water droplets to be transferred. Add about 4 g of anhydrous calcium chloride pellets to the ether extract and set it aside.

4-*tert*-Butylphenol
mp 101°C, pK_a 10.17

Acidify the contents of flask 2 by dropwise addition of concentrated hydrochloric acid while testing with litmus paper. Cool the flask in an ice bath.

Cautiously add concentrated hydrochloric acid dropwise to flask 1 until the contents are acidic to litmus and then cool the flask in ice.

Online Study Center

Video: Macroscale Crystallization

Decant (pour off) the ether from flask 3 into a tared flask, making sure to leave all of the drying agent behind. Wash the drying agent with additional ether to ensure complete transfer of the product. If decantation is difficult, then remove the drying agent by gravity filtration (*see* Fig. 4.6 on page 69). Put a boiling stick in the flask and evaporate the ether in the hood. An aspirator tube can be used for

■ FIG. 7.11
An aspirator tube in use.

this purpose (Fig. 7.11). Determine the weight of the crude *p*-dimethoxybenzene and then recrystallize it from methanol. See Chapter 4 for detailed instructions on how to carry out recrystallization.

Isolate the *t*-butylphenol from flask 2, employing vacuum filtration on a Hirsch funnel, and wash it on the filter with a small quantity of ice water. Determine the weight of the crude product and then recrystallize it from ethanol. Similarly isolate, weigh, and recrystallize from boiling water the benzoic acid in flask 1. The solubility of benzoic acid in water is 1.9 g/L at 0°C and 68 g/L at 95°C.

Dry the purified products, determine their melting points and weights, and calculate the percent recovery of each substance, bearing in mind that the original mixture contained 1 g of each compound. Hand in the three products in neatly labeled vials.

Cleaning Up. Combine all aqueous layers, washes, and filtrates. Dilute with water, neutralize using either sodium carbonate or dilute hydrochloric acid. This material can then be flushed down the drain with excess water. Methanol filtrate and any ether go in the organic solvents container. Allow ether to evaporate from the calcium chloride in the hood. Then place the calcium chloride in the nonhazardous solid waste container. If local regulations do not allow for the evaporation of solvents in a hood, dispose of the wet sodium sulfate in a special container.

4. Separation of Neutral and Basic Substances

A mixture of equal parts of a neutral substance (naphthalene) and a basic substance (4-chloroaniline) is to be separated by extraction from *t*-butyl methyl ether solution. The base will dissolve in hydrochloric acid, whereas the neutral naphthalene will remain in the *t*-butyl methyl ether solution. 4-Chloroaniline is insoluble in cold water but will dissolve to some extent in hot water and is soluble in ethanol. Naphthalene can be purified as described in Chapter 4.

Plan a procedure for separating 2.0 g of the mixture into its components and have the plan checked by your instructor before proceeding. A flow sheet is a convenient way to present the plan. Using solubility tests, select the correct solvent or

**1,4-Dimethoxybenzene
(Hydroquinone dimethyl ether)**
mp 57°C

Naphthalene
mp 82°C

4-Chloroaniline
mp 68–71°C, pK_b 10.0

mixture of solvents to recrystallize 4-chloroaniline. Determine the weights and melting points of the isolated and purified products and calculate the percent recovery of each. Turn in the products in neatly labeled vials.

Cleaning Up. Combine all aqueous filtrates and solutions, neutralize them, and flush the resulting solution down the drain with a large excess of water. Used *t*-butyl methyl ether should be placed in the organic solvents container, and the drying agent, once the solvent has evaporated from it, can be placed in the nonhazardous solid waste container. If local regulations do not allow for the evaporation of solvents in a hood, dispose of the wet sodium sulfate in a special container. Any 4-chloroaniline should be placed in the chlorinated organic compounds container.

Handle aromatic amines with care. Most are toxic, and some are carcinogenic. Avoid breathing the dust and vapor from the solid and keep the compounds off the skin, which is best done by wearing nitrile gloves.

5. Extraction and Purification of Components in an Analgesic Tablet

> **IN THIS EXPERIMENT** a powdered analgesic tablet, Excedrin, is boiled with dichloromethane and filtered. The solid on the filter is boiled with ethanol, which dissolves everything but the binder. The ethanol is evaporated and from the hot solution acetaminophen recrystallizes. The dichloromethane solution is shaken with base that converts aspirin to the water-soluble carboxylate anion. The dichloromethane is then evaporated to give caffeine that is purified by sublimation. The aqueous carboxylate anion solution is made acidic, which frees aspirin; warming the mixture and allowing it to cool allows aspirin to recrystallize. It is isolated by filtration.

Excedrin contains aspirin, caffeine, and acetaminophen as determined by thin-layer chromatography (TLC; *see* Chapter 8) or high performance liquid chromatography. A tablet is held together with a binder to prevent the components from crumbling when stored or while being swallowed. A close reading of the contents on the package will disclose the nature of the binder. Starch is commonly used, as is microcrystalline cellulose or silica gel. All of these have one property in common: They are insoluble in water and common organic solvents.

Aspirin
(Acetylsalicylic acid)
mp 135°C

Acetaminophen
(*p*-Hydroxyacetanilide)
mp 169–170.5°C

Caffeine
mp 238°C

TABLE 7.2 • Solubilities					
	Water	Ethanol	Chloroform	Diethyl ether	Ligroin
Aspirin	0.33 g/100 mL at 25°C; 1 g/100 mL at 37°C	1 g/5 mL	1 g/17 mL	1 g/13 mL	
Acetaminophen	v. sl. sol. cold; sol. hot	sol.	ins.	sl. sol.	ins.
Caffeine	1 g/46 mL at 25°C; 1 g/5.5 mL at 80°C; 1 g/1.5 mL at 100°C	1 g/66 mL at 25°C; 1 g/22 mL at 60°C	1 g/5.5 mL	1 g/530 mL	sl. sol.

Inspection of the structures of caffeine, acetylsalicylic acid, and acetaminophen reveals that one is a base, one is a strong organic acid, and one is a weak organic acid. It might be tempting to separate this mixture using exactly the same procedure employed in separating benzoic acid, 4-*t*-butylphenol, and 1,4-dimethoxybenzene (experiment 3)—that is, dissolve the mixture in dichloromethane; separate the strongly acidic component by reaction with bicarbonate ion, a weak base; then remove the weakly acidic component by reaction with hydroxide, a strong base. This process would leave the neutral compound in the dichloromethane solution.

In the present experiment the solubility data (see Table 7.2) reveal that the weak acid, acetaminophen, is not soluble in ether, chloroform, or dichloromethane, so it cannot be extracted by a strong base. We can take advantage of this lack of solubility by dissolving the other two components, caffeine and aspirin, in dichloromethane and removing the acetaminophen by filtration. The binder is also insoluble in dichloromethane, but treatment of the solid mixture with ethanol will dissolve the acetaminophen and not the binder. These can then be separated by filtration, with the acetaminophen isolated by evaporation of the ethanol.

This experiment is a test of technique. It is not easy to separate and recrystallize a few milligrams of a compound that occurs in a mixture.

Microscale Procedure

In a mortar, grind an Extra Strength Excedrin tablet to a very fine powder. The label states that this analgesic contains 250 mg of aspirin, 250 mg of acetaminophen, and 65 mg of caffeine per tablet. Place 300 mg of this powder in a reaction tube and add 2 mL of dichloromethane. Warm the mixture briefly and note that a large part of the material does not dissolve. Filter the mixture on a microscale Büchner funnel (the base of a chromatography column; Fig. 7.12) into another reaction tube. This is done by transferring the slurry to the funnel with a Pasteur pipette and completing the transfer with a small portion of dichloromethane. This filtrate is solution 1. A Hirsch funnel (Fig. 7.13) or a Wilfilter (Fig. 7.14) can also be used for this procedure. Pressure filtration is another alternative.

Transfer the powder on the filter to a reaction tube, add 1 mL of ethanol, and heat the mixture to boiling on the sand bath (with a boiling stick). Not all the material will go into solution. That which does not is the binder. Filter the mixture on

⚠ Handle dichloromethane in the hood. It is a suspected carcinogen.

✦ Online Study Center

Photos: Micro Büchner Funnel, Vacuum Filtration into Reaction Tube through Hirsch Funnel, Use of the Wilfilter

The binder can be starch, microcrystalline cellulose, or silica gel.

■ **FIG. 7.12**
A microscale Büchner funnel assembly.

Thermometer adapter

Micro Büchner funnel with fritted disk

To aspirator

Vacuum-tight connector

Reaction tube with filtrate

■ **FIG. 7.13**
A Hirsch funnel with an integral adapter, a polyethylene frit, and a 25-mL filter flask.

Filter paper, 12 mm dia.

Polyethylene filter disk (frit), 10 mm dia.

Hirsch funnel

To aspirator

25-mL Filter flask

■ **FIG. 7.14**
The Wilfilter filtration apparatus. *See* Chapter 4 for usage information.

Crystals

Wilfilter

Filtrate

Online Study Center

Photos: Vacuum Filtration into Reaction Tube through Hirsch Funnel, Micro Büchner Funnel

Acetaminophen

Online Study Center

Video: Filtration of Crystals Using the Pasteur Pipette

Check product purity by TLC (Chapter 8) using 25:1 ethyl acetate–acetic acid to elute the silica gel plates.

the same microscale Büchner funnel into a tared reaction tube and complete the transfer and washing using a few drops of hot ethanol.

Evaporate about two-thirds of the filtrate by boiling off the ethanol or, better, by warming the solution and blowing a stream of air into the reaction tube. Heat the residue to boiling (add a boiling stick to prevent bumping) and, if necessary, add more ethanol to bring the solid into solution. Allow the saturated solution to cool slowly to room temperature to deposit crystals of acetaminophen, which is reported to melt at 169°C–170.5°C. After the mixture has cooled to room temperature, cool it in ice for several minutes, remove the solvent with a Pasteur pipette, wash the crystals once with 2 drops of ice-cold ethanol, remove the ethanol, and dry the crystals under aspirator vacuum while heating the tube on a steam or sand bath.

Alternatively, the original ethanol solution can be evaporated to dryness, and the residue recrystallized from boiling water. The crystals can be collected on a Hirsch funnel (Fig. 7.13) or by use of a Wilfilter (Fig. 7.14). Once the crystals are dry, determine their weight and melting point. TLC analysis (see Chapter 8) and a determination of the melting points of these crystals and the two other components of this mixture will indicate their purity.

Online Study Center

Video: Recrystallization; Photos: Vacuum Filtration into Reaction Tube through Hirsch Funnel, Use of the Wilfilter

Video: Extraction with Dichloromethane

Photos: Sublimation Apparatus, Filtration Using a Pasteur Pipette; Videos: Recrystallization, Filtration Using a Pasteur Pipette

Caffeine

See Figure 4.13 on page 73 for drying crystals under vacuum.

The dichloromethane filtered from the binder and acetaminophen mixture (solution 1) should contain caffeine and aspirin. These can be separated by extraction either with acid (which will remove the caffeine as a water-soluble salt) or with base (which will remove the aspirin as a water-soluble salt). We shall use the latter procedure.

To the dichloromethane solution in a reaction tube, add 1 mL of 3 M sodium hydroxide solution and shake the mixture thoroughly. Remove the aqueous layer, add 0.2 mL more water, shake the mixture thoroughly, and again remove the aqueous layer, which is combined with the first aqueous extract.

To the dichloromethane, add calcium chloride pellets until the drying agent no longer clumps together. Shake the mixture over a 5-min to 10-min period to complete the drying process; then remove the solvent, wash the drying agent with more solvent, and evaporate the combined extracts to dryness under a stream of air to leave crude caffeine.

The caffeine can be purified by sublimation (Fig. 7.15) or by recrystallization. Recrystallize the caffeine by dissolving it in the minimum quantity of 30% ethanol in tetrahydrofuran. It also can be recrystallized by dissolving the product in a minimum quantity of hot toluene or acetone and adding to this solution ligroin (hexanes) until the solution is cloudy while at the boiling point. In any case, allow the solution to cool slowly to room temperature; then cool the mixture in ice and remove the solvent from the crystals with a Pasteur pipette. Remove the remainder of the solvent under aspirator vacuum and determine the weight of the caffeine and its melting point.

The aqueous hydroxide extract contains aspirin as the sodium salt of the carboxylic acid. To the aqueous solution, add 3 M hydrochloric acid dropwise until the solution tests strongly acid with indicator paper; then add 2 more drops of acid. This will give a suspension of white acetylsalicylic acid in the aqueous solution. It could be filtered off and recrystallized from boiling water, but this would cause transfer losses. An easier procedure is to heat the aqueous solution that contains the precipitated aspirin.

Online Study Center

Photos: Filtration Using a Pasteur Pipette, Use of the Wilfilter; Videos: Recrystallization, Filtration of Crystals Using the Pasteur Pipette

Aspirin

Alternative procedure: Use a Hirsch funnel or a Wilfilter to isolate the aspirin.

Add a boiling stick and heat the mixture to boiling (Fig. 7.16), at which time the aspirin should dissolve completely. If it does not, add more water. Long boiling will hydrolyze the aspirin to salicylic acid (mp 157°C–159°C). Once completely dissolved, the aspirin should be allowed to recrystallize slowly as the solution cools to room temperature in an insulated container. Once the tube has reached room temperature, it should be cooled in ice for several minutes, and then the solvent is removed with a Pasteur pipette. Wash the crystals with a few drops of ice-cold water and isolate them with a Wilfilter or scrape them out onto a piece of filter paper. Squeezing the crystals between sheets of filter paper will hasten drying. Once these crystals are completely dry, determine the weight of the acetylsalicylic acid and its melting point.

Cleaning Up. Place any dichloromethane-containing solutions in the halogenated organic waste container and the other organic liquids in the organic solvents container. The aqueous layers should be diluted and neutralized with sodium carbonate before being flushed down the drain. After it is free of solvent, the calcium

15-mL Centrifuge tube, to be filled with ice

Pipette bulb

Adapter (Pluro stopper)

25-mL Filter flask

Material to be sublimed

Sublimate

Heat source

Boiling stick

Cool at this poin

Air condenser

Boiling solvent

Temperature controlled by depth in sand

chloride can be placed in the nonhazardous solid waste container. If local regulations do not allow for the evaporation of solvents in a hood, dispose of the wet sodium sulfate in a special container.

Macroscale Procedure

In a mortar, grind two Extra Strength Excedrin tablets to a very fine powder. The label states that this analgesic contains 250 mg of aspirin, 250 mg of acetaminophen, and 65 mg of caffeine per tablet. Place this powder in a test tube and add 7.5 mL of dichloromethane. Warm the mixture briefly and note that a large part of the material does not dissolve. Filter the mixture into another test tube. This can be done by transferring the slurry to a funnel equipped with a piece of filter paper. Use a Pasteur pipette and complete the transfer with a small portion of dichloromethane. This filtrate is solution 1.

Transfer the powder on the filter to a test tube, add 4 mL of ethanol, and heat the mixture to boiling (with a boiling stick). Not all of the material will go into solution. That which does not is the binder. Filter the mixture into a tared test tube and complete the transfer and washing by using a few drops of hot ethanol. This is solution 2.

Evaporate about two-thirds of solution 2 by boiling off the ethanol (with a boiling stick) or, better, by warming the solution and blowing a stream of air into the test tube. Heat the residue to boiling (add a boiling stick to prevent bumping) and add more ethanol, if necessary, to bring the solid into solution. Allow the saturated solution to cool slowly to room temperature to deposit crystals of acetaminophen, which is reported to melt at 169°C–170.5°C. After the mixture has

Handle dichloromethane in the hood. It is a suspected carcinogen.

The binder can be starch, microcrystalline cellulose, or silica gel.

Acetaminophen

Check product purity by TLC using 25:1 ethyl acetate–acetic acid to elute the silica gel plates.

An alternative to shaking is pipette mixing or using a vortex stirrer, if available.

Caffeine

**Sodium
acetylsalicylate**
(soluble in water)

Aspirin

Alternative procedure: Use a Hirsch funnel (*see* Fig. 4.14 on page 74) to isolate the aspirin.

cooled to room temperature, cool it in ice for several minutes, remove the solvent with a Pasteur pipette, wash the crystals once with 2 drops of ice-cold ethanol, remove the ethanol, and dry the crystals under aspirator vacuum while heating the tube on a steam or sand bath.

Alternatively, the original ethanol solution is evaporated to dryness, and the residue is recrystallized from boiling water. The crystals are best collected and dried on a Hirsch funnel (*see* Fig. 7.13 on page 158). Once the crystals are dry, determine their weight and melting point. TLC analysis (*see* Chapter 8) and a determination of the melting points of these crystals and the two other components of this mixture will indicate their purity.

The dichloromethane filtered from the binder and acetaminophen mixture (solution 1) should contain caffeine and aspirin. These can be separated by extraction either with acid (which will remove the caffeine as a water-soluble salt) or with base (which will remove the aspirin as a water-soluble salt). We shall use the latter procedure.

To the dichloromethane solution in a test tube, add 4 mL of 3 *M* sodium hydroxide solution and shake the mixture thoroughly. Remove the aqueous layer, add 1 mL more water, shake the mixture thoroughly, and again remove the aqueous layer, which is combined with the first aqueous extract.

To the dichloromethane add anhydrous calcium chloride pellets until the drying agent no longer clumps together. Shake the mixture over a 5–10-min period to complete the drying process, then remove the solvent, wash the drying agent with more solvent, and evaporate the combined extracts to dryness under a stream of air to leave crude caffeine.

The caffeine can be purified by sublimation or by recrystallization. Recrystallize the caffeine by dissolving it in the minimum quantity of 30% ethanol in tetrahydrofuran. It can also be recrystallized by dissolving the product in a minimum quantity of hot toluene or acetone and adding hexanes to this solution until the solution is cloudy while at the boiling point. In any case, allow the solution to cool slowly to room temperature; then cool the mixture in ice and remove the solvent from the crystals with a Pasteur pipette. Remove the remainder of the solvent under aspirator vacuum and determine the weight of the caffeine and its melting point.

The aqueous hydroxide extract contains aspirin as the sodium salt of the carboxylic acid. To the aqueous solution add 3 *M* hydrochloric acid dropwise until the solution tests strongly acid with indicator paper; then add 2 more drops of acid. This will give a suspension of white acetylsalicylic acid in the aqueous solution. It could be filtered off and recrystallized from boiling water, but this would cause transfer losses. An easier procedure is to simply heat the aqueous solution that contains the precipitated aspirin and allow it to recrystallize on slow cooling.

Add a boiling stick and heat the mixture to boiling, at which time the aspirin should dissolve completely. If it does not, add more water. Long boiling will hydrolyze the aspirin to salicylic acid (mp 157°C–159°C). Once completely dissolved, the aspirin should be allowed to recrystallize slowly as the solution cools to room temperature in an insulated container. Once the tube has reached room temperature, it should be cooled in ice for several minutes, and then the solvent is removed with a Pasteur pipette. The crystals are to be washed with a few drops of ice-cold water and then scraped out onto a piece of filter paper. Squeezing the crystals between sheets of the filter paper will hasten drying. Once these crystals are completely dry, determine the weight of the acetylsalicylic acid and its melting point.

Cleaning Up. Place any dichloromethane-containing solutions in the halogenated organic waste container and the other organic liquids in the organic solvents container. The aqueous layers should be diluted and neutralized with sodium carbonate before being flushed down the drain. After it is free of solvent, the calcium chloride can be placed in the nonhazardous solid waste container. If local regulations do not allow for the evaporation of solvents in a hood, dispose of the wet sodium sulfate in a special container.

Extractions from Common Items

6. Extraction of Caffeine from Tea

Tea and coffee have been popular beverages for centuries, primarily because they contain caffeine, a stimulant. Caffeine stimulates respiration, the heart, and the central nervous system, and it is a diuretic (i.e., it promotes urination). It can cause nervousness and insomnia and, like many drugs, can be addictive, making it difficult to reduce the daily dose. A regular coffee drinker who consumes just 4 cups per day can experience headache, insomnia, and even nausea upon withdrawal from the drug. On the other hand, it helps people to pay attention and can sharpen moderately complex mental skills as well as prolong the ability to exercise.

Caffeine may be the most widely abused drug in the United States. During the course of a day, an average person may unwittingly consume up to 1 g of caffeine. The caffeine content of some common foods and drugs is given in Table 7.3.

Caffeine belongs to a large class of compounds known as alkaloids. These are of plant origin, contain basic nitrogen, often have a bitter taste and a complex structure, and usually have physiological activity. Their names usually end in *-ine*; many are quite familiar by name if not chemical structure—for example, nicotine, cocaine, morphine, and strychnine.

Tea leaves contain tannins, which are acidic, as well as a number of colored compounds and a small amount of undecomposed chlorophyll (soluble in dichloromethane). To ensure that the acidic substances remain water soluble and that the caffeine will be present as the free base, sodium carbonate is added to the extraction medium.

The solubility of caffeine in water is 2.2 mg/mL at 25°C, 180 mg/mL at 80°C, and 670 mg/mL at 100°C. It is quite soluble in dichloromethane, the solvent used in this experiment to extract the caffeine from water.

Caffeine can be easily extracted from tea bags. The procedure one would use to make a cup of tea—simply "steeping" the tea with very hot water for about 7 min—extracts most of the caffeine. There is no advantage to boiling the tea leaves with water for 20 min. Because caffeine is a white, slightly bitter, odorless,

TABLE 7.3 • **Caffeine Content of Common Foods and Drugs**	
Espresso	120 mg per 2 oz
Coffee, regular, brewed	103 mg per cup
Instant coffee	57 mg per cup
Coffee, decaffeinated	2–4 mg per cup
Tea	30–75 mg per cup
Cocoa	5–40 mg per cup
Milk chocolate	6 mg per oz
Baking chocolate	35 mg per oz
Coca-Cola, Classic	46 mg per 12 oz
Jolt Cola	72 mg per 12 oz
Anacin, Bromo-Seltzer, Midol	32 mg per pill
Excedrin, Extra Strength	65 mg per pill
Dexatrim, Dietac, Vivarin	200 mg per pill
Dristan	16 mg per pill
No-Doz	100 mg per pill

crystalline solid, it is obvious that water extracts more than just caffeine. When the brown aqueous solution is subsequently extracted with dichloromethane, caffeine primarily dissolves in the organic solvent. Evaporation of the solvent leaves crude caffeine, which on sublimation yields a relatively pure product. When the concentrated tea solution is extracted with dichloromethane, emulsions can form very easily. There are substances in tea that cause small droplets of the organic layer to remain suspended in the aqueous layer. This emulsion formation results from vigorous shaking. To avoid this problem, it might seem that one could boil the tea leaves with dichloromethane first and then extract the caffeine from the dichloromethane solution with water. In fact, this does not work. Boiling 25 g of tea leaves with 50 mL of dichloromethane gives only 0.05 g of residue after evaporation of the solvent. Subsequent extractions yield even less material. Hot water causes the tea leaves to swell and is obviously a far more efficient extraction solvent. An attempt to sublime caffeine directly from tea leaves is also unsuccessful.

Microscale Procedure

Online Study Center
Video: Caffeine from Tea

In a 30-mL beaker place 15 mL of water, 2 g of sodium carbonate, and a wooden boiling stick. Bring the water to a boil on the sand bath, remove the boiling stick, and brew a very concentrated tea solution by immersing a tea bag (2.4 g tea) in the very hot water for 5 min. After the tea bag cools enough to handle, and being careful not to break the bag, squeeze as much water from the bag as possible. Again bring the water to a boil and add a new tea bag to the hot solution. After 5 min, remove the tea bag and squeeze out as much water as possible. This can be done easily on a Hirsch funnel. Rinse the bag with a few mL of very hot water but be sure the total volume of aqueous extract does not exceed 12 mL. Pour the extract into a 15-mL centrifuge tube and cool the solution in ice to below 40°C (the boiling point of dichloromethane).

Using three 2-mL portions of dichloromethane, extract the caffeine from the tea. Cork the tube and use a gentle rocking motion to carry out the extraction. Vigorous shaking will produce an intractable emulsion, whereas extremely gentle mixing will fail to extract the caffeine. If you have ready access to a centrifuge, the shaking can be very vigorous because any emulsions formed can be broken fairly well by centrifugation for about 90 s. After each extraction, remove the lower organic layer into a reaction tube, leaving any emulsion layer behind. Dry the combined extracts over anhydrous calcium chloride pellets for 5–10 min in an Erlenmeyer flask. Add the drying agent in portions with shaking until it no longer clumps together. Transfer the dry solution to a tared 25-mL filter flask, wash the drying agent twice with 2-mL portions of dichloromethane, and evaporate it to dryness (*see* Fig. 7.9 on page 146). The residue will be crude caffeine (determine its weight), which is to be purified by sublimation.

Fit the filter flask with a Pluro stopper or no. 2 neoprene adapter through which is thrust a 15-mL centrifuge tube. Put a pipette bulb on the side arm. Clamp the flask with a large three-prong clamp, fill the centrifuge tube with ice and water, and heat the flask on a hot sand bath (*see* Fig. 7.15 on page 160). Caffeine is reported to sublime at about 170°C. Tilt the filter flask and rotate it in a hot sand bath to drive more caffeine onto the centrifuge tube. Use a heat gun to heat the upper walls of the filter flask. When sublimation ceases, remove the ice water from the centrifuge tube and allow the flask to cool somewhat before removing the centrifuge tube. Scrape the caffeine onto a tared weighing paper, weigh and, using a plastic funnel, transfer it to a small vial or a plastic bag. At the discretion of your instructor, determine the melting point with a sealed capillary. The melting point of caffeine is 238°C. Using the centrifugation technique to separate the extracts; about 30 mg of crude caffeine can be obtained. This will give you 10–15 mg of sublimed material, depending on the caffeine content of the particular tea being used. The isolated caffeine can be used to prepare caffeine salicylate (experiment 9).

Cleaning Up. Discard the tea bags in the nonhazardous solid waste container. Allow the solvent to evaporate from the drying agent and discard in the same container. If local regulations do not allow for the evaporation of solvents in a hood, dispose of the wet sodium sulfate in a special container. Place any unused and unrecovered dichloromethane in the chlorinated organic compounds container. The apparatus can be cleaned with soap and hot water. Caffeine can be flushed down the drain because it is biodegradable.

Macroscale Procedure

To an Erlenmeyer flask containing 25 g of tea leaves (or 10 tea bags) and 20 g of sodium carbonate, add 225 mL of vigorously boiling water. Allow the mixture to stand for 7 min and then decant into another Erlenmeyer flask. To the hot tea leaves,

CAUTION: Carry out work with dichloromethane in the hood.

Rock the separatory funnel very gently to avoid emulsions.

Dispose of used dichloromethane in the container provided.

Online Study Center

Video: Recrystallization

add another 50 mL of hot water and then immediately decant and combine with the first extract. Very little, if any, additional caffeine is extracted by boiling the tea leaves for 20 min. Decantation works nearly as well as vacuum filtration and is much faster.

Cool the aqueous solution to near room temperature and extract it twice with 30-mL portions of dichloromethane. Do not shake the separatory funnel so vigorously as to cause emulsion formation, bearing in mind that if it is not shaken vigorously enough the caffeine will not be extracted into the organic layer. Use a gentle rocking motion of the separatory funnel. Drain off the dichloromethane layer on the first extraction; include the emulsion layer on the second extraction. Dry the combined dichloromethane solutions and any emulsion layer with anhydrous calcium chloride pellets. Add sufficient drying agent until it no longer clumps together on the bottom of the flask. Carefully decant or filter the dichloromethane solution into a tared Erlenmeyer or distilling flask. Silicone-impregnated filter paper passes dichloromethane and retains water. Wash the drying agent with a further portion of solvent and evaporate or distill the solvent. A wood applicator stick is better than a boiling chip to promote smooth boiling because it is easily removed once the solvent is gone. The residue of greenish-white crystalline caffeine should weigh about 0.25 g.

Recrystallization of Caffeine

To recrystallize the caffeine, dissolve it in 5 mL of hot acetone, transfer it with a Pasteur pipette to a small Erlenmeyer flask and, while it is hot, add ligroin to the solution until a faint cloudiness appears. Set the flask aside and allow it to cool slowly to room temperature. This mixed-solvent method of recrystallization depends on the fact that caffeine is far more soluble in acetone than ligroin, so a combination of the two solvents can be found where the solution is saturated in caffeine and will appear cloudy. Cool the solution containing the crystals and remove them by vacuum filtration, employing a Hirsch funnel or a very small Büchner funnel. Use a few drops of ligroin to transfer and wash the crystals. If you wish to obtain a second crop of crystals, collect the filtrate in a test tube, concentrate it to the cloud point using an aspirator tube (*see* Fig. 7.11 on page 155), and repeat the recrystallization process.

Cleaning Up. The filtrate can be diluted with water and washed down the drain. Any dichloromethane collected goes into the halogenated organic waste container. After the solvent is allowed to evaporate from the drying agent in the hood, the drying agent can be placed in the nonhazardous solid waste container; otherwise it goes in the hazardous waste container. If local regulations do not allow for the evaporation of solvents in a hood, dispose of the wet sodium sulfate in a special container. The tea leaves go in the nonhazardous solid waste container.

7. Extraction of Caffeine from Cola Syrup

Coca-Cola was originally flavored with extracts from the leaves of the coca plant and the kola nut. Coca is grown in northern South America; the Indians of Peru and Bolivia have for centuries chewed the leaves to relieve the pangs of hunger and sensitivity to high mountain cold. The cocaine from the leaves causes local anesthesia of the stomach. It has limited use as a local anesthetic for surgery on the eye, nose, and throat. Unfortunately, it is now a widely abused and illicit drug. Kola nuts contain about 3% caffeine as well as a number of other alkaloids. The kola tree is in the same family as the cacao tree from which cocoa and chocolate are obtained. Modern cola drinks do not contain cocaine; however, Coca-Cola contains 46 mg of caffeine per 12-oz serving. The acidic taste of many soft drinks comes from citric, tartaric, phosphoric, and benzoic acids.

Caffeine
mp 238°C

Cocaine

Automatic soft drink dispensing machines mix a syrup with carbonated water. In the following experiment caffeine is extracted from concentrated cola syrup.

Microscale Procedure

Add 1 mL of concentrated ammonium hydroxide to a mixture of 5 mL of commercial cola syrup and 5 mL of water in a 15-mL centrifuge tube. Add 1 mL of dichloromethane and tip the tube gently back and forth for 5 min. Do not shake the mixture as in a normal extraction because an emulsion will form, and the layers will not separate. After the layers have separated as much as possible, remove the clear lower layer, leaving the emulsion behind. Using 1.5 mL of dichloromethane, repeat the extraction in the same way two more times. At the final separation, include the emulsion layer with the dichloromethane. If a centrifuge is available, the mixture can be shaken vigorously, and the emulsion broken by centrifugation for 90 s. Combine the extracts in a reaction tube and dry the solution with anhydrous calcium chloride pellets. Add the drying agent with shaking until it no longer clumps together. After 5–10 min, remove the solution with a Pasteur pipette and place it in a tared filter flask. Wash off the drying agent with more dichloromethane and evaporate the mixture to dryness. Determine the crude weight of caffeine; then sublime it as described in the preceding experiment.

CAUTION: Do not breathe the vapor of dichloromethane. Work with this solvent in the hood.

Macroscale Procedure

Add 10 mL of concentrated ammonium hydroxide to a mixture of 50 mL of commercial cola syrup and 50 mL of water. Place the mixture in a separatory funnel, add 50 mL of dichloromethane, and swirl the mixture and tip the funnel back and forth for at least 5 min. Do not shake the solutions together as in a normal extraction because an emulsion will form, and the layers will not separate. An emulsion is made up of droplets of one phase suspended in the other. (Milk is an emulsion.) Separate the layers. Repeat the extraction with a second 50-mL portion of dichloromethane. From your knowledge of the density of dichloromethane and water, you should be able to predict which is the top layer and which is the bottom layer. If in doubt, add a few drops of each layer to water. The aqueous layer will be soluble; the organic layer will not. Combine the dichloromethane extracts and any emulsion that has formed in a 125-mL Erlenmeyer flask; then add anhydrous calcium chloride pellets to remove water from the solution. Add the drying agent until it no longer clumps together at the bottom of the flask but swirls freely in solution. Swirl the flask with the drying agent from time to time over a 10-min period. Carefully decant (pour off) the dichloromethane or remove it by filtration through a fluted filter paper, add about 5 mL more solvent to the drying agent to wash it, and decant this also. Combine the dried dichloromethane solutions in a tared flask and remove the dichloromethane by distillation or evaporation on a steam or sand bath. Remember to add a wood applicator stick to the solution to promote even boiling. Determine the weight of the crude product.

Chlorinated solvents are toxic, insoluble in water, and expensive and should never be poured down the drain.

Recrystallization of Caffeine

To recrystallize the caffeine, dissolve it in 5 mL of hot acetone, transfer it with a Pasteur pipette to a small Erlenmeyer flask, and, while it is hot, add ligroin to the solution until a faint cloudiness appears. Set the flask aside and allow it to cool slowly to room temperature. This mixed-solvent method of recrystallization depends on the fact that caffeine is far more soluble in acetone than ligroin, so a combination of the two solvents can be found where the solution is saturated in caffeine (the cloud point). Cool the solution containing the crystals and remove them by vacuum filtration, employing a Hirsch funnel or a very small Büchner funnel. Use a few drops of ligroin to transfer and wash the crystals. If you wish to obtain a second crop of crystals, collect the filtrate in a test tube, concentrate it to the cloud point using an aspirator tube (*see* Fig. 7.11 on page 155), and repeat the recrystallization process.

Cleaning Up. Combine all aqueous filtrates and solutions, neutralize them, and flush the resulting solution down the drain. Used dichloromethane should be placed in the halogenated waste container, and the drying agent, once the solvent has evaporated from it, can be placed in the nonhazardous solid waste container. If local regulations do not allow for the evaporation of solvents in a hood, dispose of the wet sodium sulfate in a special container. The ligroin-acetone filtrates should be placed in the organic solvents container.

Sublimation of Caffeine. Sublimation is a fast and easy way to purify caffeine. Using the apparatus depicted in Figure 7.15 (on page 160), sublime the crude caffeine at atmospheric pressure following the procedure in part 3 of Chapter 6.

Online Study Center

Photos of Extraction Procedure

8. *Isolation of Caffeine from Instant Coffee*

Instant coffee, according to manufacturers, contains between 55 mg and 62 mg of caffeine per 6-oz cup, and a cup is presumably made from a teaspoon of the powder, which weighs 1.3 g; so 2 g of the powder should contain 85–95 mg of caffeine. Unlike tea, however, coffee contains other compounds that are soluble in dichloromethane, so obtaining pure caffeine from coffee is not easy. The objective of this experiment is to extract instant coffee with dichloromethane (the easy part) and then to try to devise a procedure for obtaining pure caffeine from the extract.

From TLC analysis (*see* Chapter 8), you may deduce that certain impurities have a high R_f value in hydrocarbons (in which caffeine is insoluble). Consult reference books (see especially the *Merck Index*[2]) to determine the solubility (and lack of solubility) of caffeine in various solvents. You might try trituration (grinding the crude solid with a solvent) to dissolve impurities preferentially. Column chromatography is another possible means of purifying the product. Or you might convert all of it to the salicylate and then regenerate the caffeine from the salicylate. Experiment! Or you can simply use the following procedure.

Procedure

> **IN THIS EXPERIMENT** a very concentrated aqueous solution of coffee is prepared and shaken vigorously with an organic solvent to make an intractable emulsion that can be broken (separated into two layers) by centrifugation. Caffeine is isolated by recrystallization.

In a 10-mL Erlenmeyer flask, place 2 g of sodium carbonate and 2 g of instant coffee powder. Add 9 mL of boiling water, stir the mixture well, bring it to a boil again with stirring, cool it to room temperature, and then pour it into a 15-mL plastic centrifuge tube fitted with a screw cap. Add 2 mL of dichloromethane, cap the tube, shake it vigorously for 60 s; then centrifuge it at high speed for 90 s. Remove the clear yellow dichloromethane layer and place it in a 10-mL Erlenmeyer flask. Repeat this process twice more. To the combined extracts add anhydrous calcium chloride pellets until they no longer clump together, allow the solution to dry for a few minutes; then transfer it to a tared 25-mL filter flask and wash the drying agent with more solvent. Remove the solvent as was done in the tea extraction experiment and determine the weight of the crude caffeine. You should obtain about 60 mg of crude product. Sublimation of this orange powder gives an impure orange sublimate that smells strongly of coffee, so sublimation is not a good way to purify this material.

Caffeine has no odor.

Dissolve a very small quantity of the product in a drop of dichloromethane and perform a TLC analysis of the crude material. Dissolve the remainder of the material in 1 mL of boiling 95% ethanol; then dilute the mixture with 1 mL of

2. O'Neill, M. J.; Smith, A.; Heckelman, P. E.; Budavari, S., eds. *The Merck Index*, 13th ed.; Merck and Co., Inc.: Rahway, NJ, 2001.

Online Study Center

Video: Recrystallization

t-butyl methyl ether, heat to boiling, and allow to cool slowly to room temperature. Long, needlelike crystals should form in the orange solution. Alternatively, recrystallize the product from a 1:1 mixture of ligroin (hexanes) and 2-propanol, using about 2 mL. Cool the mixture in ice for at least 10 min and then collect the product on a Hirsch funnel. Complete the transfer with the filtrate and then wash the crystals twice with cold 50/50 ethanol/*t*-butyl methyl ether. The yield of white fluffy needles of caffeine should be more than 30 mg.

Cleaning Up. Allow the solvent to evaporate from the drying agent and discard it in the nonhazardous waste container. If local regulations do not allow for the evaporation of solvents in a hood, dispose of the wet sodium sulfate in a special container. Place any unused and unrecovered dichloromethane in the chlorinated organic solvents container.

Preparation of a derivative of caffeine.

 ## 9. Caffeine Salicylate

One way to confirm the identity of an organic compound is to prepare a derivative of it. Caffeine melts and sublimes at 238°C. It is an organic base and can therefore accept a proton from an acid to form a salt. The salt formed when caffeine combines with hydrochloric acid, like many amine salts, does not have a sharp melting point; it merely decomposes when heated. But the salt formed from salicylic acid, even though ionic, has a sharp melting point and can thus be used to help characterize caffeine. Figure 7.17 is the ^{1}H NMR spectrum of caffeine.

Caffeine + **Salicylic acid** ⟶ **Caffeine salicylate**

⚠ **CAUTION**: Petroleum ether is very flammable. Extinguish all flames.

Recrystallization from mixed solvents

Online Study Center

Video: Filtration of Crystals Using the Pasteur Pipette; Photo: Drying Crystals Under Vacuum

Procedure

The quantities given can be multiplied by 5 or 10, if necessary. To 10 mg of sublimed caffeine in a tared reaction tube, add 7.5 mg of salicylic acid and 0.5 mL of dichloromethane. Heat the mixture to boiling and add petroleum ether (a poor solvent for the product) dropwise until the mixture just turns cloudy, indicating that the solution is saturated. If too much petroleum ether is added, then clarify it by adding a very small quantity of dichloromethane. Insulate the tube to allow it to cool slowly to room temperature; then cool it in ice. The needlelike crystals are isolated by removing the solvent with a Pasteur pipette while the reaction tube is in the ice bath. Evaporate the last traces of solvent under vacuum (Fig. 7.18) and

FIG. 7.17
The ^{1}H NMR spectrum of caffeine (250 MHz).

FIG. 7.18
The drying of crystals under vacuum in beaker of warm water.

determine the weight of the derivative and its melting point. Caffeine salicylate is reported to melt at 137°C.

Cleaning Up. Place the filtrate in the halogenated organic solvents container.

QUESTIONS

1. Suppose a reaction mixture, when diluted with water, afforded 300 mL of an aqueous solution of 30 g of the reaction product malononitrile [$CH_2(CN)_2$], which is to be isolated by extraction with ether. The solubility of malononitrile in ether at room temperature is 20.0 g/100 mL and in water is 13.3 g/100 mL. What weight of malononitrile would be recovered by extraction with (a) three 100-mL portions of ether and (b) one 300-mL portion of ether? *Suggestion*: For each extraction let x equal the weight extracted into the ether layer. In part (a) the concentration in the ether layer is $x/100$ and in the water layer is $(30 - x)/300$; the ratio of these quantities is equal to $k = 20/13.3$.

2. Why is it necessary to remove the stopper from a separatory funnel when liquid is being drained from it through the stopcock?

3. The pK_a of *p*-nitrophenol is 7.15. Would you expect this to dissolve in sodium bicarbonate solution? The pK_a of 2,5-dinitrophenol is 5.15. Will it dissolve in bicarbonate solution?

4. The distribution coefficient, k = conc. in ligroin ÷ conc. in water, between ligroin and water for solute A is 7.5. What weight of A would be removed from a solution of 10 g of A in 100 mL of water by a single extraction with 100 mL of ligroin? What weight of A would be removed by four successive extractions with 25-mL portions of ligroin? How much ligroin would be required to remove 98.5% of A in a single extraction?

5. In experiment 1, how many moles of benzoic acid are present? How many moles of sodium bicarbonate are contained in 1 mL of a 10% aqueous solution? (A 10% solution has 1 g of solute in 9 mL of solvent.) Is the amount of sodium bicarbonate sufficient to react with all of the benzoic acid?

6. To isolate benzoic acid from a bicarbonate solution, it is acidified with concentrated hydrochloric acid, as in experiment 1. What volume of acid is needed to neutralize the bicarbonate? The concentration of hydrochloric acid is expressed in various ways on the inside back cover of this laboratory manual.

7. How many moles of 4-*t*-butylphenol are in the mixture to be separated in experiment 1? How many moles of sodium hydroxide are contained in 1 mL of 5% sodium hydroxide solution? (Assume the density of the solution is 1.0.) What volume of concentrated hydrochloric acid is needed to neutralize this amount of sodium hydroxide solution?

8. Draw a flow sheet to show how you would separate the components of a mixture containing an acid substance, toluic acid, a basic substance, *p*-bromo-aniline, and anthracene, a neutral substance.

9. Write equations showing how caffeine could be extracted from an organic solvent and subsequently isolated.

10. Write equations showing how acetaminophen might be extracted from an organic solvent such as an ether, if it were soluble.

11. Write detailed equations showing the mechanism by which aspirin is hydrolyzed in boiling, slightly acidic water.

Online Study Center

General Resources
Web Links

Thin-Layer Chromatography: Analyzing Analgesics and Isolating Lycopene from Tomato Paste

Online Study Center

This icon will direct you to techniques, equipment setups, and online resources at http://college.hmco.com/PIC/williamsonMMOE5e.

PRELAB EXERCISE: Based on the number and polarity of the functional groups in aspirin, acetaminophen, ibuprofen, and caffeine, whose structures are shown on page 184, predict which of these four compounds has the highest R_f value and which has the lowest.

Chromatography is the separation of two or more compounds or ions caused by their molecular interactions with two phases—one moving and one stationary. These two phases can be a solid and a liquid, a liquid and a liquid, a gas and a solid, or a gas and a liquid. You very likely have seen chromatography carried out on paper towels or coffee filters to separate inks and food dyes. The cellulose paper is the stationary or solid phase, and a propanol-water mixture is the mobile or liquid phase. The samples are spotted near one edge of the paper, and this edge is dipped into the liquid phase. The solvent is drawn through the paper by capillary action, and the molecules are separated based on how they interact with the paper. Although there are several different forms of chromatography, the principles are essentially the same.

Thin-layer chromatography (*TLC*) is a sensitive, fast, simple, and inexpensive analytical technique that you will use repeatedly while carrying out organic experiments. It is a micro technique; as little as 10^{-9} g of material can be detected, although the usual sample size is from 1×10^{-6} g to 1×10^{-8} g. The stationary phase is normally a polar solid adsorbent, and the mobile phase can be a single solvent or a combination of solvents.

TLC requires micrograms of material.

Uses of Thin-Layer Chromatography

1. **To determine the number of components in a mixture.** TLC affords a quick and easy method for analyzing such things as a crude reaction mixture, an extract from a plant substance, or the ingredients in a pill. Knowing the

number and relative amounts of the components aids in planning further analytical and separation steps.

2. **To determine the identity of two substances.**   If two substances spotted on the same TLC plate give spots in identical locations, they *may* be identical. If the spot positions are not the same, the substances cannot be the same. It is possible for two or more closely related but not identical compounds to have the same positions on a TLC plate. Changing the stationary or mobile phase will usually effect their separation.

3. **To monitor the progress of a reaction.**   By sampling a reaction at regular intervals, it is possible to watch the reactants disappear and the products appear using TLC. Thus, the optimum time to halt the reaction can be determined, and the effect of changing such variables as temperature, concentrations, and solvents can be followed without having to isolate the product.

4. **To determine the effectiveness of a purification.**   The effectiveness of distillation, crystallization, extraction, and other separation and purification methods can be monitored using TLC, with the caveat that a single spot does not guarantee a single substance.

5. **To determine the appropriate conditions for a column chromatographic separation.**   In general, TLC is not satisfactory for purifying and isolating macroscopic quantities of material; however, the adsorbents most commonly used for TLC—silica gel and alumina—are also used for column chromatography, which is discussed in Chapter 9. Column chromatography is used to separate and purify up to 1 g of a solid mixture. The correct adsorbent and solvent to use for column chromatography can be rapidly determined by TLC.

6. **To monitor column chromatography.**   As column chromatography is carried out, the solvent is collected in a number of small flasks. Unless the desired compound is colored, the various fractions must be analyzed in some way to determine which ones have the desired components of the mixture. TLC is a fast and effective method for doing this.

The Principles of Chromatography

To thoroughly understand the process of TLC (and other types of chromatography), we must examine the process at the molecular level. All forms of chromatography involve a dynamic and rapid equilibrium of molecules between the liquid and the stationary phases. For the chromatographic separation of molecules A and B shown in Figure 8.1, there are two states:

1. **Free**—dissolved in the liquid or gaseous mobile phase
2. **Adsorbed**—sticking to the surface of the solid stationary phase

Molecules A and B are continuously moving back and forth between the dissolved (free) and adsorbed states, with billions of molecules adsorbing and billions of other molecules desorbing from the solid stationary phase each second. The equilibrium between the free and adsorbed states depends on the relative strength of the

■ **FIG. 8.1**
The mixture of molecules A and B is in a dynamic equilibrium between the free and adsorbed states.

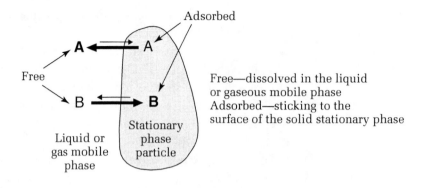

■ **FIG. 8.2**
The mixture of molecules A and B is in a dynamic equilibrium between the stationary adsorbent and a *flowing* mobile phase.

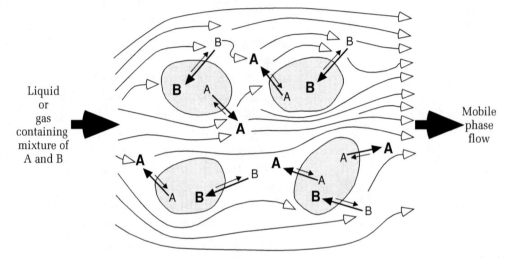

attraction of A and B to the liquid phase molecules *versus* the strength of attraction of A and B to the stationary phase structure. As discussed in the introduction to Chapter 3, the strength of these attractive forces depends on the following factors:

● Size, polarity, and hydrogen bonding ability of molecules A and B
● Polarity and hydrogen bonding ability of the stationary phase
● Polarity and hydrogen bonding ability of the mobile phase solvent

Molecules distribute themselves, or *partition*, between the mobile and stationary phases depending on these attractive forces. As implied by the equilibrium arrows in Figure 8.1, the A molecules are less polar and are thus weakly attracted to a polar stationary phase, spending most of their time in the mobile phase. In contrast, equilibrium for the more polar B molecules lies in the direction of being adsorbed onto the polar stationary phase. The equilibrium constant k (also called the *partition coefficient*) is a measure of the distribution of molecules between the mobile phase and the stationary phase and is similar to the distribution coefficient for liquid/liquid extraction. This constant changes with structure.

Simply adding a mixture to a combination of a liquid phase and a stationary phase will not separate it into its pure components. For separation to happen, the liquid phase must be mobile and be flowing past the stationary phase, as depicted in Figure 8.2. Because the A molecules spend more time in the mobile phase, they will be carried through the stationary phase and be eluted faster and move farther

■ FIG. 8.3
A chromatographic separation. Over time, the mobile phase carries the less weakly adsorbed A molecules ahead of the more strongly adsorbed B molecules.

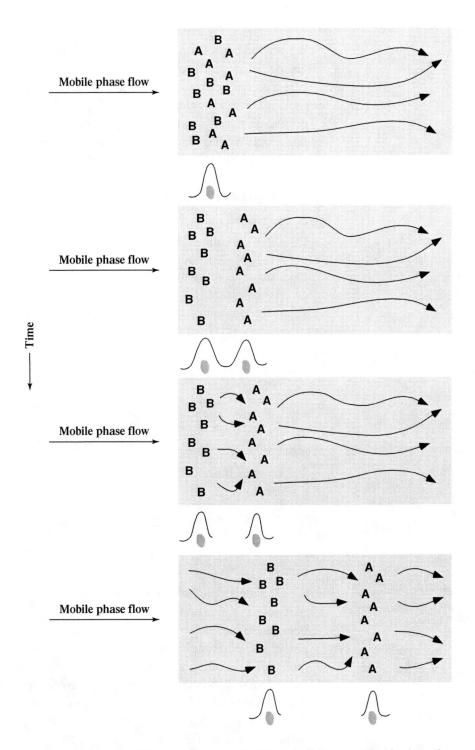

in a given amount of time. Because the B molecules are adsorbed on the stationary phase more than A molecules, the B molecules spend less time in the mobile phase and therefore migrate through the stationary phase more slowly and are eluted later. The B molecules do not migrate as far in the same amount of time. The consequence of this difference is that A is gradually separated from B by moving ahead in the flowing mobile phase as time passes, as shown in Figure 8.3.

A simple analogy may help to illustrate these concepts. Imagine a group of hungry and not-so-hungry people riding a moving sidewalk (the mobile phase in this analogy) that moves beside a long buffet table covered with all sorts of delicious food (the stationary phase). Hungry people, attracted to the food, will step off and on the moving belt many times in order to fill their plates. The not-so-hungry people will step off and on to get food far less often. Consequently, the more strongly attracted hungry people will lag behind, while the not-so-hungry ones will move ahead. The two types of people are thus separated based on the strength of their attraction for the food.

Stationary Phase Adsorbents

In TLC, the stationary phase is a polar adsorbent, usually finely ground alumina $[(Al_2O_3)_x]$ or silica $[(SiO_2)_x]$ particles, coated as a thin layer on a glass slide or plastic sheet. Silica, commonly called *silica gel* in the laboratory, is simply very pure white sand. The extended covalent network of these adsorbents creates a very polar surface. Partial structures of silica and alumina are shown below. The silicon or aluminum atoms are the smaller, darker spheres:

Silica, $(SiO_2)_x$ Alumina, $(Al_2O_3)_x$

■ FIG. 8.4
A partial silica structure showing polar Si—O bonds.

The electropositive character of the aluminum or silicon and the electronegativity of oxygen create a very polar stationary phase (Fig. 8.4). Therefore, the more polar the molecules to be separated, the stronger the attraction to the stationary phase. Nonpolar molecules will tend to stay in the mobile phase. In general, the more polar the functional group, the stronger the adsorption on the stationary phase and the more slowly the molecules will move. In an extreme situation, the molecules will not move at all. This problem can be overcome by increasing the polarity of the mobile phase so that the equilibrium between the free and adsorbed state is shifted toward the free state.

Although silica is the most common stationary phase used for TLC, many other types are used, ranging from paper to charcoal, nonpolar to polar, and reverse phase to normal phase. Several different types of stationary phases are listed according to polarity in Table 8.1.

Silica gel and alumina are commonly used in column chromatography for the purification of macroscopic quantities of material (*see* Chapter 9). Of the two,

TABLE 8.1 • Common Stationary Phases Listed by Increasing Polarity
Polydimethyl siloxane*
Methyl- or Phenylsiloxane*
Cyanopropylsiloxane*
Carbowax [poly(ethyleneglycol)]*
Reverse phase (hydrocarbon-coated silica, e.g., C_{18})
Paper
Cellulose
Starch
Calcium sulfate
Silica (silica gel)
Florisil (magnesium silicate)
Magnesium oxide
Alumina (aluminum oxide; acidic, basic, or neutral)
Activated carbon (charcoal or Norit pellets)

Stationary phase for gas chromatography

(Increasing polarity — indicated by downward arrow alongside table)

alumina, when anhydrous, is the more active; that is, it will adsorb substances more strongly. It is thus the adsorbent of choice for the separation of relatively nonpolar substrates, such as hydrocarbons, alkyl halides, ethers, aldehydes, and ketones. To separate more polar substrates, such as alcohols, carboxylic acids, and amines, the less active adsorbent, silica gel, is often used.

Molecular Polarity and Elution Sequence

Assuming we are using a polar adsorbent, how can we determine how rapidly the compounds in our particular mixture move, that is, their elution sequence? Because the more polar compounds will adsorb more strongly to the polar stationary phase, they will move the slowest and the shortest distance on a TLC plate. Nonpolar compounds will move rapidly; they will elute first or move the greatest distance on the TLC plate. Table 8.2 lists several common compound classes according to how they move or elute on silica or alumina.

You should be able to look at a molecular structure, identify its functional group(s), and easily determine whether it is more or less polar than another structure with different functional groups. Note that the polarity of a molecule increases as the number of functional groups in that molecule increases. Thus, ethyl acetoacetate, with both ketone and ester groups, is more polar than ethyl pentanoate, which has only an ester group. However, it should be noted that chromatography is not an exact science. The rules discussed here can be used to help predict the order of elution; however, only performing an experiment will give definitive answers.

Elution sequence is the order in which the components of a mixture move during chromatography.

Ethyl acetoacetate

Ethyl pentanoate

TABLE 8.2 • Elution Order for Some Common Functional Groups with a Silica or Alumina Stationary Phase
Highest/fastest (elute with nonpolar mobile phase)
Alkane hydrocarbons
Alkyl halides (halocarbons)
Alkenes (olefins)
Dienes
Aromatic hydrocarbons
Aromatic halides
Ethers
Esters
Ketones
Aldehydes
Amines
Alcohols
Phenols
Carboxylic acids
Sulfonic acids
Lowest/slowest (need polar mobile phase to elute)

Increasing polarity of functional group ↓

Mobile Phase Solvent Polarity

The key to a successful chromatographic separation is the mobile phase. You cannot change the polarities of the compounds in your mixture, and you normally use silica gel or alumina as the stationary phase. In extreme situations very polar substances chromatographed on alumina will not migrate very far from the starting point (i.e., give low R_f values), and nonpolar compounds chromatographed on silica gel will travel with the solvent front (i.e., give high R_f values). These extremes of behavior are markedly affected, however, by the solvents used to carry out the chromatography. A polar solvent will carry along with it polar substrates, and nonpolar solvents will do the same with nonpolar compounds—another example of the generalization "like dissolves like." By using different solvents, either alone or as mixtures, we can adjust the polarity of the mobile phase and affect the equilibria between the free and adsorbed states. Changing the polarity of the mobile phase can optimize the chromatographic separation of mixtures of compounds with a wide variety of polarities.

Table 8.3 lists, according to increasing polarity, some solvents that are commonly used for both TLC and column chromatography. Because the polarities of benzene, carbon tetrachloride, or chloroform can be matched by other, less toxic solvents, these three solvents are seldom used. In general, the solvents for TLC and column chromatography are characterized by having low boiling points that allow them to be easily evaporated and low viscosities that allow them to migrate

Avoid using benzene, carbon tetrachloride, and chloroform. Benzene is known to be a carcinogen when exposure is prolonged; the others are suspected carcinogens.

TABLE 8.3 •	Common Mobile Phases Listed by Increasing Polarity

Helium

Nitrogen

Pentanes (petroleum ether)

Hexanes (ligroin)

Cyclohexane

Carbon tetrachloride*

Toluene

Chloroform*

Dichloromethane (methylene chloride)

t-Butyl methyl ether

Diethyl ether

Ethyl acetate

Acetone

2-Propanol

Pyridine

Ethanol

Methanol

Water

Acetic acid

*Suspected carcinogens

(left margin, with downward arrow: Increasing polarity)

rapidly. A solvent more polar than methanol is seldom needed. Often, two solvents are used in a mixture of varying proportions; the polarity of the mixture is a weighted average of the two. Hexane and ether mixtures are often employed.

Finding a good solvent system is usually the most critical aspect of TLC. If the mobile phase has not been previously determined, start with a nonpolar solvent such as hexane or ligroin and observe the separation. If the mixture's components do not move very far, try adding a polar solvent such as ether or ethyl acetate to the hexane. Compare the separation to the previous plate. In most cases, a combination of two solvents is the best choice. If the spots stay at the bottom of the plate, add more of the polar solvent. If they run with the solvent front (move to the top), increase the proportion of the nonpolar solvent. Unfortunately, some trial and error is usually involved in determining which solvent system is the best. There is a large amount of literature on the solvents and adsorbents used in the separation of a wide variety of substances.

Spotting the TLC Plate

It is recommended that you use commercially available TLC plates, poly(ethylene terephthalate) (Mylar) sheets coated with silica gel using polyacrylic acid as a binder; these fluoresce under ultraviolet (UV) light.[1] The TLC plates must be

■ FIG. 8.5
A marked and spotted TLC plate.

Aspirin spot

Acetaminophen spot

Caffeine spot

Ibuprofen spot

Depth of solvent

Pencil line 1 cm from bottom edge

Ac As C I

■ FIG. 8.6
(a) A spotting capillary. (b) Soften the glass by heating at the base of the flame as shown and then stretch to a fine capillary.

(a)

(b)

Too much sample is a frequent problem. Use a 1% solution of the mixture. Apply very small spots.

CAUTION: Bunsen burners should be used only in lab areas that are far from flammable organic solvents.

handled gently, or the 100-mm-thick coating of silica gel can be easily scratched off. With a pencil, lightly draw a faint line 1 cm from the end and then three or four short hash marks to guide spotting. Lightly write identifying letters at the top of the plate to keep track of the placement of the compound spots (Fig. 8.5). Note that a pencil is always used to mark TLC plates because the graphite (carbon) is inert. If ink is used to mark the plate, it will chromatograph just as any other organic compound and give flawed results.

You need to dissolve only a few milligrams of material because one can detect a few micrograms of compound on a TLC plate. Choose a volatile solvent. Even if the material is only partially soluble, you will normally be able to observe the compound because only low concentrations are needed. It is extremely important that the spots be as small as possible and that they be applied using a 1% (not more than 2%) solution of the compounds being separated.

Once the sample is prepared, a spotting capillary must be used to add the sample to the plate. Spotting capillaries can be made by drawing out open-end melting point tubes or Pasteur pipette stems in a burner flame (Fig. 8.6).[2] The bore of these capillaries should be so small that once a liquid is drawn into them, it will not flow out to form a drop. Practice spotting just pure solvent onto an unmarked TLC plate. Dip the capillary into the solvent and let a 2–3 cm column of solvent flow into it by

1. Whatman flexible plates for TLC, cat. no. 4410 222 (Fisher cat. no. 05-713-162); cut with scissors to 1″ × 3″ or 2.5 × 7.5 cm Baker-flex, Silica Gel IB-F (J.T. Baker, Phillipsburg, N.J.). Unlike student-prepared plates, these coated sheets give very consistent results. A supply of these plates makes it a simple matter to examine most of the reactions in this book for completeness of reaction, purity of product, and side reactions.

2. Three-inch pieces of old and unusable gas chromatography capillary columns are also effective spotting capillaries.

■ **FIG. 8.7**
Using a wide-mouth bottle
to develop a TLC plate.

Plastic-
capped jar

Filter paper

Solvent

Plastic
chromatographic
sheet

■ **FIG. 8.8**
Using a foil-covered beaker
to develop a TLC plate.

Aluminum
foil cover

Filter paper

Beaker

Solvent

Plastic
chromatographic
sheet

■ **FIG. 8.9**
A UV lamp used to visualize spots.

capillary action, hold this vertically over the *coated* side of the plate, and lower the pipette until the tip just touches the adsorbent. Only then will liquid flow onto the plate; quickly withdraw the capillary when the spot is about 1 mm in diameter. The center of the letter *o* on this page is more than 1 mm in diameter. The distance between the sides of the letter *n* is 1 mm. The solvent should evaporate quickly, leaving your mixture behind on the plate. You may have to spot the plate a couple of times to ensure that sufficient material is present; do not spot too much sample because this will lead to a poor separation. Smearing, smudging, and overlapping of spots will make the identification of separated components difficult. Practice spotting a number of times until you develop good spotting technique. You are now ready to spot the mixture solutions as described in Experiments 1 and 2.

Development

Once the dilute solution of the mixture has been spotted on the plate, the next step is the actual chromatographic separation, called *plate development*. The marked and spotted TLC plate is inserted into a 4-oz wide-mouth bottle (Fig. 8.7) or beaker (Fig. 8.8) containing 4 mL of an organic solvent or solvent mixture. The bottle is lined with filter paper that is wet with solvent to saturate the atmosphere within the container. Use tweezers to place the plate in the development chamber; oils from your fingers can sometimes smear or ruin a TLC plate. Also make sure that the origin spots are not below the solvent level in the chamber. If the spots are submerged in the solvent, they are washed off the plate and lost. The top of the bottle is put in place and the time noted. (If a beaker is used, the beaker is to be covered with aluminium foil.) The solvent travels up the thin layer by capillary action, and if the substance is a pure colored compound, one soon sees a spot traveling either along with the solvent front or, more commonly, at some distance behind the solvent front. Once the solvent has run within a centimeter of the top of the plate, remove the plate with tweezers. Immediately, before the solvent evaporates, use a pencil to draw a line across the plate where the solvent front can be seen. The proper location of this solvent front line is important for R_f calculations.

Visualization

If you are fortunate enough to be separating organic molecules that are colored, such as dyes, inks, or indicators, then visualizing the separated spots is easy. However, because most organic compounds are colorless, this is rarely the case.

For most compounds a UV light works well for observing the separated spots. TLC plates normally contain a fluorescent indicator that makes them glow green under UV light of wavelength 254 nm. Compounds that adsorb UV light at this wavelength will quench the green fluorescence, yielding dark purple or bluish spots on the plate. Simply hold the plate by its edges under a UV lamp as shown in Figure 8.9, and the compound spots become visible to the naked eye. Lightly circle the spots with a pencil so that you will have a permanent record of their location for later calculations.

Another useful visualizing technique is to use an iodine (I_2) chamber. Certain compounds, such as alkanes, alcohols, and ethers, do not absorb UV light sufficiently

Never look into a UV lamp.

to quench the fluorescence of the TLC plate and therefore will not show up under a UV lamp. However, they will absorb iodine vapors and can be detected (after any residual solvent has evaporated) by placing the plate for a few minutes in a capped 4-oz bottle containing some crystals of iodine. Iodine vapor is adsorbed by the organic compound to form brown spots. These brown spots should be outlined with a pencil immediately after removing the plate from the iodine bottle because they will soon disappear as the iodine sublimes away; a brief return to the iodine chamber will regenerate the spots. Using both the UV lamp and iodine vapor visualization methods will ensure the location of all spots on the TLC plate.

Many specialized spray reagents have also been developed to give specific colors for certain types of compounds.

R_f Values

R_f is the ratio of the distance the spot travels from the origin to the distance the solvent travels.

In addition to qualitative results, TLC can also provide a chromatographic parameter known as an R_f value. The R_f value is the retardation factor or the ratio-to-front value expressed as a decimal fraction. The R_f value is the ratio of the distance the spot travels from the point of origin to the distance the solvent travels. The R_f value can be calculated as follows:

$$R_f = \frac{\text{distance spot travels}}{\text{distance solvent travels}}$$

This number should be calculated for each spot observed on a TLC plate. Figure 8.10 shows a diagram of a typical TLC plate and how the distances are measured to calculate the R_f value. The best separations are usually achieved when the R_f values fall between 0.3 and 0.7.

■ **FIG. 8.10**
A developed TLC plate with spots visualized and R_f values determined.

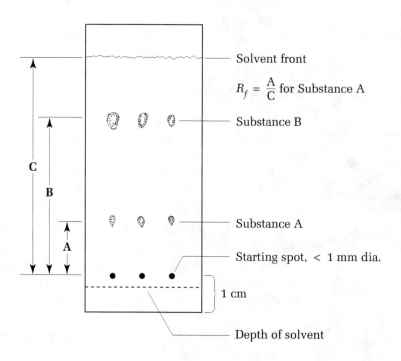

If two spots travel the same distance or have the same R_f value, then it might be concluded that the two components are the same molecule. Just as many organic molecules have the same melting point and color, many can have the same R_f value, so identical R_f values do not necessarily mean identical compounds. For comparisons of R_f values to be valid, TLC plates must be run under the exact same conditions for stationary phase, mobile phase, and temperature. Even then, additional information such as a mixed melting point or an IR spectrum should be obtained before concluding that two substances are identical.

Comparison of Different Types of Chromatography

Table 8.4 summarizes the terminology used in chromatography and how these apply to different types of chromatography. All of the chromatographic types involve the same principles but vary in the nature of the stationary phase and the mobile phase and the measure of separation.

EXPERIMENTS

1. Analgesics

Analgesics are substances that relieve pain. The most common of these is aspirin, a component of more than 100 nonprescription drugs. In Chapter 41, the history of this most popular drug is discussed. In this experiment, analgesic tablets will be analyzed by TLC to determine which analgesics they contain and whether they contain caffeine, which is often added to counteract the sedative effects of the analgesic.

In addition to aspirin and caffeine, the most common components of the currently used analgesics are acetaminophen and ibuprofen. In addition to one or

TABLE 8.4 • Chromatography Terms and Their Definitions with Examples

Chromatography Term	Definition	Examples
Mixture	A collection of different compounds	Aspirin, ibuprofen, caffeine, and fluorene/fluorenone
Stationary phase	A fixed material that can adsorb compounds	Alumina, silica gel, and silicone gum
Mobile phase	A moving liquid or gas that dissolves compounds and carries them along	Hexane, CH_2Cl_2, and ethyl acetate (TLC and column chromatography); helium gas (gas chromatography)
Adsorption	The strength of attraction between the compounds and the stationary phase	London forces, hydrogen bonds, and dipole-dipole attractive forces
Separation	A measure of the elution or migration rate of compounds	R_f (TLC); elution volume (column chromatography); retention time (gas chromatography)

more of these substances, each tablet contains a binder—often starch, microcrystalline cellulose, or silica gel. And to counteract the acidic properties of aspirin, an inorganic buffering agent is added to some analgesics. An inspection of analgesic labels will reveal that most cold remedies and decongestants contain both aspirin and caffeine in addition to the primary ingredient.

Aspirin
Acetylsalicylic acid

Acetaminophen
4-Acetamidophenol

Ibuprofen
2-(4-Isobutylphenyl)propionic acid

Caffeine

To identify an unknown by TLC, the usual strategy is to run chromatograms of known substances (the standards) and the unknown at the same time. If the unknown has one or more spots that correspond to spots with the same R_f values as the standards, then those substances are probably present.

Proprietary drugs that contain one or more of the common analgesics and sometimes caffeine are sold under some of the following brand names: Bayer Aspirin, Anacin, Datril, Advil, Excedrin, Extra Strength Excedrin, Tylenol, and Vanquish. Note that ibuprofen has a chiral carbon atom. The S-(+)-enantiomer is more effective than the other.

Procedure

Before proceeding, practice the TLC spotting technique described earlier. Following that procedure, draw a light pencil line about 1 cm from the end of a chromatographic plate. On this line spot aspirin, acetaminophen, ibuprofen, and caffeine, which are available as reference standards. Use a separate capillary for each standard (or rinse the capillary carefully before reusing). Make each spot as small as possible, preferably less than 0.5 mm in diameter. Examine the plate under UV light to see that enough of each compound has been applied; if not, add more. On a separate plate, run the unknown and one or more of the standards.

The unknown sample is prepared by crushing a part of a tablet, adding this powder to a test tube or small vial along with an appropriate amount of ethanol, and then mixing the suspension. Not all of the crushed tablet will dissolve, but enough will go into solution to spot the plate. The binder—starch or silica—will not dissolve. Weigh out only part of the tablet to try to prepare a 1% solution of the unknown. Typically, ibuprofen tablets contain 200 mg of the active ingredient, aspirin tablets contain 325 mg, and acetaminophen tablets contain 500 mg.

> Because of the insoluble binder, not all of the unknown will dissolve.

To the developing jar or beaker (*see* Fig. 8.7 or Fig. 8.8 on page 181), add 4 mL of the mobile phase, a mixture of 95% ethyl acetate and 5% acetic acid. Insert the spotted TLC plates with a tweezers. After the solvent has risen nearly to the top of the plate, remove the plate from the developing chamber, mark the solvent front with a pencil, and allow the solvent to dry. Examine the plate under UV light to see the components as dark spots against a bright green-blue background. Outline the spots with a pencil. The spots can also be visualized by putting the plate in an iodine chamber made by placing a few crystals of iodine in the bottom of a capped 4-oz jar. Calculate the R_f values for the spots and identify the components in the unknown.

Cleaning Up. Solvents should be placed in the organic solvents container; dry, used chromatographic plates can be discarded in the nonhazardous solid waste container.

2. Plant Pigments

The botanist Michael Tswett discovered the technique of chromatography and applied it, as the name implies, to colored plant pigments. The leaves of plants contain, in addition to chlorophyll-a and chlorophyll-b, other pigments that are revealed in the fall when the leaves die and the chlorophyll rapidly decomposes. Among the most abundant of the other pigments are the carotenoids, which include the carotenes and their oxygenated homologs, the xanthophylls. The bright orange β-carotene is the most important of these because it is transformed in the liver to vitamin A, which is required for night vision.

Chlorophyll-a

β-Carotene ($C_{40}H_{56}$)
mp 183°C, λ_{max}^{hexane} 451 nm

3′-Dehydrolutein (a xanthophyll)

Butter Yellow
(carcinogenic)

Lycopene ($C_{40}H_{56}$)
MW 536.85
mp 173°C, λ_{max}^{hexane} 475 nm

■ **FIG. 8.11**
An energy-minimized, space-filling model of lycopene. The molecule is flat, but steric hindrance of the methyl groups causes the molecule to bend into an S shape.

Cows eat fresh, green grass that contains carotene, but they do not metabolize the carotene entirely, so it ends up in their milk. Butter made from this milk is therefore yellow. In the winter the silage cows eat does not contain carotene because that compound readily undergoes air oxidation, and the butter made at that time is white. For some time an azo dye called Butter Yellow was added to winter butter to give it the accustomed color, but the dye was found to be a carcinogen. Now winter butter is colored with synthetic carotene, as is all margarine.

Isoprene

Lycopene from tomato paste and β-carotene from strained carrots

As an interesting variation, try extracting lycopene from commercial ketchup.

CAUTION: Do not breathe the vapors of dichloromethane. Carry out the extraction in the hood.

Lycopene (Fig. 8.11), the red pigment of the tomato, is a C_{40}-carotenoid made up of eight isoprene units. β-Carotene, the yellow pigment of the carrot, is an isomer of lycopene in which the double bonds at C_1—C_2 and C'_1—C'_2 are replaced by bonds extending from C_1 to C_6 and from C'_1 to C'_6 to form rings. The chromophore in each case is a system of 11 all-*trans* conjugated double bonds; the closing of the two rings causes β-carotene to absorb at shorter wavelengths than lycopene does, shifting its color from red to yellow.

In 1911, Richard Willstätter and Heinrich R. Escher isolated 20 mg of lycopene per kilogram of fresh tomatoes, which contain about 96% water.[3] They then found a more convenient source in commercial tomato paste: the seeds and skin were eliminated, and the water content was reduced by evaporation in vacuum to a content of 26% solids. From this they isolated 150 mg of lycopene per kilogram of paste. The expected yield in the following experiment is 0.075 mg, which is not enough to weigh on a balance.

A jar of strained carrots sold as baby food serves as a convenient source of β-carotene. The German investigators isolated 1 g of β-carotene per kilogram of dried, shredded carrots of unstated water content.

The following procedure calls for the dehydration of tomato or carrot paste with ethanol and extraction with dichloromethane, an efficient solvent for lipids.

Experimental Considerations

Carotenoids are very sensitive to light-catalyzed air oxidation. Perform this experiment as rapidly as possible; keep the solutions as cool and dark as possible. This extraction produces a mixture of products that can be analyzed by both TLC and column chromatography (*see* Chapter 9). If enough material for TLC only is desired, use one-tenth the quantities of starting material and solvents employed in the following procedure. This extraction can also be carried out with hexane if the ventilation is not adequate enough to use dichloromethane. However, hexane is more prone to form emulsions than the chlorinated solvent.

Procedure

> **IN THIS EXPERIMENT** some tomato or carrot paste is treated with acetone, which will remove water and lipids but not the highly colored carotenoid hydrocarbons. The carotenoids are extracted by dichloromethane and analyzed by TLC.

A 5-g sample of fresh tomato or carrot paste (baby food) is transferred to the bottom of a 25 × 150 mm test tube, followed by 10 mL of acetone. The mixture is stirred and shaken before being filtered on a Hirsch funnel. Scrape as much of the material from the tube as possible and press it dry on the funnel. Let the tube drain thoroughly. Place the filtrate in a 125-mL Erlenmeyer flask.

3. Willstätter, R.; Escher, H. R. *Z. Physiol. Chem.* **1911**, *64*, 47–61.

Return the solid residue to the test tube, shake it with a 10-mL portion of dichloromethane, and again filter the material on a Hirsch funnel. Add the filtrate to the 125-mL flask. Repeat this process two more times and then pour the combined filtrates into a separatory funnel. Add water and sodium chloride solution (which aids in the breaking of emulsions) and shake the funnel gently. This aqueous extraction will remove the acetone and any water-soluble components from the mixture, leaving the hydrocarbon carotenoids in the dichloromethane. Dry the colored organic layer over anhydrous calcium chloride and filter the solution into a dry flask. Remove about 0.5 mL of this solution and store it under nitrogen in the dark until it can be analyzed by TLC. Evaporate the remainder of the dichloromethane solution to dryness under a stream of nitrogen or under vacuum on a rotary evaporator. This material can be used for column chromatography (*see* Chapter 9). If it is to be stored, fill the flask with nitrogen and store it in a dark place.

> Air can be used for the evaporation, but nitrogen is better because these hydrocarbons air oxidize with great rapidity.

Thin-Layer Chromatography

Spot the mixture on a TLC plate about 1 cm from the bottom and 8 mm from the edge. Make one spot concentrated by repeatedly touching the plate, but ensure that the spot is as small as possible, certainly less than 1 mm in diameter. The other spot can be of lower concentration. Develop the plate with an 80:20 hexane-acetone mixture. With other plates you could try cyclohexane and toluene as eluents and also hexane-ethanol mixtures of various compositions.

> Many spots may be seen. There are two common carotene and chlorophyll isomers and four xanthophyll isomers.

The container in which the chromatography is carried out should be lined with filter paper that is wet with the solvent so that the atmosphere in the container will be saturated with the solvent vapor. After elution is completed, remove the TLC plate and mark the solvent front with a pencil and outline the colored spots. Examine the plate under UV light. Also place the plate in an iodine chamber to visualize the spots.

Cleaning Up. The aqueous saline filtrate containing acetone can be flushed down the drain. Recovered and unused dichloromethane should be placed in the halogenated organic waste container; the solvents used for TLC should be placed in the organic solvents container. If local regulations allow, evaporate any residual solvent from the drying agents in the hood and place the dried solid in the nonhazardous waste container. Otherwise, place the wet drying agent in a waste container designated for this purpose. Used plant material and dry TLC plates can be discarded in the nonhazardous waste container.

Procedure

In a small mortar grind 2 g of green or brightly colored fall leaves (do not use ivy or waxy leaves) with 10 mL of ethanol, pour off the ethanol (which serves to break up and dehydrate the plant cells), and grind the leaves successively with three 1-mL portions of dichloromethane that are decanted or withdrawn with a Pasteur pipette and placed in a test tube. The pigments of interest are extracted by the dichloromethane. Alternatively, place 0.5 g of carrot paste (baby food) or tomato paste in a test tube, stir and shake the paste with 3 mL of ethanol until the paste has a somewhat dry or fluffy appearance, remove the ethanol, and extract the dehydrated paste with three 1-mL portions of dichloromethane. Stir and shake the plant material with the solvent to extract as much of the pigments as possible.

Fill the tube containing the dichloromethane extract from leaves or vegetable paste with a saturated sodium chloride solution and shake the mixture. Remove the aqueous layer; add anhydrous calcium chloride pellets to the dichloromethane solution until the drying agent no longer clumps together. Shake the mixture with the drying agent for about 5 min and then withdraw the solvent with a Pasteur pipette and place it in a test tube. Add to the solvent a few pieces of Drierite to complete the drying process. Gently stir the mixture for about 5 min, transfer the solvent to a test tube, wash off the drying agent with more solvent, and then evaporate the combined dichloromethane solutions under a stream of nitrogen while warming the tube in your hand or in a beaker of warm water. Carry out this evaporation in the hood.

Immediately cork the tube filled with nitrogen and then add 1 or 2 drops of dichloromethane to dissolve the pigments for TLC analysis. Carry out the analysis without delay by spotting the mixture on a TLC plate about 1 cm from the bottom and 8 mm from the edge. Make one spot concentrated by repeatedly touching the plate, but ensure that the spot is as small as possible—less than 1.0 mm in diameter. The other spot can be of lower concentration. Develop the plate with a 70:30 hexane-acetone mixture. With other plates try cyclohexane and toluene as eluents and also hexane-ethanol mixtures of various compositions. The container in which the chromatography is carried out should be lined with filter paper that is wet with the solvent so that the atmosphere in the container will be saturated with solvent vapor. After elution is completed, mark the solvent front with a pencil and outline the colored spots. Examine the plate under the UV light. Are any new spots seen? Report colors and R_f values for all of your spots and identify each as lycopene, carotene, chlorophyll, or xanthophyll.

Cleaning Up. The ethanol used for the dehydration of the plant material can be flushed down the drain along with the saturated sodium chloride solution. Recovered and unused dichloromethane should be placed in the halogenated organic waste container. The solvents used for TLC should be placed in the organic solvents container. If local regulations allow, evaporate any residual solvent from the drying agents in the hood and place the dried solid in the nonhazardous waste container. Otherwise, place the wet drying agent in a waste container designated for this purpose. Used plant material and dry TLC plates can be discarded in the nonhazardous waste container.

3. For Further Investigation

Many of the pigments in plants are made up of compounds called *anthocyanins*. Grind about 4 g of colored plant tissue (flower petals, blueberries, strawberries, cranberries, apple skins, red cabbage, red or purple grapes, etc.) and a small amount of alumina or fine sand with about 4 mL of a mixture of 99% methanol and 1% hydrochloric acid. Spot the extract on cellulose TLC plates and elute with a solvent mixture of 20% concentrated hydrochloric acid, 40% water, and 4% formic acid. Note the number and color of the spots. Look up the structures of the possible anthocyanins, of which many are glycosides of the aglycones delphinidin, peonidin, malvidin, and cyanidin, among others.

These hydrocarbons air oxidize with great rapidity.

4. Colorless Compounds

You will now apply the thin-layer technique to a group of colorless compounds. The spots can be visualized under UV light if the plates have been coated with a fluorescent indicator; chromatograms can also be developed in a 4-oz bottle containing crystals of iodine. During development, spots will appear rapidly but remember that they also disappear rapidly. Therefore, outline each spot with a pencil immediately on withdrawal of the plate from the iodine chamber. Some suggested solvents are pure cyclohexane, pure toluene, toluene (3 mL) plus dichloromethane (1 mL), or toluene (4.5 mL) plus methanol (1/2 mL).

The compounds for trial are to be selected from the following list (all 1% solutions in toluene; those compounds with an asterisk are fluorescent under UV light):

1. Anthracene*
2. Cholesterol
3. 2,7-Dimethyl-3,5-octadiyne-2,7-diol
4. Diphenylacetylene
5. *trans,trans*-1,4-Diphenyl-1,3-butadiene*
6. *p*-Di-*t*-butylbenzene
7. 1,4-Di-*t*-butyl-2,5-dimethoxybenzene
8. *trans*-Stilbene
9. 1,2,3,4-Tetraphenylnaphthalene*
10. Tetraphenylthiophene
11. *p*-Terphenyl*
12. Triphenylmethanol
13. Triptycene

Except for tetraphenylthiophene, the structures for all of these molecules will be found in this book.

Make your own selections.

It is up to you to make selections and to plan your own experiments. Do as many as time permits. One plan would be to select a pair of compounds that are estimated to be separable and that have R_f values determinable with the same solvent. One can assume that a hydroxyl compound will travel less rapidly with a hydrocarbon solvent than a hydroxyl-free compound; you will therefore know what to expect if the solvent contains a hydroxylic component. An aliphatic solvent should carry along an aromatic compound with aliphatic substituents better than one without such groups. However, instead of relying on assumptions, you can do brief preliminary experiments on used plates on which previous spots are visible or outlined. If you spot a pair of compounds on such a plate and let the solvent rise about 3 cm from the starting line before development, you might be able to tell if a certain solvent is appropriate for a given sample. Alternatively, make some spots on a plate (new or used) and then touch each spot with a different solvent held in a capillary. In Figure 8.12a, the mixture did not move away from the point of origin; in Figure 8.12b, two concentric rings are seen between the origin and the solvent front. This is how a good solvent behaves. In Figure 8.12c, the mixture of compounds traveled with the solvent front.

Preliminary trials on used plates

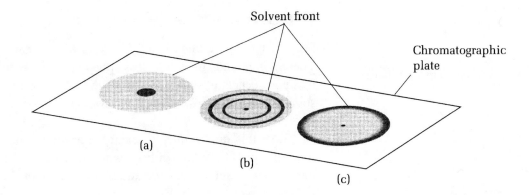

Once a solvent is chosen, run a complete chromatogram on the two compounds on a fresh plate. If separation of the two compounds seems feasible, put two spots of one compound on a plate, let the solvent evaporate, and put spots of the second compound over the first ones. Run a chromatogram and see if you can detect two spots in either lane (with colorless compounds, it is advisable not to attempt a three-lane chromatogram until you have acquired considerable practice and skill).

Cleaning Up. Solvents should be placed in the organic solvents container, and dry, used chromatographic plates can be discarded in the nonhazardous solid waste container.

Discussion

If you have investigated hydroxylated compounds, you doubtless have found that it is reasonably easy to separate a hydroxylated from a nonhydroxylated compound or a diol from a mono-ol. How, by a simple reaction followed by a thin-layer chromatogram, could you separate cholesterol from triphenylmethanol? Heating a sample of each with acetic anhydride and a trace of pyridine catalyst for 5 min on a steam bath, followed by chromatography, should do it. A first trial of a new reaction leaves questions about what has happened and how much, if any, starting material is present. A comparative chromatogram of the reaction mixture with starting material may tell the story. How crude is a crude reaction product? How many components are present? The thin-layer technique may give the answers to these questions and suggest how best to process the product. A preparative column chromatogram may afford a large number of fractions of eluent (say, 1 to 30). Some fractions probably contain nothing and should be discarded, while others should be combined for evaporation and workup. How can you identify the good and the useless fractions? Take a few used plates and put numbered circles on clean places of each; spot samples of each of the fractions; and, without any chromatography, develop the plates with iodine. Negative fractions for discard will be obvious, and the pattern alone of positive fractions may allow you to infer which fractions can be combined. Thin-layer chromatograms of the first and last fractions of each suspected group would then show whether or not your inferences are correct.

Fluorescence

Four of the compounds listed in Experiment 4 are fluorescent under UV light. These compounds give colorless spots that can be picked up on a chromatogram by fluorescence (after removal from the UV-absorbing glass bottle). If a UV light source is available, spot the four compounds on a used plate and observe the fluorescence.

Take this opportunity to examine a white shirt or handkerchief under UV light to see if it contains a brightener, that is, a fluorescent white dye or optical bleach. These substances are added to counteract the yellow color that repeated washing gives to cloth. Brighteners of the type of Calcofluor White MR, a sulfonated *trans*-stilbene derivative, are commonly used in detergent formulations for cotton; the substituted coumarin derivative is typical of brighteners used for nylon, acetate, and wool. Detergents normally contain 0.1%–0.2% of optical bleach. The amount of dye on a freshly laundered shirt is approximately 0.01% of the weight of the fabric.

⚠
Never look into a UV lamp.

Calcofluor White MR

7-Diethylamino-4-methylcoumarin

Online Study Center

General Resources
Additional Experiments

QUESTIONS

1. Why might it be very difficult to visualize the separation of *cis*- and *trans*-2-butene by TLC?
2. What error is introduced into the determination of an R_f value if the top is left off the developing chamber?
3. What problem will ensue if the level of the developing liquid is higher than the applied spot in a TLC analysis?

4. In what order (from top to bottom) would you expect to find naphthalene, butyric acid, and phenyl acetate on a silica gel TLC plate developed with dichloromethane?

5. In carrying out an analysis of a mixture, what do you expect to see when the TLC plate has been allowed to remain in the developing chamber too long, so that the solvent front has reached the top of the plate?

6. Arrange the following in order of increasing R_f with TLC: acetic acid, acetaldehyde, 2-octanone, decane, and 1-butanol.

7. What will be the result of applying too much compound to a TLC plate?

8. Why is it necessary to run TLC in a closed container and to have the interior vapor saturated with the solvent?

9. What will be the appearance of a TLC plate if a solvent of too low polarity is used for the development? a solvent of too high polarity?

10. A TLC plate showed two spots with R_f values of 0.25 and 0.26. The plate was removed from the developing chamber, the residual solvent was allowed to evaporate from the plate, and then the plate was returned to the developing chamber. What would you expect to see after the second development was complete?

11. One of the analgesics has a chiral center. Which compound is it? One of the two enantiomers is far more effective at reducing pain than the other.

12. Using a ruler to measure distances, calculate the R_f value for substance B in Figure 8.10.

Column Chromatography: Fluorenone, Cholesteryl Acetate, Acetylferrocene, and Plant Pigments

Online Study Center

This icon will direct you to techniques, equipment setups, and online resources at http://college.hmco.com/PIC/williamsonMMOE5e.

PRELAB EXERCISE: Compare column chromatography and thin-layer chromatography (TLC) with regard to the (1) quantity of material that can be separated, (2) time needed for the analysis, (3) solvent systems used, and (4) ability to separate compounds.

Column chromatography is one of the most useful methods for the separation and purification of both solids and liquids when carrying out microscale experiments. It becomes expensive and time consuming, however, when more than about 10 g of material must be purified. Column chromatography involves the same chromatographic principles as detailed for TLC in Chapter 8, so be sure that you understand those before doing the experiments in this chapter.

As discussed in Chapter 1, organic chemists obtain new compounds by synthesizing or isolating natural products that have been biosynthesized by microbes, plants, or animals. In most cases, initial reaction products or cell extracts are complex mixtures containing many substances. As you have seen, recrystallization, distillation, liquid/liquid extraction, and sublimation can be used to separate and purify a desired compound from these mixtures. However, these techniques are frequently not adequate for removing impurities that are closely related in structure. In these cases, column chromatography is often used. The broad applicability of this technique becomes obvious if you visit any organic chemistry research lab, where chromatography columns are commonplace.

Three of the five experiments in this chapter involve synthesis and may be your first experience in running an organic reaction. Experiments 1 and 2 involve the synthesis of a ketone. In Experiment 3 an ester of cholesterol is prepared. Experiment 4 demonstrates the separation of colored compounds. Experiment 5 involves the isolation and separation of natural products (plant pigments), which is analogous to Experiment 2 in Chapter 8 but on a larger scale.

The most common adsorbents for column chromatography—silica gel and alumina—are the same stationary phases as used in TLC. The sample is dissolved in a small quantity of solvent (the eluent) and applied to the top of the column. The eluent, instead of rising by capillary action up a thin layer, flows down through the column filled with the adsorbent. Just as in TLC, there is an equilibrium established between the solute adsorbed on the silica gel or alumina and the eluting solvent flowing down through the column, with the less strongly absorbed solutes moving ahead and eluting earlier.

Three mutual interactions must be considered in column chromatography: the activity of the stationary adsorbent phase, the polarity of the eluting mobile solvent phase, and the polarity of the compounds in the mixture being chromatographed.

Additional Principles of Column Chromatography

Adsorbents

A large number of adsorbents have been used for column chromatography, including cellulose, sugar, starch, and inorganic carbonates; but most separations employ alumina [$(Al_2O_3)_x$] or silica gel [$(SiO_2)_x$]. Alumina comes in three forms: acidic, neutral, and basic. The neutral form of Brockmann activity grade II or III, 150 mesh, is most commonly employed. The surface area of this alumina is about 150 m^2/g. Alumina as purchased will usually be activity grade I, meaning that it will strongly adsorb solutes. It must be deactivated by adding water, shaking, and allowing the mixture to reach equilibrium over an hour or so. The amount of water needed to achieve certain activities is given in Table 9.1. The activity of the alumina on TLC plates is usually about III. Silica gel for column chromatography, 70–230 mesh, has a surface area of about 500 m^2/g and comes in only one activity.

TABLE 9.2 • Elutropic Series for Solvents

n-Pentane (least polar)
Petroleum ether
Cyclohexane
Hexanes
Carbon disulfide
t-Butyl methyl ether
Dichloromethane
Tetrahydrofuran
Dioxane
Ethyl acetate
2-Propanol
Ethanol
Methanol
Acetic acid (most polar)

TABLE 9.1 • Alumina Activity

Brockmann activity grade	I	II	III	IV	V
Percent by weight of water	0	3	6	10	15

Solvents

Solvent systems for use as mobile phases in column chromatography can be determined from TLC, the scientific literature, or experimentally. Normally, a separation will begin with a nonpolar or low-polarity solvent, allowing the compounds to adsorb to the stationary phase; then the polarity of the solvent is *slowly* switched to desorb the compounds and allow them to move with the mobile phase. The polarity of the solvent should be changed gradually. A sudden change in solvent polarity will cause heat evolution as the alumina or silica gel adsorbs the new solvent. This will vaporize the solvent, causing channels to form in the column that severely reduce its separating power.

Several solvents are listed in Table 9.2, arranged in order of increasing polarity (elutropic series), with *n*-pentane being the least polar. The order shown in the table reflects the ability of these solvents to dislodge a polar substance adsorbed onto either silica gel or alumina, with *n*-pentane having the lowest solvent power.

Petroleum ether: mostly isometric pentanes

As a practical matter, the following sequence of solvents is recommended in an investigation of unknown mixtures: elute first with petroleum ether (pentanes); then hexanes; followed by hexanes containing 1%, 2%, 5%, 10%, 25%, and 50% ether; pure ether; ether and dichloromethane mixtures; followed by dichloromethane and methanol mixtures. Either diethyl ether or *t*-butyl methyl ether can be used, but *t*-butyl methyl ether is recommended. Solvents such as methanol and water are normally not used because they can destroy the integrity of the stationary phase by dissolving some of the silica gel. Some typical solvent combinations are hexanes-dichloromethane, hexanes–ethyl acetate, and hexanes-toluene. An experimentally determined ratio of these solvents can sufficiently separate most compounds.

Compound Mobility

The ease with which different classes of compounds elute from a column is indicated in Table 9.3. Molecules with nonpolar functional groups are least adsorbed and elute first, while more polar or hydrogen-bonding molecules are more strongly adsorbed and elute later. The order is similar to that of the eluting solvents—another application of "like dissolves like."

Sample and Column Size

Chromatography columns can be as thin as a pencil for milligram quantities to as big as a barrel for the industrial-scale separation of kilogram quantities. A microscale column for the chromatography of about 50 mg of material is shown in Figure 9.1; columns with larger diameters, as shown in Figures 9.2 and 9.3, are used for macroscale procedures. The amount of alumina or silica gel used should generally weigh at least 30 times as much as the sample, and the column, when packed, should have a height at least 10 times the diameter. The density of silica gel is 0.4 g/mL, and the density of alumina is 0.9 g/mL, so the optimum size for any column can be calculated.

Packing the Column

Microscale Procedure

Before you pack the column, tare several Erlenmeyer flasks, small beakers, or 20-mL vials to use as receivers. Weigh each one carefully and mark it with a number on the etched circle.

Uniform packing of the chromatography column is critical to the success of this technique. Two acceptable methods for packing a column are dry packing and slurry packing, which normally achieve the best results. Assemble the column as depicted in Figure 9.1. To measure the amount of adsorbent, fill the column one-half to two-thirds full; then pour the powder out into a small beaker or flask. Clamp the column in a vertical position and close the valve. Always grasp the

TABLE 9.3 • Elution Order for Solutes

Alkanes (first)

Alkenes

Dienes

Aromatic hydrocarbons

Ethers

Esters

Ketones

Aldehydes

Amines

Alcohols

Phenols

Acids (last)

Online Study Center

Photo: Column Chromatography;
Video: Column Chromatography

■ FIG. 9.1
A microscale chromatographic column.

Funnel

Glass column

Alumina

Micro Büchner funnel

Polyethylene frit

10-mL Erlenmeyer flask

■ FIG. 9.2
A macroscale chromatographic column.

← Solvent

← Sand

← Alumina or silica gel

← Sand
← Glass wool

■ FIG. 9.3
A chromatographic tube on ring stand.

valve with one hand while turning it with the other. Fill the column with a nonpolar solvent such as hexanes almost to the top.

● **Dry Packing Method.** This is the simplest method for preparing a microscale column. Slowly add the powedered alumina or silica gel through the funnel while gently tapping the side of the column with a pencil. The solid should "float" to the bottom of the column. Try to pack the column as evenly as possible; cracks, air bubbles, and channels will lead to a poor separation.

● **Slurry Packing Method.** To slurry pack a column, add about 8 mL of hexanes to the adsorbent in a flask or beaker, stir the mixture to eliminate air bubbles, and then (this is the hard part) swirl the mixture to get the adsorbent suspended in the solvent and immediately pour the entire slurry into the funnel. Open the valve, drain some solvent into the flask that had the adsorbent in it and finish transferring the slurry to the column. Place an empty flask under the column and allow the solvent to drain to about 5 mm above the top surface of the adsorbent. Tap the column with a pencil until the packing settles to a minimum height. Try to pack the column as evenly as possible; cracks, air bubbles, and channels will lead to a poor separation.

The slurry method normally gives the best column packing, but it is also the more difficult technique to master. Whether the dry packing or slurry packing method is chosen, the most important aspect of packing the column is creating an evenly distributed and packed stationary phase. The slurry method is often used for macroscale separations.

Once the column is loaded with solvent and adsorbent, place a flask under it, open the stopcock (use two hands for the microscale column), and allow the solvent level to drop to the *top* of the packing. Avoid allowing the solvent level to go below the stationary phase (known as letting the column "run dry") because this allows air bubbles and channel formation to occur, which leads to a poor separation.

Macroscale Procedure

Before you pack the column, prepare several Erlenmeyer flasks to use as receivers by taring (weighing) each one carefully and marking each with a number on the etched circle.

Extinguish all flames; work in laboratory hood.

Dry Packing Method

The column can be prepared using a 50-mL burette such as the one shown in Figure 9.2 or using the less expensive and equally satisfactory chromatographic tube shown in Figure 9.3, in which the flow of solvent is controlled by a screw pinchclamp. Weigh the required amount of silica gel (12.5 g in the first experiment), close the pinchclamp on the tube, and fill about half full with a 90:10 mixture of hexanes and ether. With a wooden dowel or glass rod, push a small plug of glass wool through the liquid to the bottom of the tube, dust in through a funnel enough sand to form a 1-cm layer over the glass wool, and level the surface by tapping the tube. Unclamp the tube. With your right hand grasp both the top of the tube and the funnel so that the whole assembly can be shaken to dislodge silica gel that may stick to the walls; with your left hand pour in the silica gel slowly (Fig. 9.4) while tapping the column with a rubber stopper fitted on the end of a pencil. If necessary, use a Pasteur pipette full of a 90:10 mixture of hexanes and ether to wash down any silica gel that adheres to the walls of the column above the liquid. When the silica gel has settled, add a little sand to provide a protective layer at the top. Open the pinchclamp, let the solvent level fall until it is just slightly above the upper layer of sand, and then stop the flow.

■ FIG. 9.4
A useful technique for filling a chromatographic tube with silica gel.

Slurry Packing Method

Alternatively, the silica gel can be added to the column (half filled with hexanes) by slurrying the silica gel with a 90:10 mixture of hexanes and ether in a beaker. The powder is stirred to suspend it in the solvent and immediately poured through a wide-mouth funnel into the chromatographic tube. Rap the column with a rubber stopper to cause the silica gel to settle and to remove bubbles. Add a protective layer of sand to the top. The column is now ready for use.

Cleaning Up. After use, the tube is conveniently emptied by pointing the open end into a beaker, opening the pinchclamp, and applying gentle air pressure to the tip. If the plug of glass wool remains in the tube after the alumina leaves, wet it with acetone and reapply air pressure. Allow the adsorbent to dry in the hood and then dispose of it in the nonhazardous waste container.

Adding the Sample

Dissolve the sample completely in a very minimum volume of dichloromethane (just a few drops) in a small flask or vial. Add to this solution 300 mg of the adsorbent, stir, and evaporate the solvent completely by heating the slurry *very gently* with *constant* stirring to avoid bumping. Remember that dichloromethane boils at 41°C. Pour this dry powder into the funnel of the chromatography column, wash it down onto the column with a few drops of hexane, and then tap the column to remove air bubbles from the layer of adsorbent-solute mixture just added. Open the valve and carefully add new solvent in such a manner that the top surface of the column is not disturbed. A thin layer of fine sand can be added to the column after the sample to avoid disturbance of the column surface when the solvent is being added. Run the solvent down near to the surface several times to apply the sample as a narrow band at the top of the column.

Eluting the Column

Fill the column with solvent, open the stopcock, and continue to add more solvent while collecting 1–3 mL fractions in small tared containers. Collecting small fractions is important to the success of your column separation. Fractions that are too small can always be pooled together; however, if the collected fractions are too large, you may get more than one compound in any particular fraction. If this occurs, the only way to attain separation is to redo the chromatography. Column chromatography is a lengthy process, so collecting large fractions is discouraged.

Isolating the Separated Compounds

If the mixture to be separated contains colored compounds, then monitoring the column is very simple. The colored bands will move down the column along with the solvent, and as they approach the end of the column, you can collect the separated colors in individual containers. However, most organic molecules are colorless. In this case, the separation must be monitored by TLC. Spot each fraction on a TLC plate (Fig. 9.5). Four or five fractions can be spotted on a single plate. Before you develop the plate, do a quick examination under UV light to see if there is any compound where you spotted. If not, you can spot the next fraction in that location. Note which fraction is in which lane. Develop the plate and use the observed spot(s) to determine which compound is in each of the collected fractions. Spotting some of the starting material or the product (if available) on the TLC plate as a standard will help in the identification.

The colors of the fractions or the results from analyzing the fractions by TLC will indicate which fractions contain the compound(s) you are interested in isolating. Combine fractions containing the same compound and evaporate the

■ FIG. 9.5
Spot each fraction on a TLC plate. Examine under UV light to see which fractions contain the compound.

solvent. Recrystallization may be used to further purify a solid product. However, on a milligram scale, there is usually not enough material to do this.

Other Types of Chromatography

Online Study Center

General Resources
Flash Chromatography

Relying only on gravity, liquid flow through a column can be quite slow, especially if the column is tightly packed. One method to speed up the process is *flash chromatography*. This method uses a pressure of about 10 psi of air or nitrogen on top of the column to force the mobile phase through the column. Normally, doing this would give a poorer separation. However, it has been found that with a finer mesh of alumina or silica gel, flash chromatography can increase the speed without lowering the quality of the separation. Go to this book's website for an illustrated set of instructions for packing and using a flash chromatography column.

High-performance liquid chromatography

High-performance liquid chromatography (HPLC) is a high-tech version of column chromatography, which is capable of separating complex mixtures with dozens of components. A high-pressure pump forces solvent at pressures up to 10,000 psi through a stainless steel tube packed tightly with extremely small adsorbent particles. The eluent flows from the column to a detector, such as a tiny UV absorbance cell or a mass spectrometer that is able to detect extremely small amounts of separated components, as little as a picogram (10^{-12} g).

Reverse-phase chromatography

HPLC is used extensively in biochemistry to separate cellular components such as proteins, lipids, and nucleic acids. Mixtures of these types of compounds can be dissolved only in a predominantly aqueous mobile phase such as methanol-water or acetonitrile-water, and normal silica gel or alumina stationary phases do not work well with high concentrations of water. Rather than polar stationary phases, highly nonpolar ones called *reverse-phase packings* are used. These are manufactured by bonding lots of hydrocarbon molecules to the surfaces of silica gel particles, which convert the particles into highly nonpolar grease balls. With this packing, the order of elution is the reverse of that observed for a normal silica gel phase. On a reverse-phase column, the more nonpolar compounds will adhere to the nonpolar stationary phase more strongly, and the polar compounds will elute first.

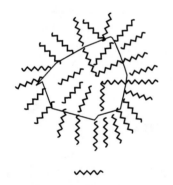

C_{18} **reverse-phase packing**

Chiral chromatography

Is it possible to separate two enantiomers (optical isomers), both of which have the same intermolecular attractive forces? Chiral stationary phases can be used to separate enantiomers. Giving the stationary phase an asymmetry or handedness allows one enantiomer to be specifically retained on the column. Such columns are quite expensive and are limited to a particular type of separation, but they have led to great achievements in separation science. This separation technique is of great importance in the pharmaceutical industry because the U.S. Food and Drug Administration (FDA) specifies the amounts of impurities, including enantiomers, that can be found in drugs. For example, Thalidomide, a drug prescribed as a sedative and an antidepressant in the 1960s, was found to be a potent teratogen that caused birth defects when pregnant women took the drug. It was quickly pulled from the market. Thalidomide has two enantiomers, and further research demonstrated that only one of the enantiomers caused the birth defects.

EXPERIMENTS

1. Air Oxidation of Fluorene to Fluorenone

The 9-position of fluorene is unusually reactive for a hydrocarbon. The protons on this carbon atom are acidic by virtue of being doubly benzylic, and, consequently, this carbon can be oxidized by several reagents, including oxygen from the air. Here the oxidation is carried out using a phase-transfer catalyst called methyltricapryl ammonium chloride, commonly known as Stark's catalyst or Aliquat 336. In the presence of this catalyst, the hydroxide is carried into the organic layer, where it can remove one of the acidic fluorene protons, creating a carbanion that can react with oxygen in the air. An intermediate hydroperoxide is formed and loses water to give the ketone.

Sufficiently acidic
to be removed
by strong base

$\rightarrow$

H   H

Fluorene
mp 114°C
MW 166.22

$+ O_2$

CH_3 Cl^-

N^+

Methyltricapryl ammonium chloride
(Aliquat 336, Stark's catalyst)

10 M NaOH
Toluene
10–60 min

O

Fluorenone
mp 83°C
MW 180.21

$+ H_2O$

Microscale Procedure

IN THIS EXPERIMENT fluorene is oxidized to fluorenone by oxygen from the air in a base-catalyzed reaction involving a phase-transfer catalyst. The reaction is monitored by TLC and stopped when about a 50:50 mixture of product and starting material has formed. The toluene layer is separated and washed with 5% hydrochloric acid and saturated sodium chloride. After drying over calcium chloride, the toluene is removed and the fluorene-fluorenone mixture is separated by microscale column chromatography on alumina, using hexanes as the mobile phase. Fractions are analyzed by TLC; common fractions are pooled and weighed after solvent removal to give pure fluorene and fluorenone.

CAUTION: Sodium hydroxide is a strong base and is very corrosive. Wash your hands immediately if contact occurs.

This experiment requires a 50-mL to 125-mL separatory funnel. To a 25-mL Erlenmeyer flask clamped to a ring stand above a magnetic stirrer, add 5 mL of 10 M NaOH and 70 mg of fluorene while stirring with a $\frac{1}{2}$-inch stir bar. Add 5 mL of toluene and stir until all of the solid has dissolved. (Observe the color and identify which layer is organic and which is aqueous.) Add approximately 3 drops of Stark's catalyst (Aliquat 336) to the solution. Stir vigorously but without splashing the solution. The reaction can take anywhere from 10 min to 30 min. Follow the rate of the reaction by TLC. Develop the TLC plate by using 20% dichloromethane in hexanes and use a UV lamp to visualize the products. Also spot the plate with a 1% fluorene standard. When approximately half of the fluorene has been converted to fluorenone (as evidenced by the fact that the product spot is about the same size and intensity), pour the reaction mixture into a separatory funnel, rinsing the beaker with an additional 3 mL of toluene, which is also added to the separatory funnel.

Separate the organic layer from the aqueous layer. Wash the organic layer in the separatory funnel with 1.5 M hydrochloric acid (three separate times with 5 mL each time) and then saturated sodium chloride (three separate times with 5 mL each time). After each washing, drain the aqueous layer from the separatory funnel into a waste beaker. Dry the remaining toluene layer over anhydrous calcium chloride pellets in a 125-mL Erlenmeyer flask. Add the pellets until they no longer clump together (3–5 scoops). Allow the product to dry for 5–10 min before decanting the toluene from the solid calcium chloride and transferring the toluene to a 100-mL tared beaker. Wash the solid calcium chloride with 3 mL of toluene, adding this to the main portion of toluene to complete the transfer of product. The crude mixture of fluorene and fluorenone will be separated by column chromatography in the next lab period. The beaker containing the toluene extract can be allowed to stand in your hood (labeled properly) until the next lab period. The toluene will evaporate in the interim. Alternatively, if you have time, reduce the volume of solvent (~1 mL) by heating gently on a sand bath. Insert a boiling stick if you do this.

Cleaning Up. Carefully dilute the strongly basic aqueous reaction layer 10- to 20-fold with water in a large beaker, add the hydrochloric acid washes, and then neutralize by slowly adding additional hydrochloric acid. Flush this and the sodium chloride washes down the drain with lots of water. If local regulations allow, evaporate any residual solvent from the drying agents in the hood and place the dried solid in the nonhazardous waste container. Otherwise, place the wet drying agent in a waste container designated for this purpose.

Column Chromatography of the Fluorene-Fluorenone Mixture

Figure 9.1 on page 197 shows the typical setup you will use for the chromatographic separation of fluorene and fluorenone, and a general outline of the procedure is given on page 196. It is essential to have at least 10 clean 10-mL Erlenmeyer flasks, reaction tubes, small beakers, test tubes, or vials available to collect the chromatography fractions as they elute. At least two of these should be weighed, with their tare weight recorded. Once you have this done and the column is assembled, you can pack the column with alumina according to the following instructions.

Packing the Column

Before you assemble the column, check the small plug that fits into the bottom of the column to make sure that it has a small fritted disk inside. Next, make sure that the plug fits snugly into the glass column and is not easy to pull out. If it is loose,

Set up a sand bath at a heating setting of 50 before you do anything else.

get a new bottom plug from the stockroom. Finish assembling the chromatography column as depicted in Figure 9.1. Be sure to clamp the column securely and vertically.

Grasp the valve with one hand and turn it with the other. Close the valve and fill the column with hexanes to the bottom of the plastic funnel. Weigh out approximately 4.5 g of activity grade III alumina in a small beaker and slowly sprinkle the dry alumina into the hexanes in the column while you tap the column with a pen or pencil. It may be necessary to drain off some of the solvent to keep it from flowing over the top. This amount of alumina should fill the column to a height of about 10 cm. It is extremely important *not* to let the column run dry at any time. This will allow air to enter the column, which will result in uneven bands and poor separation.

After all of the alumina has been added to the column, open the stopcock and continue to tap the column as you allow the solvent to drain slowly until the solvent just barely covers the surface of the alumina, collecting the solvent in an Erlenmeyer flask.

Adding the Sample

It is important to use a minimum amount of solvent when dissolving the sample. If too much is used, poor separation will result.

The solvent is drained just to the surface of the alumina, which should be perfectly flat. Dissolve the crude mixture of fluorene and fluorenone in 10 drops of dichloromethane and 10 drops of toluene and add this with a pipette to the surface of the alumina. Be sure to add the sample as a solution; should any sample crystallize, add 1 more drop of dichloromethane. (This is done so that the sample to be added to the column is in the most concentrated solution possible.) Drain some liquid from the column until the dichloromethane-toluene solution just barely covers the surface of the alumina. Then add a few drops of hexanes and drain out some solvent until the liquid just covers the alumina. Repeat until the sample is seen as a narrow band at the top of the column. Carefully add a 4–5 mm layer of sand and then fill the column with hexanes.

Collect 3-mL fractions in a combination of small vials, 10-mL Erlenmeyer flasks, 13 × 100 mm test tubes, vials, and small beakers. You will probably collect close to ten 3-mL fractions. While the chromatography is running, you will be determining the amount of fluorene or fluorenone in each fraction by TLC. Once you determine which fractions contain which compound, you will combine the "like" fractions and evaporate the solvent.

After you collect each 3-mL fraction in a flask, apply it to a TLC plate by spotting it 2 or 3 times on the plate in the same location. Four or five fractions can be applied and analyzed at the same time using one TLC plate. Allow the solvent to completely evaporate from the spot and examine the plate under a UV lamp to determine if there is any material present, as evidenced by a dark blue spot. The TLC plates can be developed using 20% dichloromethane in hexanes. You will probably collect a few fractions that contain little or no material; these fractions are likely to be the first or the middle of the series.

After spotting and developing each fraction on the TLC plate, combine like fractions and immediately start to boil off the solvent on the sand bath *in the hood* using a boiling stick broken in half. Tilt the flasks and vials on their side as much as possible to allow the heavy vapors to escape. As soon as all the liquid seems to have boiled off, set the flask *on its side* on the bench top in the hood to allow the last traces of heavy solvent vapors to escape. After the flask has cooled to room temperature, if that fraction contains any material, crystals may appear. If an oily, gooey residue is present, you may have to scratch it with a glass stirring rod to induce crystallization. With good organizational effort, you can do the TLC analysis and evaporate off the solvent at about the same rate at which you collect fractions; thus you can follow the progress of the chromatography simply by noting the amount of material in each flask, vial, or test tube. If, after solvent removal and cooling, the flasks are perfectly clean on careful inspection, they can be used to collect subsequent fractions.

If the yellow band has not moved one third of the way down the column after two fractions have been collected, you can speed up the elution by replacing the hexanes solvent at the top of the column with 20% dichloromethane in hexanes. Once the first component has completely eluted, you can speed up the elution of the second component by using 50% dichloromethane in hexanes. Decide when the product has been completely eluted from the column by using visual cues and TLC. Using a few drops of dichloromethane, wash all the fractions that contain fluorene as determined by TLC analysis into a tared container. Do the same for the fluorenone fractions. Evaporate the dichloromethane and obtain dry weights for the product and the recovered fluorene.

Mark all compound spots on all TLC plates with a pencil. Tape your developed TLC plates in your notebook with wide transparent tape. Calculate the theoretical yield and the percent yield of your pure fluorenone both with and without taking into account the amount of fluorene starting material recovered. Calculate the percent recovery of fluorene.

Cleaning Up. When you are done with the column, pour out the excess solvent into the proper waste container, pull out the bottom, and leave the wet column propped in a beaker in your desk hood. The column will dry out by the next lab, and the dry, used alumina can then be easily emptied out into a waste bin.

2. Chromium(VI) Oxidation of Fluorene to Fluorenone

Chromium(VI) oxidations are less favored today because of environmental concerns based on chromium's toxicity.

The 9-position of fluorene is unusually reactive for a hydrocarbon. The protons on this carbon atom are acidic by virtue of being doubly benzylic, and, consequently, this carbon can be oxidized by several reagents, including elemental oxygen. In this experiment, the very powerful and versatile oxidizing agent chromium(VI), in the form of chromium trioxide, is used to carry out the oxidation. Chromium(VI) in a variety of other forms is used for about a dozen oxidation reactions in this text. The *dust* of chromium(VI) salts is reported to be a carcinogen, so avoid breathing it.

Fluorene
mp 114°C
MW 166.22

$$\xrightarrow[\text{CH}_3\text{COOH}]{\text{Na}_2\text{Cr}_2\text{O}_7}$$

Fluorenone
mp 83°C
MW 180.21

Microscale Procedure

> **IN THIS EXPERIMENT** the hydrocarbon fluorene is oxidized to the ketone fluorenone by sodium dichromate in acetic acid with heating. The mixture is diluted with water, and the crude product is isolated by filtration; then—in a standard procedure—it is dissolved in ether. The ether is dried and evaporated to give a mixture of fluorene and fluorenone, which is separated by column chromatography.

CAUTION: Sodium dichromate is toxic. The dust is corrosive to nasal passages and skin and is a suspected carcinogen. Hot acetic acid is very corrosive to skin. Handle sodium dichromate and acetic acid in the hood; always wear gloves.

In a reaction tube dissolve 50 mg of fluorene in 0.25 mL of acetic acid by heating and add this hot solution to a solution of 0.15 g of sodium dichromate dihydrate in 0.5 mL of acetic acid. Heat the reaction mixture to 80°C for 15 min in a hot water bath; then cool it and add 1.5 mL of water. Stir the mixture for 2 min; then filter it on a Hirsch funnel. Wash the product well with water and press out as much water as possible. Return the product to the reaction tube, add 2 mL of ether, and add anhydrous calcium chloride pellets until it no longer clumps together. Cork and shake the tube and allow the product to dry for 5–10 min before evaporating the ether in another tared reaction tube. Use ether to wash off the drying agent and to complete the transfer of product. Use this ether solution to spot a TLC plate. This crude mixture of fluorene and fluorenone will be separated by column chromatography.

Column Chromatography of the Fluorene-Fluorenone Mixture

Online Study Center

Photo: Column Chromatography;
Video: Column Chromatography

The sample can also be applied to the column using the technique described on page 196.

Prepare a microscale chromatographic column exactly as described at the beginning of this chapter (*see* Fig. 9.1 on page 197). Use alumina as the adsorbent. Dissolve the crude mixture of fluorene and fluorenone in a mixture of 10 drops of dichloromethane and 10 drops of toluene and add this to the surface of the alumina. Be sure to add the sample as a solution; should any sample crystallize, add 1 more drop of dichloromethane. Run the hexanes down to the surface of the alumina, add a few drops more of hexanes, and repeat the process until the sample is seen as a narrow band at the top of the column. Carefully add a 3-mm layer of sand, fill the column with hexanes, and collect 5-mL fractions in tared 10-mL Erlenmeyer flasks. Sample each flask for TLC (*see* Fig. 9.5 on page 199) and evaporate each to dryness. Final drying can be done under vacuum using the technique shown in Figure 9.6. You are to decide when all of the product has been eluted from the column. The TLC plates can be developed using 20% dichloromethane in hexanes. Combine fractions that are identical and determine the melting points of the two substances.

Cleaning Up. The filtrate probably contains unreacted dichromate. To destroy it, add 3 *M* sulfuric acid until the pH is 1; then complete the reduction by adding solid sodium thiosulfate until the solution becomes cloudy and blue colored. Neutralize with sodium carbonate and then filter the flocculent precipitate of $Cr(OH)_3$ through Celite in a Büchner funnel. If regulations allow, the filtrate can be diluted with water and flushed down the drain; otherwise, it should be disposed of in a designated waste container. The precipitate and Celite should be placed in the heavy metal hazardous waste container.

Macroscale Procedure

In a 250-mL Erlenmeyer flask dissolve 5.0 g of practical grade fluorene in 25 mL of acetic acid by heating on a steam bath with occasional swirling. In a 125-mL Erlenmeyer flask dissolve 15 g of sodium dichromate dihydrate in 50 mL of acetic acid by swirling and heating on a hot plate. Adjust the temperature of the dichromate solution to 80°C, transfer the thermometer, and adjust the fluorene–acetic acid solution to 80°C; then, *in the hood*, pour in the dichromate solution. Note the time and the temperature of the solution and heat on a steam bath for 30 min. Observe the maximum and final temperature; then cool the solution and add 150 mL of water. Swirl the mixture for a full 2 min to coagulate the product and promote rapid filtration; collect the yellow solid in an 8.5-cm Büchner funnel using vacuum filtration (if filtration is slow, empty the funnel and flask into a beaker and stir vigorously for a few minutes). Wash the filter cake well with water and then suck the filter cake as dry as possible. Either let the product dry overnight or dry it quickly as follows: Put the moist solid into a 50-mL Erlenmeyer flask, add ether (20 mL) and swirl to dissolve, and add anhydrous calcium chloride (10 g) to scavenge the water. Decant the ethereal solution through a cone of anhydrous calcium chloride in a funnel into a 125-mL Erlenmeyer flask; then rinse the flask and funnel with ether. Evaporate on a steam bath under an aspirator, heat until all the ether is removed, and pour the hot oil into a 50-mL beaker to cool and solidify. Scrape out the yellow solid. The yield should be about 4.0 g.

Separation of Fluorene and Fluorenone

Prepare a column of 12.5 g of alumina, run out excess solvent, and pour onto the column a solution of 0.5 g of fluorene-fluorenone mixture. Elute at first with hexanes and use tared 50-mL flasks as receivers. The yellow color of fluorenone provides one index of the course of the fractionation, and the appearance of solid around the delivery tip provides another. Frequently wash the solid on the tip into the receiver with ether. When you believe that one component has been eluted completely, change to another receiver until you judge that the second component is beginning to appear. Then, when you are sure the second component is being eluted, change to a 1:1 hexanes and ether mixture and continue until the column is exhausted. It is possible to collect practically all of the two components in the two receiving flasks, with only a negligible intermediate fraction. After evaporation of the solvent, evacuate each flask under vacuum (Fig. 9.7) and determine the weight and melting point of the products. A convenient method for evaporating fractions is to use a rotary evaporator (Fig. 9.8).

Cleaning Up. All organic material from this experiment can go in the organic solvents container. If local regulations allow, evaporate any residual solvent from

Handle dichromate and acetic acid in laboratory hood; always wear gloves.

One-half hour unattended heating

■ FIG. 9.6
Drying a solid by reduced air pressure.

■ **FIG. 9.7**
An aspirator tube in use. A boiling stick may be necessary to promote even boiling.

■ **FIG. 9.8**
A rotary evaporator. The rate of evaporation with this apparatus is very fast due to the thin film of liquid spread over the entire inner surface of the rotating flask, which is heated under vacuum. Foaming and bumping are also greatly reduced.

the alumina in the hood and place the dried solid in the nonhazardous waste container. Otherwise, place the wet drying agent in a waste container designated for this purpose.

3. Acetylation of Cholesterol

Cholesterol is a solid alcohol; the average human body contains about 200 g distributed in brain, spinal cord, and nerve tissue and occasionally clogs the arteries and the gall bladder.

In the following experiment, cholesterol is dissolved in acetic acid and allowed to react with acetic anhydride to form the ester cholesteryl acetate. The reaction does not take place rapidly and consequently does not go to completion under the conditions of this experiment. Thus, when the reaction is over, both unreacted cholesterol and the product, cholesteryl acetate, are present. Separating these by fractional crystallization would be extremely difficult; but because they differ in polarity (the hydroxyl group of cholesterol is the more strongly adsorbed on alumina), they are easily separated by column chromatography. Both molecules are colorless and hence cannot be detected visually. Each fraction should be sampled by TLC. In that way not only the presence but also the purity of each fraction can be assessed. It is also possible to put 1 drop of each fraction on a watch glass and evaporate it to see if the fraction contains product. Solid will also appear on the tip of the column while a compound is being eluted.

Microscale Procedure

> **IN THIS EXPERIMENT** cholesterol is refluxed with acetic acid and acetic anhydride. In the standard procedure the mixture is diluted with water and extracted with ether, and the ether is dried and evaporated. The resulting mixture of cholesterol and cholesteryl acetate is separated by column chromatography on silica gel, eluting with hexanes and then hexanes and ether mixtures. Cholesteryl acetate comes off first, followed by cholesterol.

H₃C, CH₃ / CH₃ / CH₃ — Cholesterol structure with HO

$$+ \ CH_3\overset{O}{\overset{||}{C}}O\overset{O}{\overset{||}{C}}CH_3 \longrightarrow$$

Acetic anhydride

Cholesterol

Cholesteryl acetate structure

$CH_3\overset{O}{\overset{||}{C}}O$ $+ \ CH_3COOH$

Cholesteryl acetate

In a reaction tube, add 0.5 mL of acetic acid to 50 mg of cholesterol. The initial thin slurry may set into a stiff paste of the molecular complex consisting of one molecule of cholesterol and one molecule of acetic acid. Add 0.10 mL of acetic anhydride and a boiling chip and gently reflux the reaction mixture on a hot sand bath for no more than 30 min (*see* Fig. 1.1 on page 2).

While the reaction is taking place, prepare the microscale chromatography column as described previously, using silica gel as the adsorbent. Refer to Figure 9.1 on page 197 and the associated procedure earlier in the chapter. Cool the mixture, add 2 mL of water, and extract the product with three 2-mL portions of ether that are placed in the 15-mL centrifuge tube. Wash the ether extracts in the tube with two 2-mL portions of water and one 2.5-mL portion of 3 *M* sodium hydroxide (these three washes remove the acetic acid) and dry the ether by shaking it with 2.5 mL of saturated sodium chloride solution. Then complete the drying by adding enough anhydrous calcium chloride pellets to the solution so that the drying agent does not clump together.

Shake the ether solution with the drying agent for 10 min; then transfer it in portions to a tared reaction tube and evaporate to dryness. Use 1 drop of this ether solution to spot a TLC plate for later analysis. If the crude material weighs more than the theoretical weight, you will know that it is not dry or that it contains acetic acid, which can be detected by its odor. Dissolve this crude cholesteryl acetate in the minimum quantity of ether and apply it to the top of the chromatography column.

To prevent the solution from dribbling from the pipette, use a pipette pump to make the transfer. It also could be applied as a dry powder adsorbed on silica gel, as in Experiment 1. Elute the column with hexanes, collecting two 5-mL fractions

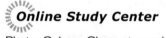

Online Study Center

Photo: Column Chromatography;
Video: Column Chromatography

in tared 10-mL Erlenmeyer flasks or other suitable containers. Add a boiling stick to each flask and evaporate the solvent under an aspirator tube on a steam bath or a sand bath (*see* Fig. 9.7). If the flask appears empty, it can be used to collect later fractions. Lower the solvent layer to the top of the sand and elute with 15 mL of a 70:30 mixture of hexanes and ether, collecting five 3-mL fractions. Evaporate the solvent under an aspirator tube (Fig. 9.7). The last traces of solvent can be removed using reduced pressure, as shown in Figure 9.6 on page 206. Follow the 70:30 mixture with 10 mL of a 50:50 mixture of hexanes and ether, collecting four 2-mL fractions. Save any flask that has any visible residue. Analyze the original mixture and each fraction by TLC on silica gel plates using a 1:1 mixture of hexanes and ether to develop the plates and either UV light or iodine vapor to visualize the spots.

Cholesteryl acetate (mp 115°C) and cholesterol (mp 149°C) should appear, respectively, in early and late fractions with a few empty fractions (no residue) in between. If so, combine consecutive fractions of early and late material and determine the weights and melting points. Calculate the percentage of the acetylated material compared to the total recovered and calculate the percentage yield from cholesterol.

Cleaning Up. After neutralization, acetic acid, the aqueous layers, and the saturated sodium chloride layers from the extraction can be flushed down the drain with water. Ether, hexanes, and TLC solvents should be placed in the organic solvents container. If local regulations allow, evaporate any residual solvent from the drying agents and the chromatography packing in the hood and place the dried solid in the nonhazardous waste container. Otherwise, place the wet materials in waste containers designated for this purpose.

Macroscale Procedure

Carry out procedure in laboratory hood.

Cover 0.5 g of cholesterol with 5 mL of acetic acid in a small Erlenmeyer flask; swirl and note that the initially thin slurry soon sets to a stiff paste of the molecular compound $C_{27}H_{45}OH \cdot CH_3CO_2H$. Add 1 mL of acetic anhydride and heat the mixture on a steam bath for any convenient period of time from 15 min to 1 h; record the actual heating period. While the reaction takes place, prepare the chromatographic column. Cool the reaction mixture, add 20 mL of water, and extract with two 25-mL portions of ether. Wash the combined ethereal extracts twice with 15-mL portions of water and once with 25 mL of 3 *M* sodium hydroxide and dry by shaking the ether extracts with 25 mL of saturated sodium chloride solution; then dry the ether over anhydrous calcium chloride pellets for 10 min in an Erlenmeyer flask, filter, and evaporate the ether. Save a few crystals of this material for TLC analysis. Dissolve the residue in 3–4 mL of ether, transfer the solution with a Pasteur pipette onto a column of 12.5 g of silica gel, and rinse the flask with another small portion of ether.[1] In order to apply the ether solution to the top of the sand and avoid having it coat the interior of the column, pipette the solution down a 6-mm-diameter glass tube that is resting on the top of the sand. Label a series of

1. Ideally, the material to be adsorbed is dissolved in hexanes (ligroin), the solvent of lowest elutant power. The present mixture is not soluble enough in hexanes, and so ether is used, but the volume is kept to a minimum.

50-mL Erlenmeyer flasks as fractions 1 to 10. Open the pinchclamp, run the eluant solution into a 50-mL Erlenmeyer flask, and as soon as the solvent in the column has fallen to the level of the upper layer of sand, fill the column with a part of a measured 125 mL of a 70:30 mixture of hexanes and ether. When about 25 mL of eluant has collected in the flask (fraction 1), change to a fresh flask; add a boiling stone to the first flask and evaporate the solution to dryness on a steam bath under an aspirator tube (*see* Fig. 9.7 on page 207). Evacuation using an aspirator helps to remove last traces of ligroin (*see* Figure 9.6 on page 206). If fraction 1 is negative (no residue), use the flask for collecting further fractions. Continue adding the hexanes and ether mixture until the 125-mL portion is exhausted; then use 100 mL of a 1:1 hexanes and ether mixture. A convenient bubbler (Fig. 9.9) made from a 125-mL Erlenmeyer flask, a short piece of 10-mm-diameter glass tubing, and a cork will automatically add solvent. A separatory funnel with a stopper and a partially open stopcock serves the same purpose. Collect and evaporate successive 25-mL fractions of eluant. Save any flask that has any visible solid residue. The ideal method for the removal of solvents involves the use of a rotary evaporator (*see* Fig. 9.8 on page 207). Analyze the original mixture and each fraction by TLC on silica gel plates using a 1:1 mixture of hexanes-ether to develop the plates and either UV light or iodine vapor to visualize the spots.

Cholesteryl acetate (mp 115°C) and cholesterol (mp 149°C) should appear, respectively, in early and late fractions with a few empty fractions (no residue) in between. If so, combine consecutive fractions of early and of late material and determine the weights and melting points. Calculate the percentage of the acetylated material compared to the total recovered and compare your result with those of others in your class employing different reaction periods.

Cleaning Up. After neutralization, acetic acid, the aqueous layers, and the saturated sodium chloride layers from the extraction can be flushed down the drain with water. Ether, hexanes, and TLC solvents should be placed in the organic solvents container. Hexanes and other from the chromatography go into the organic solvents container. If local regulations allow, evaporate any residual solvent from the drying agents and silica gel in the hood and place the dried solid in the nonhazardous waste container. Otherwise, place the wet drying agent and silica gel in waste containers designated for this purpose.

4. Chromatography of a Mixture of Ferrocene and Acetylferrocene

Online Study Center

Photo: Column Chromatography;
Video: Column Chromatography

⚠

CAUTION: Acetylferrocene is toxic.

> **IN THIS EXPERIMENT** a mixture of two compounds is separated by chromatography on alumina. The first compound to come down the column is ferrocene (a yellow band). The solvent polarity is changed so that acetylferrocene is eluted as an orange band. The solvents are evaporated from the collection flasks and the compounds recrystallized. Both of these compounds are colored (see Chapter 49 for their preparation), so it is easy to follow the progress of the chromatographic separation.

Prepare the microscale alumina column exactly as described at the beginning of the chapter. Then add a dry slurry of 90 mg of a 50:50 mixture of acetylferrocene

(a)

Ferrocene
MW 186.04
mp 172–174°C

(b)

CH₃

Acetylferrocene
MW 228.08
mp 85–86°C

■ **FIG. 9.10**
Evaporation of a low-boiling liquid under vacuum. Heat is supplied by the hand, the contents of the flask are swirled, and the vacuum is controlled with the thumb.

To aspirator

Isoprene

and ferrocene that has been adsorbed onto 300 mg of alumina, following the procedure for preparing and adding the sample given at the beginning of the chapter.

Carefully add hexanes to the column, open the valve (use both hands), and elute the two compounds. The first to be eluted, ferrocene, will be seen as a yellow band. Collect this in a 10-mL flask. Any crystalline material seen at the tip of the valve should be washed into the flask with a drop or two of ether. Without allowing the column to run dry, add a 50:50 mixture of hexanes and ether, and elute the acetylferrocene, which will be seen as an orange band. Collect it in a 10-mL flask. Spot a silica gel TLC plate with these two solutions. Evaporate the solvents from the two flasks and determine the weights of the residues. An easy way to evaporate the solvent is to place it in a tared 25-mL filter flask and heat the flask in your hand under vacuum while swirling the contents (Fig. 9.10).

Recrystallize the products from the minimum quantities of hot hexanes. Isolate the crystals, dry them, and determine their weights and melting points. Calculate the percent recovery of the crude and recrystallized products based on the 45 mg of each in the original mixture.

The TLC plate is eluted with a 30:1 mixture of toluene and absolute ethanol. Do you detect any contamination of one compound by the other?

Cleaning Up. If regulations allow, empty the chromatography column onto a piece of aluminum foil in the hood. After the solvent has evaporated, place the alumina and sand in the nonhazardous waste container. Otherwise, place the wet alumina and sand in a designated waste container. Evaporate the crystallization mother liquor to dryness and place the residue in the hazardous waste container.

5. Isolation of Lycopene and β-Carotene

Lycopene, the red pigment in tomatoes, is a C_{40}-carotenoid made up of eight five-carbon isoprene units. β-Carotene, the yellow pigment of the carrot, is an isomer of lycopene in which the double bonds at C_1—C_2 and C'_1—C'_2 are replaced by bonds extending from C_1 to C_6 and from C'_1 to C'_6 to form rings. The chromophore in each case is a system of 11 all-*trans* conjugated double bonds; the closing of the two rings renders β-carotene less highly pigmented than lycopene.

These colored hydrocarbons have been encountered in the TLC experiment (*see* Chapter 8). The isolation procedure described here affords sufficient carotene and lycopene to carry out analytical spectroscopy and some isomerization reactions. It might be of interest if some students isolate carotene from strained carrot baby food while others isolate lycopene from tomato paste.

Lycopene is responsible not only for the red color of tomatoes but also of red grapefruit and flamingos. If flamingos do not include foods containing lycopene in their diet, they will be white.

Until recently, lycopene was thought to have no utility until a study showed a lower incidence of prostate cancer among men who consumed such foods as spaghetti and pizza (but not tomato juice). It is theorized that the lycopene, which is insoluble in water, is dissolved in the fat of pasta sauce and pizza and thus absorbed through the intestine. Carotene does not have the same anticancer effect.

Lycopene (C₄₀H₅₆)
MW 536.85
mp 173°C, λ_{max}^{hexane} 475 nm

β-Carotene (C₄₀H₅₆)
mp 183°C, λ_{max}^{hexane} 451 nm

Lycopene is the predominant carotenoid in blood plasma and prostate tissue. It is not converted into vitamin A as carotene is, but it is a powerful antioxidant and is an efficient scavenger of singlet oxygen.

Carotenoids are highly sensitive to photochemical air oxidation; therefore, protect solutions and solids from undue exposure to light and heat and work as rapidly as possible. Do not heat solutions when evaporating solvents and, if possible, flush apparatus with nitrogen to exclude oxygen. Research workers isolate these compounds in dimly lit rooms and/or wrap all containers and chromatographic columns in aluminum foil and carry out extractions and crystallizations using solvents that have been deoxygenated.

Dehydration and Extraction of Tomato or Carrot Paste

> **IN THIS EXPERIMENT** a vegetable paste is stirred with acetone to remove water, but not the coloring matter, from the paste. The mixture is filtered, the yellow filtrate discarded, and the material on the filter squeezed as dry as possible. This solid is then extracted three times with dichloromethane; the solution is dried over calcium chloride and evaporated at room temperature under vacuum to leave the crude carotenoids.

Add 5 g of tomato or carrot paste to a 15-mL centrifuge tube or 25 × 150-mm test tube; then add about 7 mL of acetone and stir the paste for several minutes until it is no longer gummy. This acetone treatment removes most of the water from the cellular mixture. Filter the mixture on a small Büchner funnel. Scrape out the tube with a spatula, let it drain thoroughly, and squeeze out as much liquid as possible from the solid residue in the funnel with a spatula. Discard the yellow filtrate. Then return the solid residue to the centrifuge tube and add 5 mL of dichloromethane to effect extraction. Cap the tube and shake the mixture vigorously. Filter the mixture on a Büchner funnel once more, repeat the extraction and filtration with two or three further 5-mL portions of dichloromethane, clean the tube thoroughly, and place the filtrates in it. Dry the solution over anhydrous calcium chloride pellets, filter the solution into a small flask, and evaporate the solution to dryness with a stream of nitrogen or under vacuum using a rotary evaporator (Fig. 9.8 on page 207) or the apparatus shown in Figure 9.10 on page 211, never heating the sample above 50°C.

Determine the weight of the crude material. It will be very small. If the residue is dry, as it should be, add just enough dichloromethane to dissolve the residue. Save 1 drop of this solution to carry out a TLC analysis (using dichloromethane as the eluent on silica gel plates; *see* Chapter 8). Then add 200 mg of alumina to the remaining dichloromethane solution and evaporate the mixture to dryness, again without heat.

Column Chromatography

Online Study Center

Video: Column Chromatography;
Photo: Column Chromatography

The crude carotenoid is to be chromatographed on an 8-cm column of basic or neutral alumina, prepared with hexanes as solvent (see the detailed procedure at the beginning of this chapter). Run out excess solvent or remove it from the top of the chromatography column with a Pasteur pipette. Using the dry sample loading method described at the beginning of this chapter, add the 300 mg of alumina that has the crude carotenoids absorbed on it. Add a few drops of hexanes to wash down the inside of the chromatography column and to consolidate the carotenoid mixture at the top of the column. Elute the column with hexanes, discard the initial colorless eluate, and collect all yellow or orange eluates together. Place a drop of solution on a microscope slide and evaporate the remainder to dryness using a stream of nitrogen or a rotary evaporator (*see* Fig. 9.8 on page 207). Examination of the material spotted on the slide may reveal crystallinity. If you are using tomato paste, a small amount of yellow β-carotene will come off first, followed by lycopene. Collect the red lycopene separately by eluting with a mixture of 10% acetone in hexane and also evaporate that solution to dryness.

Finally, dissolve the samples obtained by evaporating the solvent in the least possible amount of dichloromethane and carry out TLC of the two products in order to ascertain their purity (*see* Chapter 8, Experiment 2). You may want to combine your purified products with those of several other students, evaporate the solution to dryness, dissolve the residue in deuterochloroform, $CDCl_3$, and determine the ^1H NMR spectrum (*see* Chapter 12). Also obtain an infrared spectrum and a visible spectrum (in hexane).

Note that β-carotene is in demand as a source of vitamin A and is manufactured by an efficient synthesis. Until very recently no use for lycopene had been found.

Cleaning Up. Place recovered and unused dichloromethane in the halogenated organic waste container; the solvents used for TLC in the organic solvents container. If local regulations allow, evaporate any residual solvent from the drying agents in the hood and place the dried solid in the nonhazardous waste container. Otherwise, place the wet drying agent in a waste container designated for this purpose. Used plant material and dry TLC plates can be discarded in the nonhazardous waste container.

For Further Investigation

The carotenoids of any leaf can be isolated in the manner described in this experiment. Grind the leaf material (about 10 g) in a mortar with some sand; then follow the above procedure. Waxy leaves do not work well. The carotenoids are present in the leaf during its entire life span, so a green leaf from a maple tree or euonymus shrub, also known as burning bush, known to turn bright red in the fall will show lycopene even when the leaf is green. In the fall the chlorophyll decomposes before the carotenoids, so the leaves appear in a variety of orange and red hues.

It is of interest to investigate the carotenoids of the tomato, of which there are some 80 varieties. The orange-colored tangerine tomato contains an isomer of lycopene. If a hexane solution of the prolycopene from this tomato is treated with a drop of a very dilute solution of iodine in hexane and then exposed to bright light, the solution will turn deep-orange in color, indicating that a *cis*-double bond has isomerized to the *trans* form. The product is, however, still not identical to natural lycopene.

Isomerization

Prepare a hexane solution of either carotene or lycopene and save a drop for TLC. Treat the solution with a very dilute solution of iodine in hexane, expose the resulting mixture to strong light for a few minutes, and then carry out TLC on the resulting solution. Also compare the visible spectrum before and after isomerization.

Iodine serves as a catalyst for the light-catalyzed isomerization of some of the *trans*-double bonds to an equilibrium mixture containing *cis*-isomers.

QUESTIONS

1. Predict the order of elution of a mixture of triphenylmethanol, biphenyl, benzoic acid, and methyl benzoate from an alumina column.
2. What would be the effect of collecting larger fractions when carrying out the experiments in this chapter?
3. What would have been the result if a large quantity of petroleum ether alone were used as the eluent in either of the experiments described?
4. Once the chromatographic column has been prepared, why is it important to allow the level of the liquid in the column to drop to the level of the alumina before applying the solution of the compound to be separated?
5. A chemist started to carry out column chromatography on a Friday afternoon, reached the point at which the two compounds being separated were about three-fourths of the way down the column, and then returned on Monday to find that the compounds came off the column as a mixture. Speculate the reason for this. The column had not run dry over the weekend.
6. Write a detailed mechanism for the formation of fluorenone from fluorene. Explain the purpose of the phase-transfer catalyst.
7. The primary cause of low yields in the isolation of lycopene is oxidation of the product during the procedure. Once crystalline, it is reasonably stable. Speculate on the primary products formed by photochemical air oxidation of lycopene.

Online Study Center

General Resources
Web Links

CHAPTER
58

The Synthesis of an Alkyne from an Alkene; Bromination and Dehydrobromination: Stilbene and Diphenylacetylene

Online Study Center

This icon will direct you to techniques, equipment setups, and online resources at http://college.hmco.com/ PIC/williamsonMMOE5e.

PRELAB EXERCISE: Calculate the theoretical quantities of thionyl chloride and sodium borohydride needed to convert benzoin to *E*-stilbene.

E-Stilbene
mp 125°C, MW 180.24
λ_{max}^{EtOH} 301 nm (ϵ = 28,500)
226 nm (ϵ = 17,700)

Heat of hydrogenation, −20.1 kcal/mol

Z-Stilbene
mp 6°C, MW 180.24
λ_{max}^{EtOH} 280 nm (ϵ = 13,500)
223 nm (ϵ = 23,500)

Heat of hydrogenation, −25.8 kcal/mol

In this chapter's experiments, benzoin, which was prepared in Chapter 53, is converted to the alkene *trans*-stilbene (*E*-stilbene), which is in turn brominated and dehydrobrominated to form diphenylacetylene, an alkyne.

One method of preparing *E*-stilbene is the reduction of benzoin with zinc amalgam in a mixture of ethanol and hydrochloric acid, presumably through an intermediate:

Benzoin

$\xrightarrow[\text{EtOH}]{\text{Zn/Hg, HCl}}$

$\xrightarrow{-\text{H}_2\text{O}}$

E-Stilbene

The procedure that follows is quick and affords very pure hydrocarbon. It involves three steps: (1) replacing the hydroxyl group of benzoin by chlorine to form desyl chloride, (2) reducing the keto group with sodium borohydride to give what appears to be a mixture of the two diastereoisomeric chlorohydrins, and (3) eliminating the elements of hypochlorous acid with zinc and acetic acid. The last step is analogous to the debromination of an olefin dibromide.

Benzoin
MW 212.24

$\xrightarrow[\substack{\text{Thionyl} \\ \text{chloride} \\ \text{MW 118.97}}]{\text{SOCl}_2}$

Desyl chloride
mp 68°C

$\xrightarrow[\substack{\text{Sodium} \\ \text{borohydride} \\ \text{MW 37.85}}]{\text{NaBH}_4}$

Mixture of both diasteromers

$\xrightarrow{\text{Zn/HOAc}}$

E-Stilbene

The minimum energy conformations of *E*- and *Z*-stilbene are shown in Figures 58.1 and 58.2, respectively. These have been calculated using Spartan's

■ **FIG. 58.1**
The minimum energy conformation of *E*-stilbene.

■ **FIG. 58.2**
The minimum energy conformation of *Z*-stilbene.

molecular mechanics routine.[1] Note that the *E*-isomer is planar, whereas the *Z*-isomer is markedly distorted from planarity.

EXPERIMENTS

1. Stilbene

IN THIS EXPERIMENT the hydroxyl group of solid benzoin is converted to a chloride by heating with liquid thionyl chloride, which acts as both a solvent and a reactant. The hydrogen chloride that is evolved is captured in a gas trap. The thionyl chloride is evaporated under vacuum to leave the oily product—a keto chloride. This material is dissolved in ethanol and reduced to a mixture of isomeric hydroxy chlorides (chlorohydrins) with sodium borohydride. Without isolation this solution of chlorohydrins is reduced again, this time with zinc dust and acetic acid. This process removes the elements of hypochlorus acid (HOCl) to give the product—stilbene.

Microscale Procedure

Place 100 mg of benzoin (crushed to a powder) in a reaction tube, cover it with 0.15 mL of thionyl chloride, and add a boiling chip and a rubber septum bearing a polyethylene tube leading to another reaction tube bearing a plug of damp cotton (Fig. 58.3). This will serve to trap the hydrogen chloride and sulfur dioxide

■ **FIG. 58.3**
A trap for hydrogen chloride and sulfur dioxide. Warm the tubing in a steam bath to bend it permanently.

Polyethylene tubing

Rubber septum

Reaction tubes

Damp cotton

Thionyl chloride and benzoin

1. Spartan molecular modeling software is available from Wavefunction, Inc., Irvine, California.

■ FIG. 58.4
The Pasteur pipette filtration
technique.

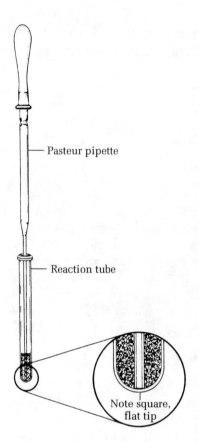

— Pasteur pipette

— Reaction tube

Note square,
flat tip

evolved in this reaction. Warm the reaction mixture gently on a steam bath or on
a warm sand bath until the solid has dissolved and then more strongly for 5 min.

Caution: If the mixture of benzoin and thionyl chloride is allowed to stand at
room temperature for an appreciable time before being heated, an undesired reaction intervenes,[2] and the synthesis of *E*-stilbene is spoiled.

To remove excess thionyl chloride (bp 77°C), connect the reaction tube to an
aspirator for a few minutes, add 0.5 mL of petroleum ether (bp 30°C–60°C), boil it
off, and evacuate again. Desyl chloride is thus obtained as a viscous, pale-yellow oil
(it will solidify on standing). Dissolve it in 1 mL of 95% ethanol, cool under the tap,
and add 9 mg of sodium borohydride (an excess is harmful to the success of the reaction). Stir to break up any lumps of the borohydride; after 10 min, add to the solution of chlorohydrins 60 mg of zinc dust and 0.15 mL of acetic acid; then reflux
for 1 h and cool under the tap. When white crystals separate, add 2 mL of *t*-butyl
methyl ether, wash the ether solution once with an equal volume of water containing 1 drop of concentrated hydrochloric acid (to dissolve basic zinc salts), and then
wash with water. Dry the ether over calcium chloride pellets, which is added until it
no longer clumps together. Remove the ether from the drying agent with a Pasteur
pipette (Fig. 58.4), wash the drying agent with ether, evaporate the ether to dryness

2. $C_6H_5C{=}O$
$|$
C_6H_5CHOH $\xrightarrow{SOCl_2}$ C_6H_5C-O
$\underset{C_6H_5C-O}{\overset{\parallel}{}}{>}SO$ $\xrightarrow{NaBH_4}$ C_6H_5CO
$|$
$C_6H_5CH_2$

Desoxybenzoin

under the hood, dissolve the residue in a minimum amount of hot 95% ethanol (about 1 mL), and let the product crystallize. *E*-Stilbene separates in diamond-shaped iridescent plates (mp 124°C–125°C); the yield is about 50 mg. *E*-Stilbene can be isolated easily using the Pasteur pipette technique (Fig. 58.4) or a Wilfilter (*see* Fig. 4.14 on page 74).

Cleaning Up. Combine the washings from the cotton in the trap and all aqueous layers, neutralize with sodium carbonate, remove zinc salts by vacuum filtration, and flush the filtrate down the drain with excess water. The zinc salts are placed in the nonhazardous solid waste container. Allow the ether to evaporate from the calcium chloride pellets in the hood and then place the drying agent in the nonhazardous solid waste container. If local regulations do not allow for the evaporation of solvents in a hood, the wet solid should be disposed in a special container. Ethanol mother liquor goes in the organic solvents container. Spread out any isolated zinc on a watch glass to dry and air oxidize. Wet it with water and place in the nonhazardous solid waste container.

Macroscale Procedure

Place 2 g of benzoin (crushed to a powder) in a 50-mL round-bottomed flask, cover it with 4 mL of thionyl chloride,[3] warm gently on a steam bath (in the hood) until all the solid has dissolved, and then heat more strongly for 5 min.

Caution: If the mixture of benzoin and thionyl chloride is left standing at room temperature for an appreciable time before being heated, an undesired reaction intervenes,[4] and the synthesis of *E*-stilbene is spoiled.

To remove excess thionyl chloride (bp 77°C), evacuate on an aspirator for a few minutes, add 5 mL of petroleum ether (bp 30°C–60°C), boil it off (in the hood), and again evacuate. Desyl chloride is thus obtained as a viscous, pale-yellow oil (it will solidify on standing). Dissolve it in 20 mL of 95% ethanol, cool under the tap, and add 180 mg of sodium borohydride (an excess is harmful to the success of the reaction). Stir to break up any lumps of the borohydride; after 10 min, add to the solution of chlorohydrins 1 g of zinc dust and 2 mL of acetic acid and reflux for 1 h. Then cool under the tap. When white crystals separate, add 25 mL of *t*-butyl methyl ether and decant the solution from the bulk of the zinc into a separatory funnel. Wash the solution twice with an equal volume of water containing 0.5–1 mL of concentrated hydrochloric acid (to dissolve basic zinc salts) and then, in turn, with sodium carbonate solution and saturated sodium chloride solution. Dry the ether over anhydrous calcium chloride pellets (2 g), filter

Sometimes zinc dust from a reaction like this is pyrophoric (spontaneously flammable in air) because it is so finely divided and has such a large, clean surface area able to react with air.

Carry out the procedure in the hood.

---

3. The reagent can be dispensed from a burette or measured by pipette; in the latter case the liquid should be drawn into the pipette with a pipette bulb, *not by mouth.*

4.

$$\underset{\underset{\displaystyle C_6H_5CHOH}{|}}{C_6H_5C=O} \xrightarrow{\text{SOCl}_2} \underset{\underset{\displaystyle C_6H_5C-O}{\|}}{\overset{C_6H_5C-O}{}}\!\!\!SO \xrightarrow{\text{NaBH}_4} \underset{\underset{\displaystyle C_6H_5CH_2}{|}}{C_6H_5CO}$$

Desoxybenzoin

■ **FIG. 58.5**
The UV spectra of *Z*- and
E-stilbene. *Z*: λ_{max}^{EtOH} = 224 nm
(ε = 23,300) and 279 nm
(ε = 11,100); *E*: λ_{max}^{EtOH} = 226 nm
(ε = 18,300) and 295 nm
(ε = 27,500). As in the diacetates,
steric hindrance and the lack
of coplanarity in these
hydrocarbons cause the
long-wavelength absorption of
the *Z*-isomer to be of diminished
intensity relative to the *E*-isomer.

Wavelength (nm)

to remove the drying agent, evaporate the filtrate to dryness under the hood, dissolve the residue in a minimum amount of hot 95% ethanol (15–20 mL), and let the product crystallize. *E*-Stilbene separates in diamond-shaped iridescent plates (mp 124°C–125°C); the yield is about 1 g. The UV spectrum is shown in Figure 58.5.

Cleaning Up. Combine the washings from the cotton in the trap and all aqueous layers, neutralize with sodium carbonate, remove zinc salts by vacuum filtration, and flush the filtrate down the drain with excess water. The zinc salts are placed in the nonhazardous solid waste container. Allow the ether to evaporate from the calcium chloride in the hood and then place it in the nonhazardous solid waste container. If local regulations do not allow for the evaporation of solvents in a hood, the wet solid should be disposed in a special container. Ethanol mother liquor goes in the organic solvents container. Any zinc isolated should be spread out on a watch glass to dry and air oxidize. It should then be wetted with water and placed in the nonhazardous solid waste container.

> Sometimes zinc dust from a
> reaction like this is pyrophoric
> (spontaneously flammable in air)
> because it is so finely divided and
> has such a large, clean surface
> area able to react with air.

2. *meso*-Stilbene Dibromide

> **IN THIS EXPERIMENT** an acetic acid solution of stilbene, an alkene, is brominated with a solid bromine donor to give a dibromide that crystallizes and is isolated by filtration.

E-Stilbene reacts with bromine predominantly by the usual process of *trans*-addition and affords the optically inactive, nonresolvable *meso*-dibromide; the much lower melting enantiomeric mixture of dibromides is a very minor product of the reaction.

Pyridine + HBr + Br$_2$

↓

Pyridinium hydrobromide perbromide

In this procedure, the brominating agent will be pyridinium hydrobromide perbromide,[5] a crystalline, nonvolatile, odorless complex of high molecular weight (319.86), which dissociates, in the presence of a bromine acceptor such as an alkene, to liberate 1 mol of bromine. For microscale experiments the perbromide is far more convenient and agreeable to measure and use than free bromine.

E-Stilbene MW 180.24	**Pyridinium hydro-bromide perbromide** MW 319.86	**(1R,2S)-*meso*-Stilbene dibromide** mp 236–237°C, MW 340.07

Microscale Procedure

In a reaction tube, dissolve 50 mg of *E*-stilbene in 1 mL of acetic acid by heating on a steam bath or a hot water bath; then add 100 mg of pyridinium hydrobromide perbromide. Mix by swirling; if necessary, rinse crystals of the reagent down the walls of the flask with a little acetic acid and continue the heating for an additional 1–2 min. The dibromide separates in small plates. Cool this mixture under the tap, collect the product on a Wilfilter (*see* Fig. 4.14 on page 74) or on a Hirsch funnel, and wash it with methanol to remove any color; the yield of colorless crystals (mp 236°C–237°C) is 80 mg. Use this material to prepare the diphenylacetylene after determining the percent yield and the melting point.

Cleaning Up. To the filtrate add sodium bisulfite (until a negative test with starch-iodide paper is observed) to destroy any remaining perbromide, neutralize with sodium carbonate, and extract the pyridine released with ether, which goes in the organic solvents container. The aqueous layer can then be diluted with water and flushed down the drain.

⚠ **CAUTION**: Pyridinium hydrobromide perbromide is corrosive and a lachrymator (tear producer).

Carry out the procedure in the hood.

Online Study Center

Photo: Use of the Wilfilter; Video: Microscale Filtration on the Hirsch Funnel

Total time required: 10 min

5. Crystalline pyridinium hydrobromide perbromide suitable for small-scale experiments is available from the Aldrich Chemical Company. Massive crystals commercially available should be recrystallized from acetic acid (4 mL/g). Pyridinium hydrobromide perbromide can also be prepared as follows: Mix 15 mL of pyridine with 30 mL of 48% hydrobromic acid and cool. Add 25 g of bromine gradually with swirling, cool, and collect the product (use acetic acid for rinsing and washing). Without drying the solid, crystallize it from 100 mL of acetic acid. The yield of orange needles should be 33 g (69%).

Macroscale Procedure

In a 50-mL Erlenmeyer flask dissolve 1 g of *E*-stilbene in 20 mL of acetic acid, by heating on a steam bath; then add 2 g of pyridinium hydrobromide perbromide.[6] Mix by swirling; if necessary, rinse crystals of the reagent down the walls of the flask with a little acetic acid; continue the heating for an additional 1–2 min. The dibromide separates almost at once in small plates. Cool the mixture under the tap, collect the product, and wash it with methanol; the yield of colorless crystals (mp 236°C–237°C) is about 1.6 g. Use 0.5 g of this material to prepare the diphenylacetylene and turn in the remainder to your instructor.

Cleaning Up. To the filtrate add sodium bisulfite (until a negative test with starch-iodide paper is observed) to destroy any remaining perbromide, neutralize with sodium carbonate, and extract the pyridine released during the reaction with ether, which goes in the organic solvents container. The aqueous layer can then be diluted with water and flushed down the drain.

CAUTION: Pyridium hydrobromide perbromide is corrosive and a lachrymator (tear producer).

Carry out the procedure in the hood.

Total time required: 10 min

3. Synthesis of Diphenylacetylene

$$H_2NNH_2$$ ... HOCH$_2$CH$_2$OCH$_2$CH$_2$OCH$_2$CH$_2$OH

+ 2 KOH, MW 56.00, Triethylene glycol, bp 290°C

(1R,2S)-*meso*-Stilbene dibromide
MW 340.07

Diphenylacetylene
mp 61°C, MW 178.22

One method for the preparation of diphenylacetylene involves the oxidation of benzil dihydrazone with mercuric oxide; the intermediate diazo compound loses nitrogen as it is formed to give the hydrocarbon:

Benzil + 2 H$_2$NNH$_2$ → **Benzil hydrazone** $\xrightarrow{\text{HgO} / C_6H_6}$ ... $\xrightarrow{-2 N_2}$ **Diphenylacetylene**

---

6. *See* footnote 5.

The method used in the following procedure involves the dehydrohalogenation of *meso*-stilbene dibromide. An earlier procedure in the chemical literature called for refluxing the dibromide with 43% ethanolic potassium hydroxide in an oil bath at 140°C for 24 h. In the following procedure the reaction time is reduced to a few minutes by using high-boiling triethylene glycol as the solvent to permit operation at a higher reaction temperature, a technique introduced by Louis Fieser.

IN THIS EXPERIMENT a solution of stilbene dibromide in a very high-boiling solvent reacts with potassium hydroxide to remove 2 mol of HBr to give an alkyne. After the reaction mixture is diluted with water, the product crystallizes, is isolated by filtration, and is recrystallized from ethanol to give pure diphenylacetylene.

Microscale Procedure

In a reaction tube place 80 mg of *meso*-stilbene dibromide, 40 mg of potassium hydroxide,[7] and 0.5 mL of triethylene glycol. Heat the mixture on a hot sand bath to 160°C, at which point potassium bromide begins to separate. By intermittent heating, keep the mixture at 160°C–170°C for an additional 5 min; then cool to room temperature, remove the thermometer, and add 2 mL of water. The diphenylacetylene that separates as a nearly colorless, granular solid is collected with a Pasteur pipette. The crude product need not be dried but can be crystallized directly from 95% ethanol. Let the solution stand undisturbed to observe the formation of beautiful, very large spars of colorless crystals. After a first crop has been collected, the mother liquor can be concentrated to afford a second crop of pure product; the total yield is 35 mg (mp 60°C–61°C).

Cleaning Up. Combine the crystallization mother liquor with the filtrate from the reaction, dilute with water, neutralize with 3 *M* hydrochloric acid, and flush down the drain.

Macroscale Procedure

In a 20 × 150-mm test tube place 0.5 g of *meso*-stilbene dibromide, 3 pellets of potassium hydroxide[8] (250 mg), and 2 mL of triethylene glycol. Insert a thermometer into a 10 × 75-mm test tube containing enough triethylene glycol to cover the bulb and then slip this assembly into the larger tube. Clamp the tube in a vertical position in a hot sand bath and heat the mixture to 160°C, at which point potassium bromide begins to separate. By intermittent heating, keep the mixture at 160°C–170°C for an additional 5 min; then cool to room temperature, remove the thermometer and small tube, and add 10 mL of water. The diphenylacetylene that separates as a nearly colorless, granular solid is collected by suction filtration. The

CAUTION: Potassium hydroxide is corrosive to skin.

Reaction time: 5 min

Online Study Center

Photo: Filtration Using a Pasteur Pipette; Video: Filtration of Crystals Using the Pasteur Pipette

CAUTION: Potassium hydroxide is corrosive to skin.

Reaction time: 5 min

---

7. Potassium hydroxide pellets consist of 85% KOH and 15% water.

8. *See* footnote 7.

■ **FIG. 58.6**

The UV spectrum of diphenylacetylene. $\lambda_{max}^{EtOH} = 279$ nm ($\varepsilon = 31,400$). This spectrum is characterized by considerable fine structure (multiplicity of bands) and a high extinction coefficient.

Wavelength (nm)

crude product need not be dried but can be crystallized directly from 95% ethanol. Let the solution stand undisturbed to observe the formation of beautiful, very large spars of colorless crystals. After a first crop has been collected, the mother liquor can be concentrated to afford a second crop of pure product; the total yield is about 0.23 g (mp 60°C–61°C). The UV spectrum is shown in Figure 58.6.

Cleaning Up. Combine the crystallization mother liquor with the filtrate from the reaction, dilute with water, neutralize with 3 *M* hydrochloric acid, and flush down the drain.

QUESTIONS

1. Using a molecular mechanics program, calculate the energy difference or the difference in heats of formation between *Z*- and *E*-stilbene. How do your computed values compare to the difference in heats of hydrogenation of the two isomers (refer to the structures on the first page of this chapter)?
2. Why is *Z*-stilbene not planar? Explain.
3. How do you account for the large difference in the extinction coefficients (ε) for the long-wavelength peaks for *Z*- and *E*-stilbene (*see* Fig. 58.5 on page 734)?

Nucleophilic Substitution
Reactions of Alkyl Halides

Online Study Center

This icon will direct you to
techniques, equipment setups,
and online resources at
http://college.hmco.com/PIC/
williamsonMMOE5e.

PRELAB EXERCISE: Predict the outcomes of the two sets of
experiments to be carried out with the 11 halides used in this
chapter.

The alkyl halides, R—X (where X = Cl, Br, I, and sometimes F), play a
central role in organic synthesis. These can easily be prepared from, among
others, alcohols, alkenes, and, industrially, alkanes. In turn, they are the starting
materials for the synthesis of a large number of new functional groups. The syntheses are often carried out by nucleophilic substitution reactions in which the
halide is replaced by another group such as cyano, hydroxyl, ether, ester, alkyl—
the list is long. As a consequence of the importance of this substitution reaction, it
has been studied carefully by employing reactions such as the two used in this
chapter. Some of the questions that can be asked are as follows:

- How does the structure of the alkyl part of the alkyl halide affect the
  reaction?
- What is the effect of changing the . . .

  nature of the halide?
  nature of the solvent?
  relative concentrations of the reactants?
  temperature of the reaction?
  nature of the nucleophile?

In this chapter we explore the answers to some of these questions.

In free radical reactions the covalent bond undergoes homolysis when it
breaks:

$$R\!:\!\ddot{\underset{\cdot\cdot}{Cl}}\!: \longrightarrow R\!\cdot\; +\; \cdot\ddot{\underset{\cdot\cdot}{Cl}}\!:$$

A carbocation is planar and has an empty *p*-orbital.

Order of carbocation stability

Nucleophilic substitution

One step

Two steps

Reaction kinetics

whereas in ionic reactions it undergoes heterolysis:

$$R{:}\ddot{C}l{:} \longrightarrow R^+ + {:}\ddot{C}l{:}^-$$

A carbocation is often formed as a reactive intermediate in these reactions. This carbocation is sp^2 hybridized and trigonal-planar in structure with a vacant *p*-orbital. Much experimental evidence of the type obtained in this chapter indicates that the order of stability of carbocations is

$$
\begin{array}{cccc}
\quad R & \quad R & \quad H & \quad H \\
\quad | & \quad | & \quad | & \quad | \\
R\!-\!C^+ > & R\!-\!C^+ > & R\!-\!C^+ > & H\!-\!C^+ \\
\quad | & \quad | & \quad | & \quad | \\
\quad R & \quad H & \quad H & \quad H
\end{array}
$$

The alkyl (R) groups stabilize the positive charge of the carbocation by displacing or releasing electrons toward the positive charge. As the number of alkyl groups attached to the carbocation increases, the stabilization increases.

Many organic reactions occur when a nucleophile (a species with an unshared pair of electrons) reacts with an alkyl halide to replace the halogen with the nucleophile.

$$Nu{:}^- + R{:}\ddot{X}{:} \longrightarrow Nu{:}R + {:}\ddot{X}{:}^-$$

This substitution reaction can occur in one smooth step:

$$Nu{:}^- + R{:}\ddot{X}{:} \longrightarrow \left[\overset{\delta-}{Nu} \cdots R \cdots \overset{\delta-}{\ddot{X}{:}} \right] \longrightarrow Nu{:}R + {:}\ddot{X}{:}^-$$

or it can occur in two discrete steps:

$$R{:}\ddot{X}{:} \longrightarrow R^+ + {:}\ddot{X}{:}^-$$

$$Nu{:}^- + R^+ \longrightarrow Nu{:}R$$

depending primarily on the structure of the R group. The nucleophile ($Nu{:}^-$) can be a substance with a full negative charge, such as $:\ddot{I}:^-$ or $H{:}\ddot{O}:^-$, or an uncharged molecule with an unshared pair of electrons such as exists on the oxygen atom in water, $H{-}\ddot{O}{-}H$. Not all of the halides, $:\ddot{X}:^-$, depart with equal ease in nucleophilic substitution reactions. In this chapter we investigate the ease with which the different halogens leave in one of the substitution reactions.

To distinguish between the reaction that occurs as one smooth step and the reaction that occurs as two discrete steps, it is necessary to study the kinetics of the reaction. If the reaction were carried out with several different concentrations of $R{:}\ddot{X}{:}^-$ and $Nu{:}^-$, we could determine if the reaction is bimolecular or unimolecular.

In the case of the smooth, one-step reaction, the nucleophile must collide with the alkyl halide. The kinetics of the reaction

$$\text{Nu:}^- + \text{R:}\ddot{\text{X}}: \longrightarrow \left[\overset{\delta-}{\text{Nu}} \cdots \text{R} \cdots \overset{\delta-}{\ddot{\text{X}}:} \right] \longrightarrow \text{Nu:R} + :\ddot{\text{X}}:^-$$

$$\text{Rate} = k\left[\text{Nu:}^- \right]\left[\text{R} :\ddot{\text{X}}: \right]$$

are found to depend on the concentration of both the nucleophile and the halide. Such a reaction is said to be a bimolecular nucleophilic substitution reaction, S_N2. If the reaction occurs as a two-step process,

$$\text{R:}\ddot{\text{X}}: \xrightarrow{\text{slow}} \text{R}^+ + :\ddot{\text{X}}:^-$$

$$\text{Nu:}^- + \text{R}^+ \xrightarrow{\text{fast}} \text{Nu:R}$$

$$\text{Rate} = k\left[\text{R:}\ddot{\text{X}}: \right]$$

the rate of the first step, the slow step, depends only on the concentration of the halide, and it is said to be a unimolecular nucleophilic substitution reaction, S_N1.

The S_N1 reaction proceeds through a planar carbocation. Even if the starting material were chiral, the product would be a 50:50 mixture of enantiomers because the planar intermediate can form a bond with the nuceophile on either face.

Racemization: S_N1

Chiral alkyl chloride   **Planar carbocation**

(1)

(2)

Enantiomers

Inversion: S_N2

The S_N2 reaction occurs with inversion of configuration to give a product of the opposite chirality from the starting material.

$$Nu:^- \; + \quad \underset{D\;\;R}{\overset{H}{C}}{-}Cl \quad \longrightarrow \quad \overset{\delta^-}{Nu}\text{------}\underset{D\;\;R}{\overset{H}{C}}\text{------}\overset{\delta^-}{Cl} \quad \longrightarrow \quad Nu{-}\underset{R\;\;D}{\overset{H}{C}} \; + \; :\ddot{\underset{..}{Cl}}:^-$$

The order of reactivity for *simple* alkyl halides in the S_N2 reaction is

Order of S_N2 reactivity

$$CH_3{-}X > R{-}CH_2{-}X > R{-}\underset{R}{\overset{|}{\underset{|}{C}}}H{-}X > R{-}\underset{R}{\overset{R}{\underset{|}{\overset{|}{C}}}}{-}X$$

The tertiary halide is in parentheses because it usually does not react by an S_N2 mechanism. The primary factor in this order of reactivity is steric hindrance, that is, the ease with which the nucleophile can come within bonding distance of the alkyl halide; 2,2-dimethyl-1-bromopropane, even though it is a primary halide, reacts 100,000 times slower than ethyl bromide (CH_3CH_2Br) because of steric hindrance to attack on the bromine atom in the dimethyl compound.

Steric hindrance toward S_N2

$$CH_3{-}\underset{CH_3}{\overset{CH_3}{\underset{|}{\overset{|}{C}}}}{-}CH_2{-}Br \qquad CH_3CH_2Br$$

$$Rate = 1 \qquad\qquad Rate = 100,000$$

The primary factor in S_N1 reactivity is the relative stability of the carbocation that is formed. For simple alkyl halides, this means that only tertiary halides react by this mechanism. The tertiary halide must be able to form a planar carbocation. Only slightly less reactive are the allyl carbocations, which derive their great stability from the delocalization of the charge on the carbon by resonance.

The allyl carbocation

$$CH_2{=}CH{-}CH_2{-}\ddot{\underset{..}{Br}}: \quad \longrightarrow \quad CH_2{=}CH{-}\overset{+}{CH_2} \quad \longleftrightarrow \quad \overset{+}{CH_2}{-}CH{=}CH_2 \; + \; :\ddot{\underset{..}{Br}}:^-$$

Solvent effects

The nature of the solvent has a large effect on the rates of S_N2 reactions. In a solvent with a hydrogen atom attached to an electronegative atom such as oxygen, the protic solvent forms hydrogen bonds to the nucleophile. These solvent molecules get in the way during an S_N2 reaction.

Aprotic: no ionizable protons

If the solvent is polar and aprotic, solvation of the nucleophile cannot occur, and the S_N2 reaction can occur up to a million times faster. Some common polar, aprotic solvents are N,N-dimethylformamide and dimethylsulfoxide:

N,N-Dimethylformamide   **Dimethylsulfoxide**

In the S_N1 reaction a polar protic solvent such as water stabilizes the transition state more than it does the reactants, lowering the energy of activation for the reaction and thus increasing the rate, relative to the rate in a nonpolar solvent. Acetic acid, ethanol, and acetone are relatively nonpolar solvents and have lower dielectric constants than the polar solvents water, dimethylsulfoxide, and N,N-dimethylformamide.

The leaving group

The rate of S_N1 and S_N2 reactions depends on the nature of the leaving group, the best leaving groups being the ones that form stable ions. Among the halogens we find that the iodide ion (I^-) is the best leaving group as well as the best nucleophile in the S_N2 reaction.

Vinylic and aryl halides

do not normally react by S_N1 reactions because the resulting carbocations

TABLE 17.1 • Summary of S$_N$1 and S$_N$2 Reactions

	Unimolecular Nucleophilic Substitution (S$_N$1)	Second-Order Nucleophilic Substitution (S$_N$2)
Kinetics	First order	Second order
Mechanism	Two steps; unimolecular in the rate-determining step via a carbocation	One-step, bimolecular
Stereochemistry	Racemization predominates	Inversion of configuration
Reactivity of structure	$3° > 2° > 1° > CH_3 >$ vinyl	$3° < 2° < 1° < CH_3 <$ vinyl
Rearrangements	May occur	No rearrangements because no carbocation intermediate
Effect of leaving group	$—I > —Br > —Cl >> —F$	$—I > —Br > —Cl >> —F$
Effect of nucleophile	Not important because it is not in the rate-determining step	$I^- > Br^- > Cl^- > F^-$
Concentration of nucleophile	S$_N$1 is favored by low concentration	S$_N$2 is favored by high concentration
Solvent polarity	High, favors S$_N$1	Low, favors S$_N$2

are relatively difficult to form. For S$_N$2 reactions, electrons in the nearby double bonds repel the nucleophile, which is either an ion or a polarized neutral species.

Temperature dependence   The rates of both S$_N$1 and S$_N$2 reactions depend on the temperature of the reaction. As the temperature increases, the kinetic energy of the molecules increases, leading to a greater rate of reaction. The rate of many organic reactions will approximately double when the temperature increases about 10°C. This information is summarized in Table 17.1.

EXPERIMENTS

In the experiments that follow, 11 representative alkyl halides are treated with sodium iodide in acetone and with an ethanolic solution of silver nitrate.

1. Sodium Iodide in Acetone

Acetone, with a dielectric constant of 21, is a relatively nonpolar solvent that will readily dissolve sodium iodide. The iodide ion is an excellent nucleophile, and the nonpolar solvent (acetone) favors the S$_N$2 reaction; it does not favor ionization of the alkyl halide. The extent of reaction can be observed because sodium bromide and sodium chloride are not soluble in acetone and precipitate from solution if a reaction occurs.

Organic halides that can react by an S$_N$2 mechanism give a precipitate of NaX with sodium iodide in acetone.

$$Na^+I^- + R{—}Cl \longrightarrow R{—}I + NaCl\downarrow$$

$$Na^+I^- + R{—}Br \longrightarrow R{—}I + NaBr\downarrow$$

2. Ethanolic Silver Nitrate Solution

When an alkyl halide is treated with an ethanolic solution of silver nitrate, the silver ion coordinates with an electron pair of the halogen. This weakens the carbon-halogen bond because a molecule of insoluble silver halide is formed, thus promoting an S_N1 reaction of the alkyl halide. The solvent, ethanol, favors ionization of the halide, and the nitrate ion is a very poor nucleophile, so alkyl nitrates do not form by an S_N2 reaction.

Organic halides that can react by an S_N1 mechanism give a precipitate of AgX with ethanolic silver nitrate solution.

$$R—\overset{..}{\underset{..}{X}}: \underset{}{\overset{Ag^+}{\rightleftharpoons}} \overset{\delta^+}{R} \overset{..}{\underset{..}{X}} \overset{\delta^+}{Ag} \longrightarrow R^+ + AgX \downarrow$$

On the basis of the foregoing discussion, tertiary halides would be expected to react with silver nitrate most rapidly and primary halides least rapidly. The R^+ ion can react with the solvent to give either an alkene or an ether.

Microscale Procedure

Label 11 small containers (reaction tubes, 3-mL centrifuge tubes, 10 × 75-mm test tubes, or 1-mL vials), and place 0.1 mL or 100 mg of each of the following halides in the tubes.

$CH_3CH_2CH_2CH_2Cl$

1-Chlorobutane
bp 77–78°C

$CH_3CH_2CH_2CH_2Br$

1-Bromobutane
bp 100–104°C

$CH_3CH_2\overset{Cl}{\underset{|}{C}}HCH_3$

2-Chlorobutane
bp 68–70°C

$CH_3—\overset{CH_3}{\underset{\underset{CH_3}{|}}{\overset{|}{C}}}—Cl$

2-Chloro-2-methylpropane
bp 51–52°C

Bromobenzene
bp 156°C

$CH_3CH=CHCH_2Cl$

**1-Chloro-2-butene mixture
of *cis* and *trans* isomers**
bp 635°C (*cis*)
bp 68°C (*trans*)

$CH_3\overset{CH_3}{\underset{|}{C}}HCH_2Cl$

1-Chloro-2-methylpropane
bp 68–69°C

1-Chloroadamantane
mp 165–166°C

$CH_3CH_2\overset{Br}{\underset{|}{C}}HCH_3$

2-Bromobutane
bp 91°C

$CH_2CH=C(Cl)CH_3$

**2-Chloro-2-butene
(mixture of isomers)**
bp 62–67°C

CH_3CH_2I

Iodoethane
bp 72°C

To each tube then rapidly add 1 mL of an 18% solution of sodium iodide in acetone, stopper each tube, mix the contents thoroughly, and note the time. Note the time of first appearance of any precipitate. If no reaction occurs within about 5 min, place those tubes in a 50°C water bath and watch for any reaction over the next 5 or 6 min.

Empty the tubes, rinse them with ethanol, place the same amount of each of the alkyl halides in each tube as in the first part of the experiment, add 1 mL of 1% ethanolic silver nitrate solution to each tube, mix the contents well, and note the time of addition as well as the time of appearance of the first traces of any precipitate. If a precipitate does not appear in 5 min, heat the tubes containing these unreactive halides in a 50°C water bath for 5 to 6 min and watch for any reaction.

To test the effect of solvent on the rate of S_N1 reactivity, compare the time needed for a precipitate to appear when 2-chlorobutane is treated with 1% ethanolic silver nitrate solution and when treated with 1% silver nitrate in a mixture of 50% ethanol and 50% water.

In your analysis of the results from these experiments, consider the following for both S_N1 and S_N2 conditions:

- the nature of the leaving group (Cl vs. Br) in the 1-halobutanes
- the effect of structure, that is, compare simple primary, secondary, and tertiary halides, unhindered primary vs. hindered primary halides, a simple tertiary halide vs. a complex tertiary halide, and an allylic halide vs. a tertiary halide
- the effect of solvent polarity on the S_N1 reaction
- the effect of temperature on the reaction

Online Study Center

General Resources
Additional Experiments

Cleaning Up. Because all of the test solutions contain halogenated material, all test solutions and washes as well as unused starting materials should be placed in the halogenated organic waste container.

QUESTIONS

1. What would be the effect of carrying out the sodium iodide in acetone reaction with the alkyl halides using an iodide solution half as concentrated?
2. The addition of sodium or potassium iodide catalyzes many S_N2 reactions of alkyl chlorides or bromides. Explain.
3. In S_N1 reactions, the intermediate carbocations can eliminate a proton to yield alkenes or react with the solvent to yield ethers. Draw the structures of the byproducts of this type that would be derived from the reaction of the carbocation derived from 2-bromo-2-methylbutane in ethanol.

p-Terphenyl by the Diels–Alder Reaction

PRELAB EXERCISE: Why does the dicarboxylate (5) undergo double decarboxylation to give terphenyl, whereas the diacid formed from the reaction of cyclopentadiene with maleic anhydride (*see* Chapter 48) does not undergo decarboxylation under the same reaction conditions?

(1)
***E,E*-1,4-Diphenyl-1,3-butadiene**
MW 206.27

s-*trans* form ⇌ s-*cis* form

(2)
MW 142.11

(3)
MW 348.38, mp 98°C

(4)
mp 170°C

(5)

(6)
***p*-Terphenyl**
MW 230.29, mp 209–210°C

Diels–Alder reaction

E,E-1,4-Diphenyl-1,3-butadiene (**1**) is most stable in the s-*trans* form, but at a suitably elevated temperature the s-*cis* form present in the equilibrium adds to dimethyl acetylenedicarboxylate (**2**) to give dimethyl 1,4-diphenyl-1,4-dihydrophthalate (**3**). This low-melting ester is obtained as an oil that, when warmed briefly with methanolic potassium hydroxide, is isomerized to the high-melting E-ester (**4**). The free E-acid can be obtained in 86% yield by refluxing the suspension of (**3**) in methanol for 4 h; but in the recommended procedure the isomerized ester is collected, washed to remove the dark mother liquor, and hydrolyzed by brief heating with potassium hydroxide in a high-boiling solvent. The final step, an oxidative decarboxylation, is rapid and nearly quantitative. It probably involves reaction of the oxidant with the dianion (**5**) with removal of two electrons and formation of a diradical, which loses carbon dioxide with the formation of p-terphenyl (**6**).

EXPERIMENTS

1. Microscale Synthesis of p-Terphenyl

> **IN THIS EXPERIMENT** a previously prepared diene reacts with a dieneophile, an acetylenic diester, in a very high-boiling solvent. The mixture is dissolved in ether, and the water-soluble solvent is removed by extraction with water. The ether solution is dried and evaporated to give the diester intermediate (**3**), which is hydrolyzed in a high-boiling solvent to a dianion. The dianion is oxidized with ferricyanide to the product that is collected on a Hirsch funnel.

CAUTION: Handle dimethyl acetylenedicarboxylate with care.[1]

$$CH_3OCH_2CH_2OCH_2$$
$$|$$
$$CH_3OCH_2CH_2OCH_2$$

Triethylene glycol dimethyl ether (triglyme)
Miscible with water; bp 222°C

Reaction time: 30 min

Online Study Center

Video: Extraction with Ether;
Photos: Extraction with Ether,
Drying Crystals Under Vacuum

In a 10 × 100-mm reaction tube, place 100 mg of E,E-1,4-diphenyl-1,3-butadiene prepared by the Wittig reaction in Chapter 39. Add 74 mg of dimethyl acetylenedicarboxylate (*Caution*: skin irritant), followed by 0.35 mL of triethylene glycol dimethyl ether (triglyme; bp 222°C) and a boiling chip. Reflux the mixture on a hot sand bath for 30 min.

Cool the yellowish solution in cold water, add 2.5 mL of ether (*t*-butyl methyl ether is strongly recommended), and extract the solution three times with 1.5-mL portions of water to remove the high-boiling solvent, shake the ethereal solution once with saturated sodium chloride solution, and dry the solution over calcium chloride pellets. Add the drying agent until it no longer clumps together. Remove the ether solution with a Pasteur pipette and place it in a tared reaction tube. Wash off the calcium chloride pellets with more ether. Evaporate the solvent in the hood under a stream of nitrogen or air, removing the last traces under aspirator vacuum.

While the evaporation is in progress, dissolve 35 mg of potassium hydroxide in 0.35 mL of methanol by heating and stirring. Crystallization of the yellow oil

1. This ester is a powerful lachrymator (tear producer) and vesicant (blistering agent) and should be dispensed from a bottle provided with a pipette and a pipetter. Even a trace of ester on the skin should be washed off promptly with methanol, followed by soap and water.

Potassium hydroxide is easily powdered in a blender.

Methanol solutions are strongly fluorescent.

⚠ **CAUTION**: Triglyme forms peroxides. Discard 90 days after container is opened.

Rapid hydrolysis of the hindered ester (**4**)

🌀 **Online Study Center**

Video: Microscale Filtration on the Hirsch Funnel

⚠ **CAUTION**: Handle dimethyl acetylenedicarboxylate with care.[2]

Triethylene glycol dimethyl ether (triglyme)
Miscible with water; bp 222°C

Reaction time: 30 min; reflux on a sand bath or a hot plate

containing compound **3** can be initiated by cooling and scratching; this provides assurance that the reaction has proceeded properly. Transfer the methanolic potassium hydroxide to the yellow oil and heat with stirring on a hot sand bath for about 1 min until a stiff paste of crystals of the isomerized ester (**4**) appears. Cool, thin the mixture with methanol, collect the product on a Hirsch funnel, wash it free of the dark mother liquor, and spread it thinly on a filter paper for rapid drying. The yield of pure, white ester (**4**) is about 120 mg. Solutions in methanol are strongly fluorescent.

Place the ester (**4**) in a reaction tube, add 50 mg of potassium hydroxide, and add 0.35 mL of triethylene glycol. Stir the mixture with a stirring rod and heat, raising the temperature to 140°C in the course of about 5 min. By intermittent heating, keep the temperature close to 140°C for an additional 5 min; then cool the mixture under the tap. Pour this cooled mixture into a 4-in. test tube and rinse the reaction tube with about 3.3 mL of water. Heat to boiling; in case there is a small precipitate or the solution is cloudy, add a little pelletized Norit decolorizing charcoal, swirl, and filter the alkaline solution. Then add 225 mg of potassium ferricyanide and heat on a hot sand bath for about 5 min to dissolve the oxidant and to coagulate the white precipitate, which soon separates and is collected by filtration on a Hirsch funnel. The product can be air-dried overnight or dried to constant weight by heating in an evacuated reaction tube on a steam bath. The yield of colorless *p*-terphenyl (mp 209°C–210°C) is 50–60 mg.

Cleaning Up. The aqueous layer from the reaction after dilution can be flushed down the drain. Allow the ether to evaporate from the calcium chloride in the hood; then discard the drying agent in the nonhazardous solid waste container. If local regulations do not allow for the evaporation of solvents in a hood, the wet solid should be disposed in a special container. The aqueous reaction mixture after dilution with water is neutralized with dilute hydrochloric acid and flushed down the drain.

2. Macroscale Synthesis of *p*-Terphenyl

Place 1.5 g of *E,E*-1,4-diphenyl-1,3-butadiene (from the Wittig reaction, Chapter 39) and 1.0 mL (1.1 g) of dimethyl acetylenedicarboxylate (*Caution*: skin irritant) in a 25 × 150-mm test tube and rinse down the walls with 5 mL of triethylene glycol dimethyl ether (triglyme; bp 222°C). Clamp the test tube in a vertical position, introduce a cold finger condenser, and reflux the mixture gently for 30 min. Alternatively, carry out the experiment in a 25-mL round-bottomed flask equipped with a reflux condenser. Cool the yellowish solution under the tap, pour into a separatory funnel, and rinse out the reaction vessel with about 50 mL of ether. Extract twice with water (50–75 mL portions) to remove the high-boiling solvent, shake the ethereal solution with saturated sodium chloride solution, and dry the ether layer over anhydrous calcium chloride pellets. Filter or decant the ether solution into a tared 125-mL Erlenmeyer flask and evaporate the ether on a

2. This ester is a powerful lachrymator (tear producer) and vesicant (blistering agent) and should be dispensed from a bottle provided with a pipette and a pipetter. Even a trace of ester on the skin should be washed off promptly with methanol, followed by soap and water.

CAUTION: Extinguish all flames before working with ether.

Potassium hydroxide is easily powdered in a blender.

steam bath, eventually with evacuation at an aspirator, until the weight of yellow oil is constant; the yield is about 2.5–2.8 g.

While evaporation is in progress, dissolve 0.5 g of potassium hydroxide (about 5 pellets) in 10 mL of methanol by heating and swirling; this process is greatly hastened by crushing the lumps using a stirring rod with a flattened head. Crystallization of the yellow oil containing compound **3** can be initiated by cooling and scratching; this provides assurance that the reaction has proceeded properly. Pour in the methanolic potassium hydroxide and heat with swirling on a hot plate for about 1 min until a stiff paste of crystals of the isomerized ester (**4**) appears. Cool, thin the mixture with methanol, collect the product, wash it free of the dark mother liquor, and spread it thinly on a filter paper for rapid drying. The yield of pure, white ester (**4**) is 1.7–1.8 g. Solutions in methanol are highly fluorescent.

Rapid hydrolysis of the hindered ester (**4**)

Place the ester (**4**) in a 25 × 150-mm test tube, add 0.7 g of potassium hydroxide (7–8 pellets), and pour in 5 mL of triethylene glycol. Stir the mixture with a stirring rod and heat, raising the temperature to 140°C in the course of about 5 min. By intermittent heating, keep the temperature close to 140°C for an additional 5 min; then cool the mixture under the tap. Pour into a 125-mL Erlenmeyer flask and rinse the tube with about 50 mL of water. Heat to boiling; in case there is a small precipitate or the solution is cloudy, add a little pelletized Norit decolorizing charcoal, swirl, and filter the alkaline solution by gravity. Then add 3.4 g of potassium ferricyanide and heat on a hot plate with swirling for about 5 min to dissolve the oxidant and to coagulate the white precipitate that soon separates. The product can be air-dried overnight or dried to constant weight by heating in an evacuated Erlenmeyer flask on a steam bath. The yield of colorless *p*-terphenyl (mp 209°C–210°C) is 0.7–0.8 g.

Cleaning Up. The aqueous layer from the reaction after dilution can be flushed down the drain if local regulations permit. Allow the ether to evaporate from the calcium chloride in the hood; then discard the drying agent in the nonhazardous solid waste container. If local regulations do not allow for the evaporation of solvents in a hood, the wet solid should be disposed in a special container. The aqueous reaction mixture after dilution with water is neutralized with dilute hydrochloric acid and then flushed down the drain.

Computational Chemistry

Using a molecular mechanics program, calculate the steric energies of all the possible *cis*- and *trans*- isomers as well as all the s-*cis* and s-*trans* forms. There are six possible combinations of these. Which is the most stable?

QUESTIONS

1. What is the driving force for the isomerization of compound **3** to compound **4**?

2. Why is the *trans*- and not the *cis*- diester (**4**) formed in the isomerization of compound **3** to compound **4**?

3. Why does hydrolysis of compound **4** in methanol require 4 h, whereas hydrolysis in triethylene glycol requires only 10 min?

Friedel–Crafts Alkylation of Benzene and Dimethoxybenzene; Host-Guest Chemistry

Online Study Center

This icon will direct you to techniques, equipment setups, and online resources at http://college.hmco.com/PIC/ williamsonMMOE5e.

PRELAB EXERCISE: Prepare a flow sheet for the alkylation of benzene and the alkylation of dimethoxybenzene, indicating how the catalysts and unreacted starting materials are removed from the reaction mixture.

The Friedel–Crafts[1] alkylation of aromatic rings most often employs an alkyl halide and a strong Lewis acid catalyst. Some of the catalysts that can be used, in order of decreasing activity, are the halides of aluminum, antimony, iron, titanium, tin, bismuth, and zinc. Although useful, the reaction has several limitations. The aromatic ring must be unsubstituted or bear activating groups; because the product—an alkylated aromatic molecule—is more reactive than the starting material, multiple substitution usually occurs. Furthermore, primary halides will rearrange under the reaction conditions:

⬡ + $CH_3CH_2CH_2Cl$ $\xrightarrow{AlCl_3}$ ⬡$CH_2CH_2CH_3$ + ⬡$\overset{\overset{\displaystyle H}{|}}{\underset{H_3C \quad CH_3}{C}}$

−6°C: 60%   40%
+35°C: 40%   60%

---

1. Charles Friedel and James Crafts (who later became the president of MIT) discovered this reaction in 1879.

In this reaction a tertiary halide and the most powerful Friedel–Crafts catalyst, $AlCl_3$, are allowed to react with benzene. (If you prefer not to work with benzene, you can carry out alkylations of dimethoxybenzene or *m*-xylene.) The initially formed *t*-butylbenzene is a liquid, whereas the product, 1,4-di-*t*-butylbenzene, which has a symmetrical structure, is a beautiful crystalline solid. The alkylation reaction probably proceeds through the carbocation under the conditions of the experiments in this chapter:

Benzene
MW 78.11, den. 0.88
bp 80°C

2-Chloro-2-methylpropane
(*t*-Butyl chloride)
MW 92.57, den. 0.85
bp 51°C

1,4-Di-*t*-butylbenzene
MW 190.32, mp 77–79°C
bp 167°C

The reaction is reversible. If 1,4-di-*t*-butylbenzene is allowed to react with *t*-butyl chloride and 1.3 mol of aluminum chloride at 0°C–5°C, 1,3-di-*t*-butylbenzene, 1,3,5-tri-*t*-butylbenzene, and unchanged starting material are found in the reaction mixture. Thus, the mother liquor from crystallization of 1,4-di-*t*-butylbenzene probably contains *t*-butylbenzene, the desired 1,4-di-product, the 1,3-di-isomer, and 1,3,5-tri-*t*-butylbenzene.

Inclusion Complexes: Host-Guest Chemistry

Although the mother liquor probably contains a mixture of several components, the 1,4-di-*t*-butylbenzene can be isolated easily as an inclusion complex. Inclusion complexes are examples of host-guest chemistry. The host molecule thiourea, NH_2CSNH_2, has the interesting property of crystallizing in a helical crystal lattice that has a cylindrical hole in it. The guest molecule can reside in this hole if it is the correct size. It is not bound to the host; nuclear magnetic resonance (NMR) studies indicate the guest molecule can rotate longitudinally within the helical crystal lattice. There are often nonintegral numbers (on the average) of host molecules per guest. The inclusion complex of thiourea and 1,4-di-*t*-butylbenzene crystallizes quite nicely from a mixture of the other hydrocarbons; thus more of the product can be obtained. Because thiourea is very soluble in water, the product is recovered from the complex by shaking it with a mixture of ether and water. The complex immediately decomposes, and the product dissolves in the ether layer, from which it can be recovered.

Compare the length of the 1,4-di-*t*-butylbenzene molecule to the length of various *n*-alkanes and predict the host-guest ratio for a given alkane. You can then check your prediction experimentally. *n*-Hexane can be isolated from the mixture of isomers sold under the name *hexanes*.

EXPERIMENTS

1. 1,4-Di-*t*-Butylbenzene

IN THIS EXPERIMENT a mixture of benzene and an alkyl choride are treated with aluminum chloride, a Lewis acid catalyst. During the alkylation reaction hydrogen chloride is evolved and must be trapped. The dialkyl product is isolated by adding water to the reaction mixture and extracting it with ether. In the usual way the ether solution is washed, dried, and evaporated to give the product. This crude material is recrystallized from methanol to give the pure dialkyl product.

CAUTION: Benzene is a mild carcinogen. Handle it in the hood; do not breathe its vapors or allow the liquid to come in contact with the skin.

Online Study Center

Photos: Removing a Reagent from a Septum-Capped Bottle, Polypropylene Syringe Containing Ether

Aluminum chloride dust is extremely hygroscopic and irritating. It hydrolyzes to hydrogen chloride on contact with moisture. Clean up any spilled material immediately.

Online Study Center

Photos: Gas Trap, Placing a Polyethylene Tube through a Septum, Extraction with Ether

Add anhydrous calcium chloride until it no longer clumps together.

Using a 1.0-mL plastic syringe, measure 0.40 mL of dry 2-chloro-2-methylpropane (*t*-butyl chloride) and 0.20 mL of dry benzene into a dry 10 × 100 mm reaction tube equipped with a septum and tubing (Fig. 29.1). The benzene and the alkyl chloride will usually be found in septum-stoppered containers. Cool the tube in ice and then add 20 mg of aluminum chloride. Weighing and transferring this small quantity is difficult because aluminum chloride reacts with great rapidity with moist air. Keep the reagent bottle closed as much of the time as possible while weighing the reagent into a very small, dry, capped vial. Because the aluminum chloride is a catalyst, the amount need not be exactly 20 mg.

Mix the contents of the reaction tube by flicking the tube with a finger. After an induction period of about 2 min, a vigorous reaction sets in, with bubbling and liberation of hydrogen chloride. The hydrogen chloride is trapped using the apparatus depicted in Figure 29.1. The wet cotton in the empty reaction tube will dissolve and trap the hydrogen chloride. Figure 29.2 illustrates how to thread a polyethylene tube through a septum. Near the end of the reaction, the product separates as a white solid. When this occurs, remove the tube from the ice and let it stand at room temperature for 5 min.

Add about 1.0 mL of ice water to the reaction mixture, mix the contents thoroughly, and extract the product with three 0.8-mL portions of ether. Wash the combined ether extracts with about 1.5 mL of saturated sodium chloride solution and dry the ether over anhydrous calcium chloride pellets. Add sufficient drying agent so that it does not clump together. After 5 min, transfer the ether solution to a dry, tared reaction tube, using more ether to wash the drying agent, and evaporate the ether under a stream of air in the hood. Remove the last traces of ether under water aspirator vacuum (Fig. 29.3). The oily product should solidify on cooling and weigh about 300 mg.

■ FIG. 29.1

A hydrogen chloride gas trap for the Friedel–Crafts reaction.

Polyethylene
tubing

Rubber
septum

Reaction
tubes

Damp
cotton

Ice bath

■ FIG. 29.2

To thread a polyethylene tube through a septum, make a hole through the septum with a needle, then push a toothpick through the hole. Push the polyethylene tube firmly onto the toothpick, then pull and push on the toothpick. The tube will slide through the septum. Finally, pull the tube from the toothpick. A blunt syringe needle can be used instead of a toothpick.

Polyethylene
tube

Septum

Toothpick or
syringe needle

To aspirator

Glass tube

Thermometer
adapter

Reaction tube

Beaker
of warm
water

Crystals to
be dried

■ FIG. 29.3

Drying crystals under reduced pressure.

Spontaneous crystallization gives beautiful needles or plates.

Online Study Center

Video: Filtration of Crystals
Using the Pasteur Pipette

For crystallization, dissolve the product in 0.40 mL of methanol and allow the solution to come to room temperature without disturbance. After thorough cooling at 0°C, remove the methanol with a Pasteur pipette and rinse the crystals with a drop of ice-cold methanol while keeping the reaction tube in ice. Save this methanol solution for analysis by thin-layer chromatography (TLC). The yield of recrystallized material after drying under aspirator vacuum should be about 160 mg. Remove a sample of crystals for analysis by infrared (IR) or NMR spectroscopy, TLC, and melting-point determination (Fig. 29.4 and Fig. 29.5). Using TLC, compare the pure crystalline product to the residue left after evaporation of the methanol.

Cleaning Up. Place any unused *t*-butyl chloride in the halogenated organic waste container and any unused benzene in the hazardous waste container for benzene. Any unused aluminum chloride should be mixed thoroughly with a large excess of sodium carbonate, and the solid mixture should be added to a large volume of water before being flushed down the drain. The combined aqueous layers from the reaction should be neutralized with sodium carbonate and then flushed down the drain. Methanol from the crystallization is to be placed in the organic solvents container.

2. Preparation of the Thiourea Inclusion Complex

$$\begin{array}{c} S \\ \| \\ H_2NCNH_2 \end{array}$$

Thiourea
MW 76.12

IN THIS EXPERIMENT an inclusion complex is prepared by simply cooling a solution of thiourea and di-*t*-butylbenzene. The complex is isolated, weighed, and decomposed with water; then the dialkyl benzene is extracted into ether that is dried and evaporated. The residue is weighed to calculate how many molecules of thiourea complex with a molecule of the di-*t*-butylbenzene.

CAUTION: Thiourea is a mild carcinogen. Handle the solid in a hood. Do not breathe its dust.

The inclusion complex starts to crystallize in 10 min.

In a tared reaction tube, dissolve 200 mg of thiourea and 120 mg of 1,4-di-*t*-butylbenzene in 2.0 mL of methanol at room temperature; then cool the mixture in ice, at which time the inclusion complex will crystallize. Using a Pasteur pipette, remove the solvent and wash the product twice with just enough methanol to cover the crystals while keeping the tube on ice. Connect the reaction tube to a water aspirator and, using the heat of your hand, evaporate the remaining methanol under reduced pressure until the weight of the tube is constant. The yield should be about 200 mg.

Remove a small sample and set it aside; carefully determine the weight of the remaining complex and then add about 1.2 mL of water and 1.2 mL of ether to the tube. Shake the mixture until the crystals disappear. This causes the complex to break up, with the thiourea remaining in the aqueous layer and the 1,4-di-*t*-butylbenzene passing into the ether layer. Draw off the aqueous layer and dry the ether layer with anhydrous calcium chloride pellets. Add sufficient drying agent so that it does not clump together. More ether can be added if necessary. Transfer the ether to a tared reaction tube and wash the drying agent twice with fresh portions of ether. The objective is to make a quantitative transfer of the butylbenzene. Evaporate the ether and remove the last traces under aspirator vacuum. After the weight of the tube is constant, record the weight of the hydrocarbon. Calculate the number of molecules of thiourea per molecule of hydrocarbon (probably *not* an integral number).

Cleaning Up. Place any unused thiourea and the 1.2 mL of the aqueous solution containing thiourea in the hazardous waste container for thiourea. Alternatively, treat the thiourea with excess aqueous 5.25% sodium hypochlorite solution (household bleach), dilute the mixture with a large amount of water, and flush it down the drain. If local regulations allow, evaporate any residual solvent from the drying agent in the hood and place the dried solid in the nonhazardous waste container. Otherwise, place the wet drying agent in a waste container designated for this purpose.

3. 1,4-Di-*t*-Butylbenzene

CAUTION: Benzene is a mild carcinogen. Handle it in the hood; do not breathe its vapors or allow the liquid to come in contact with the skin.

Aluminum chloride dust is extremely hygroscopic and irritating. It hydrolyzes to hydrogen chloride on contact with moisture. Clean up any spilled material immediately.

Reaction time: about 15 min

Measure in the hood 20 mL of 2-chloro-2-methylpropane (*t*-butyl chloride) and 10 mL of benzene in a 125-mL filter flask equipped with a one-holed rubber stopper fitted with a thermometer. Place the flask in an ice-water bath to cool. Weigh 1 g of fresh aluminum chloride onto a creased paper and scrape it with a small spatula into a 10 × 75-mm test tube; close the tube at once with a cork.[2] Connect the side arm of the flask to an aspirator (preferably one made of plastic) and operate it at a rate sufficient to carry away hydrogen chloride formed in the reaction; alternatively, make a trap for the hydrogen chloride similar to that shown in Figure 18.3 (on page 348). Cool the liquid to 0°C–3°C, add about one-quarter of the aluminum chloride, replace the thermometer, and swirl the flask vigorously in the ice bath. After an induction period of about 2 min, a vigorous reaction sets in, with bubbling and liberation of hydrogen chloride. Add the remainder of the catalyst in

---

2. Alternative scheme: Put a wax pencil mark on the test tube 37 mm from the bottom and fill the tube with aluminum chloride to this mark.

Add anhydrous calcium chloride
pellets until they no longer
clump together.

Spontaneous crystallization gives
beautiful needles or plates.

Online Study Center

Video: Macroscale Crystallization

CAUTION: Thiourea is a
carcinogen. Handle the solid in a
hood. Do not breathe its dust.

Thiourea
MW 76.12
The inclusion complex starts
to crystallize in 10 min.

Workup of mother liquor

three portions at intervals of about 2 min. Toward the end, the reaction product begins to separate as a white solid. When this occurs, remove the flask from the bath
and let stand at room temperature for 5 min. Add ice and water to the reaction
mixture, allow most of the ice to melt, and then add ether for extraction of the
product, stirring with a rod or spatula to help bring the solid into solution. Transfer the solution to a separatory funnel and shake; draw off the lower layer and
wash the upper ether layer first with water then with a saturated sodium chloride
solution. Dry the ether solution over anhydrous calcium chloride pellets for 5 min,
filter the solution to remove the drying agent, remove the ether by evaporation on
a steam bath, and evacuate the flask using an aspirator to remove traces of solvent
until the weight is constant; the yield of crude product should be 15 g.

The oily product should solidify on cooling. For crystallization, dissolve the
product in 20 mL of hot methanol and let the solution come to room temperature
without disturbance. If you are in a hurry, with minimal agitation, place it gently
in an ice-water bath and observe the result. After thorough cooling at 0°C, collect
the product and rinse the flask and product with a little ice-cold methanol. The
yield of 1,4-di-*t*-butylbenzene from the first crop is 8.2–8.6 g of satisfactory material. Save the product for the next step as well as the mother liquor, in case you
later wish to work it up for a second crop.

Inclusion Complex Formation

In a 25-mL Erlenmeyer flask dissolve 5 g of thiourea and 3 g of 1,4-di-
t-butylbenzene in 50 mL of warm methanol (break up lumps with a flattened
stirring rod) and let the solution stand for crystallization of the complex, which
occurs with ice cooling. Collect the crystals, rinse with a little methanol, and dry
to constant weight; the yield is 5.8 g. Remove a small sample and set it aside;
carefully determine the weight of the remaining complex and place the material in
a separatory funnel along with about 25 mL each of water and ether. Shake until
the crystals disappear, draw off the aqueous layer containing thiourea, wash the
ether layer with saturated sodium chloride, and dry the ether layer over anhydrous
calcium chloride pellets. Remove the drying agent by filtration and collect the filtrate in a tared 125-mL Erlenmeyer flask. Evaporate and evacuate as before, being
sure the weight of hydrocarbon is constant before you record it. Calculate the
number of molecules of thiourea per molecule of hydrocarbon (probably *not* an
integral number).

To work up the mother liquor from the crystallization, first evaporate the
methanol. Note that the residual oil does not solidify on ice cooling. Next, dissolve the oil, together with 5 g of thiourea, in 50 mL of methanol, collect the inclusion complex that crystallizes (3.2 g), and recover 1,4-di-*t*-butylbenzene from
the complex as before (0.8 g before crystallization). The IR and ¹H NMR spectra
of the product are seen in Figures 29.4 and 29.5.

Cleaning Up. Place any unused *t*-butyl chloride in the halogenated organic waste
container and any unused benzene in the hazardous waste container for benzene.
Any unused aluminum chloride should be mixed thoroughly with a large excess

of sodium carbonate, and the solid mixture should be added to a large volume of water before being flushed down the drain. The combined aqueous layers from the reaction should be neutralized with sodium carbonate and then flushed down the drain. Methanol from the crystallization is to be placed in the organic solvents container.

4. 1,4-Di-*t*-Butyl-2,5-Dimethoxybenzene

1,4-Dimethoxybenzene (Hydroquinone dimethyl ether)
MW 138.16, mp 57°C

2-Methyl-2-propanol (*t*-Butyl alcohol)
MW 74.12, den. 0.79
mp 25.5°C, bp 82.8°C
n_D^{20} 1.3820

1,4-Di-*t*-butyl-2,5-dimethoxybenzene
MW 250.37, mp 104–105°C

Trimethylcarbocation

This experiment illustrates the Friedel–Crafts alkylation of an activated benzene molecule with a tertiary alcohol in the presence of sulfuric acid as the Lewis acid catalyst. Like the reaction of benzene and *t*-butyl chloride, the substitution involves attack by the electrophilic trimethylcarbocation.

Microscale Procedure

> **IN THIS EXPERIMENT** a mixture of dimethoxybenzene and *t*-butyl alcohol is dissolved in acetic acid and treated with sulfuric acid, a Lewis acid catalyst. Water is added to the reaction mixture, and the solid product is isolated by removing the aqueous material with a Pasteur pipette. The dialkylated product is recrystallized from methanol.

CAUTION: Handle concentrated sulfuric acid with care.

In a 10 × 100 mm reaction tube dissolve 120 mg of 1,4-dimethoxybenzene (hydroquinone dimethyl ether) in 0.4 mL of acetic acid with gentle warming and add 0.2 mL of *t*-butyl alcohol (it may be necessary to melt this alcohol). Cool the mixture in ice and then add to it 0.4 mL of concentrated sulfuric acid dropwise from a Pasteur pipette. After each drop of acid is added, mix the solution thoroughly. At the end of this addition, considerable solid reaction product should have separated. Stir the mixture thoroughly with a glass stirring rod, remove the

Stir **thoroughly** after each drop of water is added.

reaction tube from the ice, and allow it to warm to room temperature and remain at 20°C–25°C for at least 10 min to complete the reaction. Next, cool the mixture in ice to cause crystallization to occur. Measure 2.5 mL of water into a container. Very carefully add 1 drop of water to the reaction mixture, stir with the glass rod, and continue to add the remainder of the water dropwise with cooling and stirring. Remove the solvent from the cold solution with a Pasteur pipette and wash the crystals thoroughly with water. Recrystallize the product from methanol. After allowing the mixture to cool to room temperature and then to 0°C in ice, remove the solvent using a Pasteur pipette. The last traces of methanol can be removed under aspirator vacuum while warming the tube in your hand or in a beaker of warm water (Fig. 29.3). The yield of large plates of 1,4-di-*t*-butyl-2,5-dimethoxybenzene should be about 80–100 mg. Analyze the product by IR spectroscopy and TLC, using ligroin as the eluent. Determine the melting point and the percentage yield.

Cleaning Up. Combine the aqueous layer, the methanol washes, and the crystallization mother liquor; dilute with water; neutralize with sodium carbonate; and flush down the drain. Any spilled sulfuric acid should be covered with a large excess of solid sodium carbonate, and the mixture should be added to water before being flushed down the drain.

Macroscale Procedure

Place 3 g of 1,4-dimethoxybenzene (hydroquinone dimethyl ether) in a 125-mL Erlenmeyer flask, add 5 mL of *t*-butyl alcohol and 10 mL of acetic acid, and place the flask in an ice-water bath to cool. Measure 15 mL of concentrated sulfuric acid into a 25-mL Erlenmeyer flask and place the flask—properly supported—in an ice bath to cool. For good thermal contact the ice bath should be an ice-water mixture. Put a thermometer in the larger flask, swirl in the ice bath until the temperature is in the range 0°C–3°C, and remove the thermometer (solid, if present, will dissolve later). Do not use the thermometer as a stirring rod. Clamp a small separatory funnel in a position to deliver into the 125-mL Erlenmeyer flask so that the flask can remain in the ice-water bath, wipe the smaller flask dry, and pour the chilled sulfuric acid solution into the funnel. While swirling the 125-mL flask in the ice bath, run in the chilled sulfuric acid by rapid drops during the course of 4–7 min.

By this time considerable solid reaction product should have separated, and insertion of a thermometer should show that the temperature is in the 15°C–20°C range. Swirl the mixture while maintaining the temperature at about 20°C–25°C for an additional 5 min and then cool in ice. Add ice to the mixture to dilute the sulfuric acid; then add water to nearly fill the flask, cool, and collect the product on a Büchner funnel with suction. It is good practice to clamp the filter flask so it does not tip over. Apply only very gentle suction at first to avoid breaking the filter paper, which is weakened by the strong sulfuric acid solution. Wash liberally with water and then turn on the suction to full force. Press down the filter cake with a spatula and let it drain well. Meanwhile, cool a 15-mL portion of methanol for washing to remove a little oil and a yellow impurity. Release the suction, cover the filter cake with one-third of the chilled methanol, and then apply suction. Repeat the washing two more times.

CAUTION: Handle concentrated sulfuric acid with care.

Total reaction time: about 12 min

Because air-drying of the crude reaction product takes time, the following short procedure is suggested: Place the moist material in a 50-mL Erlenmeyer flask, add a little dichloromethane (5–8 mL) to dissolve the organic material, and note the appearance of aqueous droplets. Add enough anhydrous calcium chloride pellets to the flask so that the drying agent no longer clumps together, let drying proceed for 10 min, and then remove the drying agent by gravity filtration or careful decantation into another 50-mL Erlenmeyer flask. Add 15 mL of methanol (bp 65°C) to the solution. Remove the dichloromethane (bp 41°C) using a rotary evaporator or by evaporation on a steam bath in a hood. When the volume is estimated to be about 15 mL, let the solution stand for crystallization. When crystallization is complete, cool in ice and collect.

From an environmental standpoint, it would be better to eliminate the solvents by simple distillation using the apparatus depicted in Figure 5.10 (on page 100). Leave 15 mL in the flask and allow the mixture to cool slowly. Large crystals will form. Collect the product on a small Büchner funnel. The yield of large plates of pure 1,4-di-*t*-butyl-2,5-dimethoxybenzene is 2–2.5 g.

Antics of Growing Crystals

Robert Stolow of Tufts University reported[3] that growing crystals of the di-*t*-butyldimethoxy compound change shape in a dramatic manner: Thin plates curl and roll up and then uncurl so suddenly that they propel themselves for a distance of several centimeters. If you do not observe this phenomenon during crystallization of a small sample, you may be interested in consulting the papers cited and pooling your sample with others for trial on a large scale. The solvent mixture recommended by the Tufts workers for observing the phenomenon is 9.7 mL of acetic acid and 1.4 mL of water per gram of product.

■ **FIG. 29.6**
The IR spectrum of 1,4-dimethoxybenzene (KBr disk). Note water contaminant at $3437 \ cm^{-1}$.

3. Stolow, R. D.; Larsen, J. W. *Chem. Ind.* **1963**, *449*. See also Blatchly, J. M.; Hartshorne, N. H. *Trans. Faraday Soc.* **1966**, *62*, 512.

Figures 29.6 and 29.7 present the IR and NMR spectra of the starting hydro-quinone dimethyl ether. Can you predict the appearance of the NMR spectrum of the product?

Cleaning Up. Combine the aqueous layer, and the methanol washes, and the crystallization mother liquor; dilute with water; neutralize with sodium carbonate; and flush down the drain. Any spilled sulfuric acid should be covered with a large excess of solid sodium carbonate, and the mixture should be added to water before being flushed down the drain. Dichloromethane mother liquor from the crystallization is placed in the halogenated organic waste container. If local regulations allow, evaporate any residual solvent from the drying agent in the hood and place the dried solid in the nonhazardous waste container. Otherwise, place the wet drying agent in a waste container designated for this purpose.

5. For Further Investigation

Alkylation of m-Xylene

m-Xylene	2-Chloro-2-methylpropane	
MW 106.17	MW 92.57	
den. 0.868	den. 0.851	
bp 139°C	bp 51°C	

IN THIS EXPERIMENT an excess of *m*-xylene (1,3-dimethylbenzene) and *t*-butyl chloride (2-chloro-2-methylpropane) is treated with iron(III) chloride, a Lewis acid catalyst. Hydrogen chloride gas is trapped. When the reaction is complete, water is added; the organic layer is washed, dried, and subjected to instant microscale distillation to remove excess 1,3-dimethylbenzene. The residual alkylated product is analyzed by IR spectroscopy to determine the structure of the product.

The objective of this experiment is to determine the structure of the product formed when *m*-xylene (not benzene, as in Experiment 1) is alkylated with *t*-butyl chloride. Although aluminum chloride is the catalyst most often used for the Friedel–Crafts reaction, it is difficult to store and weigh out because it reacts very rapidly with moisture in the air. Therefore, in this experiment, another Lewis acid catalyst, iron(III) chloride is used. The methyl groups in *m*-xylene are *ortho-para* directors and activators of the benzene ring, but other factors may intervene in this particular experiment. Read about the factors affecting alkylations in the first part of this chapter.

An excess of *m*-xylene is used in this reaction to ensure that the product will be monoalkylated by the *t*-butyl cation. Because the boiling points of the reactants and the product differ highly, a crude but very rapid and efficient distillation is done to remove unreacted xylene and *t*-butyl chloride, leaving only the product. This instant microscale distillation is carried out by boiling the mixture in a reaction tube and then pulling the hot vapors into a Pasteur pipette where they condense. After about half the material has been distilled in this way, the high-boiling residue will consist of almost pure product.

IR spectroscopy can be used to determine unequivocally the structure of the product. It has been found that the hydrogen atoms on a benzene ring give rise to one or two intense, characteristic peaks in the region of 730 to 885 cm^{-1} regardless of the nature of the substituents on the benzene ring. For instance, monosubstituted benzenes have two peaks: one in the range of 770 to 730 cm^{-1}, and the other in the range of 710 to 690 cm^{-1} (*see* Table 29.1). NMR spectroscopy can also be used to determine the structure of the product.

Molecular mechanics calculations on the three possible monosubstitution products from this reaction may help you to predict the outcome or help confirm conclusions drawn from experimental evidence.

Online Study Center

Photos: Gas Trap, Placing a Polyethylene Tube through a Septum

Iron(III) Chloride Catalyzed Reaction

Place 0.6 mL of *m*-xylene and 0.5 mL of *t*-butyl chloride in a dry reaction tube equipped with a septum and a polyethylene tube that leads to a tube containing a small wad of damp cotton. See Figures 29.1 and 29.2 (on page 439) for threading a polyethylene tube through a septum. The cotton, dampened with 2 or 3 drops of water, serves to trap the hydrogen chloride evolved during the reaction. Cool the mixture in an ice bath (Fig. 29.1), add 30 mg of iron(III) chloride (purple, free-flowing crystals when pure and dry), and replace the septum and polyethylene

TABLE 29.1 • Infrared C—H Out-of-Plane Bending Vibrations of Substituted Benzenes		
Substituted Benzene	**Peak 1 (cm^{-1})**	**Peak 2 (cm^{-1})**
Benzene	671	—
Monosubstituted benzenes	770–730	710–690
1,2-Disubstituted	770–735	—
1,3-Disubstituted	810–750	710–690
1,4-Disubstituted	835–810	—
1,2,3-Trisubstituted	780–760	745–705
1,2,4-Trisubstituted	825–805	885–870
1,3,5-Trisubstituted	865–810	730–675
1,2,3,4-Tetrasubstituted	810–800	—
1,2,3,5-Tetrasubstituted	850–840	—
1,2,4,5-Tetrasubstituted	870–855	—
Pentasubstituted	870	—

tube. After a short induction period, the reaction will begin a vigorous evolution of hydrogen chloride.

When the vigorous part of this reaction is over, remove the ice bath and allow the reaction mixture to warm to room temperature. When bubbles of hydrogen chloride cease to be evolved or after 15 min, add 1 mL of water to the reaction mixture, mix well, and then remove the water layer with a Pasteur pipette. Repeat this process using about 1 mL of saturated aqueous sodium bicarbonate solution followed by 1 mL of saturated sodium chloride solution. Transfer the organic layer to another reaction tube and dry it with anhydrous calcium chloride pellets.

Transfer the organic layer once again to a dry reaction tube, add a boiling chip, and heat the mixture to boiling. Allow the refluxing vapors to rise about 3 cm in the tube and then draw them into a Pasteur pipette. Squirt the condensate into another reaction tube held in the same hand (Fig. 29.8). Repeat this until about half the mixture has been distilled.

Online Study Center

Video: Instant Microscale
Distillation

Analyze the residue by IR spectroscopy, which is most easily done as a thin film between sodium chloride or silver chloride plates. The IR spectrum of *m*-xylene is shown in Figure 29.9. Refer to Table 29.1 for the IR absorption frequencies assigned to the different benzene substitution patterns. Note the two strong peaks in Figure 29.9 for *m*-xylene and the frequencies expected for 1,3-disubstitution from Table 29.1. From this correlation chart for the aromatic C—H out-of-plane bending modes, deduce the structure of your product. In your laboratory report, write a mechanism for this reaction that illustrates all the details of your conclusions. Discuss the structure of the product in terms of directive effects of substituents on the benzene ring, the steric effects of substituents, and thermodynamic versus kinetic control of the reaction.

■ **FIG. 29.8**

An apparatus for instant microscale distillation.

Refluxing vapor

Boiling liquid

Boiling chip

■ **FIG. 29.9**

The IR spectrum of *m*-xylene (thin film) from 500 cm⁻¹ to 1000 cm⁻¹ to show C–H out-of-plane bending vibrations.

Carry out molecular mechanics calculations on the three possible products to determine their relative steric energies or heats of formation. Do these calculations corroborate your conclusions?

Cleaning Up. Place any unused *t*-butyl chloride in the halogenated organic waste container and any unused *m*-xylene in the organic solvents container. Unused iron(III) chloride and wash solutions should be combined and neutralized with sodium bicarbonate solution, diluted with water, and flushed down the drain. If local regulations allow, evaporate any residual solvent from the drying agent in the hood and place the dried solid in the nonhazardous waste container. Otherwise, place the wet drying agent in a waste container designated for this purpose.

QUESTIONS

1. Write equations to explain why the reaction of 1,4-di-*t*-butylbenzene with *t*-butyl chloride and aluminum chloride gives 1,3,5-tri-*t*-butylbenzene.
2. Why must aluminum chloride be protected from exposure to the air?
3. Would you expect to find two strong peaks at $\sim$690 cm^{-1} and $\sim$770 cm^{-1} (Fig. 29.9) in your product from the alkylation of *m*-xylene? Why or why not?
4. Draw a detailed mechanism for the formation of *t*-butyl-2,5-dimethoxybenzene.
5. Why is the 1,4 isomer, 1,4-di-*t*-butyl-2,5-dimethoxybenzene, the major product in the alkylation of dimethoxybenzene? Would you expect either of the following compounds to be formed as side products: 1,3-di-*t*-butyl-2,5-dimethoxybenzene or 1,4-dimethoxy-2,3-di-*t*-butylbenzene? Why or why not?
6. Suggest two other compounds that might be used in place of *t*-butyl alcohol to form 1,4-di-*t*-butyl-2,5-dimethoxybenzene.
7. Can you locate the two peaks in Figure 28.3 (on page 435) that show that methyl 3-nitrobenzoate is indeed 1,3-disubstituted? (See Experiment 5 and Table 29.1.)

CHAPTER

28

Nitration of Methyl Benzoate

PRELAB EXERCISE: Draw the complete mechanism for the nitration of chlorobenzene. Chlorine is an *ortho-para* director and deactivator of the benzene ring.

The nitration of methyl benzoate is a typical electrophilic aromatic substitution reaction. The electrophile is the nitronium ion generated by the interaction of concentrated nitric and sulfuric acids:

$$HNO_3 + 2H_2SO_4 \rightleftharpoons NO_2^+ + 2HSO_4^- + H_3O^+$$

Nitronium ion

Sulfuric acid protonates the methyl benzoate:

The nitronium ion then reacts with this protonated intermediate at the *meta* position, where the electron density is highest, that is, where there is no positively charged resonance form and yields the intermediate arenium ion which has the four resonance forms shown here:

The arenium ion intermediate then transfers a proton to the basic bisulfate ion to give methyl 3-nitrobenzoate:

The ester group is a *meta* director and deactivator of the benzene ring. It is much easier to nitrate a molecule such as anisole, where the methoxyl group is an *ortho-para* director and an activator of the benzene ring, as the following resonance structures indicate:

EXPERIMENTS

1. Microscale Nitration of Methyl Benzoate

$$HNO_3 + 2H_2SO_4 \rightleftharpoons NO_2^+ + 2HSO_4^- + H_3O^+$$

                             Nitronium ion   Hydronium ion

Methyl benzoate
MW 136.16
bp 199.6°C
den. 1.09
n_D^{20} 1.5170

Methyl 3-nitrobenzoate
MW 181.15
mp 78°C

IN THIS EXPERIMENT a cold solution of an aromatic ester that has been dissolved in sulfuric acid is reacted with nitric acid. This highly exothermic reaction is kept under control by cooling; then the mixture is poured onto ice. The solid product is isolated by filtration and recrystallized from methanol, in which it is very soluble.

Do not use a plastic syringe and needle to measure either sulfuric acid or nitric acid. The acids react with the metal needle.

Use care in handling concentrated sulfuric and nitric acids.

Online Study Center

Videos: Microscale Filtration on the Hirsch Funnel, Recrystallization

To 0.6 mL of concentrated sulfuric acid in a 10 × 100 mm reaction tube, add 0.30 g of methyl benzoate. Flick the tube or use magnetic stirring. Cool the mixture to 0°C; add dropwise, using a Pasteur pipette, a mixture of 0.2 mL of concentrated sulfuric acid and 0.2 mL of concentrated nitric acid. Keep the reaction mixture in ice. Using a stirring rod, keep the reaction well mixed during the addition of the acids and do not allow the temperature of the mixture to rise above about 15°C, as judged by touching the reaction tube.

After all the nitric acid has been added, warm the mixture to room temperature and, after 15 min, pour it onto 2.5 g of ice in a small beaker. Isolate the solid product by suction filtration using a Hirsch funnel and a 25-mL filter flask. Wash the product well with water and then with one 0.2-mL portion of ice-cold methanol. If the methanol is not ice-cold, some product can be lost in this washing step. Save a small sample for a melting-point determination and analysis by thin-layer chromatography (TLC) and infrared (IR) spectroscopy.

The remainder is weighed and recrystallized from an equal weight of methanol in a reaction tube. Alternatively, the sample can be dissolved in a slightly larger quantity of methanol, and water is added dropwise to make the hot solution saturated with the product. Slow cooling should produce large crystals with a melting point of 78°C. The crude material can be obtained in about 80% yield with a melting point of 74°C–76°C. If the yield is not as large as expected, concentrate the filtrate and collect a second crop of product.

Cleaning Up. Dilute the filtrate from the reaction with water, neutralize with sodium carbonate, and flush down the drain. The methanol from the crystallization should be placed in the organic solvents container.

2. Macroscale Nitration of Methyl Benzoate

In a 125-mL Erlenmeyer flask, cool 12 mL of concentrated sulfuric acid to 0°C and then add 6.1 g of methyl benzoate. Again, cool the mixture to 0°C–10°C. Now add dropwise, using a Pasteur pipette, a cooled mixture of 4 mL of concentrated sulfuric acid and 4 mL of concentrated nitric acid. During the addition of the acids, swirl the mixture frequently (or use magnetic stirring) and maintain the temperature of the reaction mixture in the range of 5°C–15°C.

When all of the nitric acid has been added, warm the mixture to room temperature and, after 15 min, pour it on 50 g of cracked ice in a 250-mL beaker. Isolate the solid product by suction filtration using a small Büchner funnel, wash well with water, and then wash with two 10-mL portions of ice-cold methanol. A small sample is saved for a melting-point determination. The remainder is weighed and crystallized from an equal weight of methanol. The crude product should be

Use care in handling concentrated sulfuric and nitric acids.

Online Study Center

Video: Macroscale Crystallization

■ **FIG. 28.1**
The ^{1}H NMR spectrum of
methyl 3-nitrobenzoate
(250 MHz).

■ **FIG. 28.2**
The ^{13}C NMR spectrum of methyl
3-nitrobenzoate (22.6 MHz).

obtained in about 80% yield with a melting point of 74°C–76°C. The recrystallized product should have a melting point of 78°C. For your reference, the carbon and proton nuclear magnetic resonance (NMR) spectra of the product are presented in Figures 28.1 and 28.2.

Cleaning Up. Dilute the filtrate from the reaction with water, neutralize with sodium carbonate, and flush down the drain. The methanol from the crystallization should be placed in the organic solvents container.

QUESTIONS

1. Hydrocarbons do not dissolve in concentrated sulfuric acid, but methyl benzoate does. Explain this difference and write an equation showing the ions that are produced.

2. What would you expect the structure of the dinitro ester to be? Consider the directing effects of the ester and the first nitro group on the addition of the second nitro group.

3. Draw resonance structures to show in which position nitrobenzene will nitrate to form dinitrobenzene.

4. Assign the peaks at 3101 cm^{-1}, 1709 cm^{-1}, and 1390 cm^{-1} in the IR spectrum of methyl 3-nitrobenzoate (Fig. 28.3).

■ **FIG. 28.3**
The IR spectrum of methyl 3-nitrobenzoate. The broad peak at 3400 cm^{-1} comes from water in the KBr disk.

CHAPTER

26

Sodium Borohydride Reduction of 2-Methylcyclohexanone: A Problem in Conformational Analysis

Online Study Center

This icon will direct you to techniques, equipment setups, and online resources at http://college.hmco.com/PIC/williamsonMMOE5e.

PRELAB EXERCISE: Using carefully prepared drawings, try to predict whether *cis*- or *trans*-2-methylcyclohexanol will predominate in this reduction. Then use molecular models to check your conclusion. Finally, if you have access to the appropriate software, see if semiempirical molecular orbital calculations will change your conclusions.

The objective of this experiment is to determine the structures and relative percentage yields of the products formed when 2-methylcyclohexanone is reduced with sodium borohydride. We also compare these results to predictions made using molecular mechanics and semiempirical molecular orbital calculations.

In the reduction of 2-methylcyclohexanone, both the *cis* and *trans* isomers of 2-methylcyclohexanol can be formed:

		cis	*trans*

2-Methylcyclohexanone   2-Methylcyclohexanol

An examination of the models reveals that the two cyclohexanols can, in principle, exist in four chair conformations:

trans, **diequatorial**   *trans*, **diaxial**

229

OH

CH₃ ⇌ OH

CH₃

cis, **equatorial methyl,**
axial hydroxyl

cis, **axial methyl,**
equatorial hydroxyl

A molecular mechanics program can be used to calculate the relative energies of these four isomers and help you to predict the most stable *trans* and *cis* conformations. Even without calculation, you should be able to predict which of the two *trans* conformations is the more stable.

By carrying out semiempirical molecular orbital calculations on the starting material (*see* Chapter 15), you may be able to decide, based on the shape and location of the lowest unoccupied molecular orbital (LUMO), whether the borohydride anion will attack the carbonyl group from the top, to give predominantly the *trans* isomer, or from the bottom, to give mostly the *cis* isomer. You may also be able to make this prediction by studying a molecular model or even a drawing of 2-methylcyclohexanone:

You can determine the structures and relative percentage yields of the products in this reaction using nuclear magnetic resonance (NMR) spectroscopy. The 250-MHz ^{1}H NMR spectrum of a 50:50 mixture of methylcyclohexanols is given in Figure 26.1. The two lowest field groups of peaks are from the hydrogen atom on the hydroxyl-bearing carbon atom.

The reduction of 2-methylcyclohexanone with sodium borohydride will give a mixture of products but not necessarily a 50:50 mixture. Integration of the two low-field groups of peaks will allow determination of the actual percentages of products in this reaction. First, however, the peaks must be assigned to the *cis* and *trans* isomers. The groups of peaks have been expanded and numbered on the spectrum in Figure 26.1, and the frequencies of the 11 peaks are listed in the caption.

The NMR coupling constant of the proton on the hydroxyl-bearing carbon is a function of the dihedral angle between that proton and an adjacent vicinal proton. This is seen most easily by examining molecular models and Newman projections. For the *trans* isomer of 2-methylcyclohexanol, the predominant conformer is the one in which both the methyl group and hydroxyl group are equatorial, and H$_A$ and H$_B$ are diaxial with a dihedral angle of 180° between them. The coupling constant for dihedral hydrogens is normally in the 9–12 Hz range. For the less favorable conformer, H_A and H_B are both equatorial, and the dihedral angle between them is 60°. This results in a coupling constant in the 2–5 Hz range.

■ FIG. 26.1
The 250-MHz NMR spectrum of a mixture of *cis-* and *trans-*2-methylcyclohexanol. The frequencies of peaks 1 to 5 are 950.3, 947.5, 944.8, 942.2, and 939.5 Hz, respectively. The frequencies of peaks 6 to 11 are 791.2, 786.9, 781.6, 777.1, 771.6, and 767.4 Hz, respectively.

For *cis*-2-methylcyclohexanol, the two possible conformers are about equal in energy. In either conformer, H$_A$ and H$_B$ are in a 60° axial-equatorial stereochemical relationship, which results in a coupling constant in the 4–7 Hz range.

From this information, it should be possible to assign the groups of peaks at 3.1 and 3.8 ppm to either *cis*- or *trans*-2-methylcyclohexanol. From the areas of the two sets of peaks, the relative percentages of the isomers can be determined.

EXPERIMENT

Borohydride Reduction of 2-Methylcyclohexanone

This reaction can be run on a scale four times larger in a 25-mL Erlenmeyer flask.

IN THIS EXPERIMENT a liquid ketone in methanol is reduced with solid sodium borohydride. Base is added, and the product is extracted into dichloromethane. In the usual way this organic layer is dried and evaporated to leave the liquid alcohol. The same procedure could be used to reduce most ketones to their corresponding alcohols.

To a reaction tube add 1.25 mL of methanol and 300 mg of 2-methylcyclohexanone. Cool this solution in an ice bath contained in a small beaker. While the reaction tube is in the ice bath, carefully add 50 mg of sodium borohydride to the solution. After the vigorous reaction has ceased, remove the tube from the ice bath and allow it to stand at room temperature for 10 min, at which time the reaction should appear to be finished. To decompose the borate ester, add 1.25 mL of 3 *M* sodium hydroxide solution. To the resulting cloudy

■ FIG. 26.2
The IR spectrum of a mixture of *cis*- and *trans*-2-methylcyclohexanol (thin film).

solution, add 1 mL of water. The product will separate as a small, clear upper layer. Remove as much of this as possible, place it in a reaction tube, and then extract the remainder of the product from the reaction mixture with two 0.5-mL portions of dichloromethane. Add these dichloromethane extracts to the small product layer and dry the combined extracts over anhydrous sodium sulfate (not calcium chloride). After a few minutes, transfer the solution to a dry reaction tube containing a boiling chip. In the hood, boil off the dichloromethane (and any accompanying methanol) and use the residue to run an NMR spectrum in the usual way.

Integrate the two low-field sets of peaks at 3.1 and 3.8 ppm, analyze the coupling constant patterns to assign the two sets of peaks, and report the percentage distribution of *cis*- and *trans*-2-methylcyclohexanol formed in this reaction. The relative amounts of the products can, of course, also be determined by gas chromatography. How do these results compare to your predictions and calculations? Which *cis* and which *trans* conformation is the more stable?

Run an infrared (IR) spectrum of the product as a thin film to determine whether the reduction of the starting material has been completed (Fig. 26.2).

Cleaning Up. The reaction mixture is neutralized with acetic acid (to react with sodium borohydride) and flushed down the drain with water.

Computational Chemistry

Using a molecular mechanics program, calculate the steric energies of *cis*- and *trans*-2-methylcyclohexanol. Each of these isomers has two principal conformations. Does reduction of 2-methylcyclohexanone give the more stable isomer? Explain.

Online Study Center

General Resources
Additional Experiments

QUESTIONS

1. Draw the NMR peak expected for H_A when H_A couples with H_B in the following structure.

2. Draw the NMR peak expected when H_A couples with both H_B and H_C. Remember that the coupling constants are not equal.

3. What is the approximate frequency of the most important peak in the starting material that should be absent in the IR spectrum of the product?

38

Grignard Synthesis of Triphenylmethanol and Benzoic Acid

PRELAB EXERCISE: Prepare a flow sheet for the preparation of triphenylmethanol. Using your knowledge of the physical properties of the solvents, reactants, and products, show how the products can be purified. Indicate which layer should contain the product in the liquid/liquid extraction steps.

In 1912 Victor Grignard received the Nobel Prize in Chemistry for his work on the reaction that bears his name, a carbon-carbon bond-forming reaction by which almost any alcohol may be formed from appropriate alkyl halides and carbonyl compounds. The Grignard reagent is easily formed by reacting an alkyl halide, in particular a bromide, with magnesium metal in anhydrous diethyl ether. The reaction can be written and thought of as simply

$$R\!-\!Br + Mg \longrightarrow R\!-\!Mg\!-\!Br$$

However, the structure of the material in solution is rather more complex. There is evidence that dialkylmagnesium is present:

$$2\ R\!-\!Mg\!-\!Br \rightleftharpoons R\!-\!Mg\!-\!R + MgBr_2$$

The magnesium atoms, which have the capacity to accept two electron pairs from donor molecules to achieve a four-coordinated state, are solvated by the unshared pairs of electrons on diethyl ether:

Structure of the Grignard reagent

$$
\begin{array}{ccc}
\overset{\displaystyle Et\diagdown\ \ \diagup Et}{\underset{\displaystyle Et\diagup\ \ \diagdown Et}{\overset{\ddot{O}}{R\!-\!\underset{\ddot{O}}{Mg}\!-\!Br}}} & \text{and} & \overset{\displaystyle Et\diagdown\ \ \diagup Et}{\underset{\displaystyle Et\diagup\ \ \diagdown Et}{\overset{\ddot{O}}{R\!-\!\underset{\ddot{O}}{Mg}\!-\!R}}}
\end{array}
$$

The Grignard reagent is both a strong base and a strong nucleophile. As a base it will react with all protons that are more acidic than those found on alkenes and alkanes. Thus, Grignard reagents react readily with water, alcohols, amines, thiols, and so on to regenerate an alkane:

$$R\text{---}Mg\text{---}Br + H_2O \longrightarrow R\text{---}H + MgBrOH$$

$$R\text{---}Mg\text{---}Br + R'OH \longrightarrow R\text{---}H + MgBrOR'$$

$$R\text{---}Mg\text{---}Br + R'NH_2 \longrightarrow R\text{---}H + MgBrNHR'$$

$$R\text{---}Mg\text{---}Br + R'C \equiv C\text{---}H \longrightarrow R\text{---}H + R'C \equiv CMgBr$$
$$\text{(an acetylenic Grignard reagent)}$$

The starting material for preparing the Grignard reagent cannot contain any acidic protons. The reactants and apparatus must be completely and absolutely dry; otherwise the reaction will not start. If proper precautions are taken, however, the reaction proceeds smoothly.

Magnesium metal, in the form of a coarse powder, has a coat of oxide on the outside. A fresh surface can be exposed by crushing the powder under absolutely dry ether in the presence of an organic halide. The reaction will begin at exposed surfaces, as evidenced by a slight turbidity in the solution and evolution of bubbles. Once the exothermic reaction starts, it proceeds easily, the magnesium dissolves, and a solution of the Grignard reagent is formed. The solution is often turbid and gray due to impurities in the magnesium. The reagent is not isolated but reacted immediately with, most often, an appropriate carbonyl compound

$$R\text{---}Mg\text{---}Br + R'\text{---}\overset{\overset{\ddot{O}:}{\|}}{C}\text{---}R'' \longrightarrow R'\text{---}\overset{\overset{:\ddot{O}:^- MgBr^+}{|}}{\underset{\underset{R}{|}}{C}}\text{---}R''$$

to give, in another exothermic reaction, magnesium alkoxide, a salt insoluble in ether. In a simple acid-base reaction, this alkoxide is reacted with acidified ice water to give the covalent, ether-soluble alcohol and the ionic water-soluble magnesium salt:

$$R'\text{---}\overset{\overset{:\ddot{O}:^- MgBr^+}{|}}{\underset{\underset{R}{|}}{C}}\text{---}R'' + H^+Cl^- \longrightarrow R'\text{---}\overset{\overset{:\ddot{O}\text{---}H}{|}}{\underset{\underset{R}{|}}{C}}\text{---}R'' + Mg^{2+}Br^-Cl^-$$

The great versatility of this reaction lies in the wide range of reactants that undergo it. Thirteen representative reactions are shown in Figure 38.1. In every case except reaction 1, the intermediate alkoxide must be hydrolyzed to give the product. The reaction with oxygen (reaction 2) is usually not a problem because the ether vapor over the reagent protects it from attack by oxygen, but this reaction is one reason why the reagent cannot usually be stored without special precautions. The reaction with solid carbon dioxide (dry ice) occurs readily to produce a carboxylic acid (reaction 3). Reactions 5, 6, and 7 with aldehydes and ketones giving, respectively, primary, tertiary, and secondary alcohols are among the most common. Ring-opening of an epoxide via Grignard addition (reaction 4) yields an alcohol as well. Reactions 8–13 are not nearly so common.

■ **FIG. 38.1**
The versatility of the Grignard reaction is illustrated by the wide range of reactants that undergo it.

In one of the experiments in this chapter, we will carry out another common type of Grignard reaction, the formation of a tertiary alcohol from 2 moles of the reagent and 1 mole of an ester. The ester employed is the methyl benzoate, which can be synthesized in Chapter 40. The initially formed product is unstable and decomposes to a ketone, which, being more reactive than an ester, immediately reacts with more Grignard reagent:

Bromobenzene[1]
MW 157.02
bp 156.4°C
den. 1.491

Magnesium
At Wt 24.1

Phenylmagnesium bromide

Methyl benzoate
MW 136.16
bp 199.6°C
den. 1.09

$-Mg^{2+}Br^{-}OCH_3^{-}$

Triphenylmethanol
MW 260.34
mp 164.2°C

The primary impurity in these experiments is biphenyl, formed by reacting phenylmagnesium bromide with unreacted bromobenzene. (Figure 38.2 shows the ^{13}C NMR spectrum of bromobenzene.) The most effective way to lessen this side reaction is to add the bromobenzene slowly to the reaction mixture so it will

■ **FIG. 38.2**
The ^{13}C NMR spectrum of bromobenzene (22.6 MHz).

react with the magnesium and not be present in high concentration to react with previously formed Grignard reagent. The impurity is easily eliminated because it is much more soluble in hydrocarbon solvents than triphenylmethanol.

Biphenyl has a characteristic odor. Triphenylmethanol is odorless.

![reaction scheme: phenylmagnesium bromide + bromobenzene → biphenyl + MgBr₂]

Biphenyl
mp 72°C

Triphenylmethanol can also be prepared from benzophenone.

![reaction scheme of phenylmagnesium bromide with benzophenone to triphenylmethanol]

Phenylmagnesium bromide

Benzophenone
MW 182.22
mp 48°C

Triphenylmethanol
MW 260.34
mp 164.2°C

EXPERIMENTS

1. Phenylmagnesium Bromide (Phenyl Grignard Reagent)

Br   +   Mg $\xrightarrow{\text{anhydrous ether}}$ MgBr

Bromobenzene
MW 157.02
bp 156°C
den. 1.491

Magnesium
At Wt
24.31

Phenylmagnesium bromide
not isolated, used in situ

Advance Preparation

It is imperative that all equipment and reagents be absolutely dry. The magnesium and the glassware to be used—two reaction tubes, two 1-dram vials (1 dram = 1.78 mL), and a stirring rod—can be dried in a 110°C oven for at least 30 min. Alternatively, if the glassware, syringe, septa, and magnesium appear to be perfectly dry, they can be used without special drying. The plastic and rubber components should be rinsed with acetone if either appears to be dirty or wet with water; then place these components in a desiccator for at least 12 h. Do not place plastic or rubber components in the oven. New, factory-sealed packages of syringes can be used without prior drying. The ether used throughout this reaction must be absolutely dry (absolute ether).

To prepare the Grignard reagent, absolute diethyl ether must be used; else-where, ordinary ether (diethyl or *t*-butyl methyl) can be used; for example, ether extractions of aqueous solutions do not need to be carried out with dry ether. It is strongly recommended that *t*-butyl methyl ether be used in all cases except in the preparation of the Grignard reagent itself.

A very convenient container for absolute diethyl ether is a 50-mL septum-capped bottle. This method of dispensing the solvent has three advantages: The ether is kept anhydrous, the exposure to oxygen is minimized, and there is little possibility of its catching fire. Ether is extremely flammable; do not work with this solvent near flames.

To remove ether from a septum-capped bottle, inject a volume of air into the bottle equal to the amount of ether being removed. Pull more ether than needed into the syringe and then push the excess back into the bottle before removing the syringe. In this way there will be no air bubbles in the syringe, and it will not dribble (Fig. 38.3).

Procedure

CAUTION: Ether is extremely flammable. Extinguish all flames before using ether.

Online Study Center

Video: The Grignard Reaction: Removing a Liquid from a Septum-Capped Bottle with Syringe; Photos: Removing a Reagent from a Septum-Capped Bottle, Polypropylene Syringe Containing Ether

IN THIS EXPERIMENT magnesium and absolutely dry diethyl ether in a dry, septum-capped tube are reacted with an aromatic halide to give phenylmagnesium bromide. The exothermic reaction is started by crushing the magnesium. If the reaction does not start in 2–3 min, it will be necessary to start again, using equipment that was not used in the first attempt.

Remove a reaction tube from the oven and immediately cap it with a septum. In the operations that follow, keep the tube capped except when it is necessary to open it. After the tube cools to room temperature, add about 2 mmol (about 50 mg) of magnesium powder. Record the weight of magnesium used to the nearest milligram. The magnesium will become the limiting reagent by using a 5% molar excess of bromobenzene (about 2.1 mmol).

Using a dry syringe, add to the magnesium by injection through the septum 0.5 mL of anhydrous diethyl ether. Your laboratory instructor will demonstrate the transfer from the storage container used in your laboratory.

Into an oven-dried vial weigh about 2.1 mmol (about 330 mg) of dry (stored over molecular sieves) bromobenzene. Using a syringe, add to this vial 0.7 mL anhydrous diethyl ether and *immediately*, with the same syringe, remove all the solution from the vial. This can be done virtually quantitatively so you do not need to rinse the vial. Immediately cap the empty vial to keep it dry for later use. Inject

Diethyl ether can be made and kept anhydrous by storing over Linde 5A molecular sieves. Discard diethyl ether within 90 days because of peroxide formation. *t*-Butyl methyl ether does not have this problem.

■ FIG. 38.3
A polypropylene syringe (1 mL, with 0.01-mL graduations). The needle is blunt. When there are no air bubbles in the syringe, it will not dribble ether.

■ FIG. 38.4
Once the reaction has started, bromobenzene in ether is added slowly from the syringe. The empty needle is for pressure relief, but if condensation is complete (aided by the damp pipe cleaner), it will not be needed. Once the reaction slows down, stir it with a magnetic stirrer and stirring bar.

■ FIG. 38.5
To start the Grignard reaction, remove the septum and apply pressure to the stirring rod while rotating the reaction tube on a hard surface that will not scratch the tube, such as a book.

Read volume here

about 0.1 mL of the bromobenzene-ether mixture into the reaction tube and mix the contents by flicking the tube. Pierce the septum with another syringe needle for pressure relief (Fig. 38.4).

The reaction will not ordinarily start at this point, so remove the septum, syringe, and empty syringe needle and crush the magnesium with a dry stirring rod. You can do this easily in the confines of the 10-mm-diameter reaction tube while it is positioned on a hard surface. There is little danger of poking the stirring rod through the bottom of the tube (Fig. 38.5). Immediately replace the septum, syringe, and empty syringe needle (for pressure relief). The reaction should start within seconds. The formerly clear solution becomes cloudy and soon begins to boil as the magnesium metal reacts with the bromobenzene to form the Grignard reagent—phenylmagnesium bromide.

If the reaction does not start within 1 min, begin again with completely different, dry equipment (syringe, syringe needle, reaction tube, etc.). Once the Grignard reaction begins, it will continue. To prevent the ether from boiling away, wrap a pipe cleaner around the top part of the reaction tube. Dampen the pipe cleaner with water or, if the room temperature is very hot, with alcohol.

To the refluxing mixture add slowly and dropwise over a period of several minutes the remainder of the bromobenzene-ether solution at a rate such that the reaction remains under control at all times. After all the bromobenzene solution is added, spontaneous boiling of the diluted mixture may be slow or become slow. At this point, add a magnetic stirring bar to the reaction tube and stir the reaction mixture with a magnetic stirrer. If the rate of reaction is too fast, slow down the stirrer. The reaction is complete when none or a very small quantity of the metal remains. Check to see that the volume of ether has not decreased. If it has, add more anhydrous diethyl ether. Because the solution of the Grignard reagent deteriorates on standing, Experiment 2 should be started at once. The phenylmagnesium bromide can be converted to triphenylmethanol or to benzoic acid.

2. Triphenylmethanol

Phenylmagnesium bromide

Benzophenone
MW 182.22
mp 48°C

Triphenylmethanol
MW 260.34
mp 164.2°C

It takes much force to crush the magnesium. Place the tube on a hard surface and bear down with the stirring rod while twisting the reaction tube. Do not pound the magnesium.

Online Study Center

Video: The Grignard Reaction: Starting the Reaction

Online Study Center

Video: The Grignard Reaction: Addition of Bromobenzene and Refluxing of Reaction Mixture

> **IN THIS EXPERIMENT** the Grignard reagent prepared in Experiment 1 is added to a dry ether solution of benzophenone. Very thorough mixing is required. When the red color disappears, the salt is hydrolyzed by adding hydrochloric acid. More ether is added, the layers separated, and the ether dried and evaporated to give crude product. An impurity, biphenyl, is removed by dissolving it in hexanes, and the product is recrystallized from 2-propanol. The product recrystallizes very slowly, so do not collect the product immediately.

Make *t*-butyl methyl ether anhydrous by storing it over molecular sieves.

Online Study Center

Videos: The Grignard Reaction: Dissolution of Benzophenone in Ether, Addition to Grignard Reagent; The Grignard Reaction: Mixing Reaction Mixture by Flicking Reaction Tube

Mixing the reaction mixture is very important.

Online Study Center

Videos: The Grignard Reaction: Final Addition of Benzophenone Solution; The Grignard Reaction: Color Change at Completion of Reaction

Online Study Center

Videos: The Grignard Reaction: Addition of Hydrochloric Acid; The Grignard Reaction: Solution Treated with Saturated Sodium Chloride Solution

In an oven-dried vial dissolve 2.0 mmol (0.364 g) of benzophenone in 1.0 mL of anhydrous ether by capping the vial and mixing the contents thoroughly. With a dry syringe, remove all the solution from the vial and add it dropwise with *thorough* mixing (magnetic stirring, flicking of the tube, or stirring with a stirring rod near the end of the addition) after each drop to the solution of the Grignard reagent. Add the benzophenone at a rate so as to maintain the ether at a gentle reflux. Rinse the vial with a few drops of anhydrous ether after all the first solution has been added; then add this rinse to the reaction tube.

After all the benzophenone has been added, the mixture should be homogeneous. If not, mix it again, using a stirring rod if necessary. The syringe can be removed but leave the pressure-relief needle in place. Allow the reaction mixture to stand at room temperature. The reaction apparently is complete when the red color disappears.

At the end of the reaction period, cool the tube in ice and add to it dropwise with stirring (use a glass rod or a spatula) 2 mL of 3 M hydrochloric acid. A creamy-white precipitate of triphenylmethanol will separate between the layers. Add more ether (it need not be anhydrous) to the reaction tube and shake the contents to dissolve all the triphenylmethanol. The result should be two perfectly clear layers. Remove a drop of the ether layer for thin-layer chromatographic (TLC) analysis. Any bubbling seen at the interface or in the lower layer is leftover magnesium reacting with the hydrochloric acid. Remove the aqueous layer and shake the ether layer with an equal volume of saturated aqueous sodium chloride solution to remove water and any remaining acid. Carefully remove the entire aqueous layer; then dry the ether layer by adding anhydrous calcium chloride pellets to the reaction tube until the drying agent no longer clumps together. Cork the tube and shake it from time to time over 5–10 min to complete the drying.

Using a Pasteur pipette, remove the ether from the drying agent and place it in another tared, dry reaction tube or a centrifuge tube. Use more ether to wash off the drying agent and combine these ether extracts. Evaporate the ether in a hood by blowing nitrogen or air onto the surface of the solution while warming the tube in a beaker of water or in the hand.

After all the solvent has been removed, determine the weight of the crude product. Note the odor of the biphenyl, the product of the side reaction that takes place between bromobenzene and phenylmagnesium bromide during the first reaction.

Trituration (grinding) of the crude product with petroleum ether will remove the biphenyl. Stir the crystals with 0.5 mL of petroleum ether in an ice bath, remove

■ **FIG. 38.6**

An apparatus for drying crystals in a reaction tube under vacuum.

■ **FIG. 38.7**

A semimicroscale, research-type apparatus for the Grignard reaction, with provision for a motor-driven stirrer and an inlet and outlet for dry nitrogen.

Online Study Center

Videos: The Grignard Reaction: Crude Product Triturated and Recrystallized—Pure Triphenylcarbinol Isolated; Microscale Filtration on the Hirsch Funnel

Online Study Center

Photo: Filtration Using a Pasteur Pipette; Video: Filtration of Crystals Using the Pasteur Pipette

the solvent as thoroughly as possible, add a boiling stick, and recrystallize the residue from boiling 2-propanol (no more than 2 mL). Allow the solution to cool slowly to room temperature and then cool it thoroughly in ice. Triphenylmethanol crystallizes slowly, so allow the mixture to remain in the ice as long as possible. Stir the ice-cold mixture well and collect the product by vacuum filtration on a Hirsch funnel. Save the filtrate. Concentration may give a second crop of crystals.

An alternative method for purifying the triphenylmethanol utilizes a mixed solvent. Dissolve the crystals in the smallest possible quantity of warm ether and add 1.5 mL of hexanes to the solution. Add a boiling stick to the solution and boil off some of the ether until the solution becomes slightly cloudy, indicating that it is saturated. Allow the solution to cool slowly to room temperature. Triphenylmethanol is deposited slowly as large, thick prisms. Cool the solution in ice; after allowing time for complete crystallization to occur, remove the ether with a Pasteur pipette and wash the crystals once with a few drops of a cold 1:4 ether-hexanes mixture. Dry the crystals in the tube under a vacuum (Fig. 38.6).

Determine the weight, melting point, and percent yield of the triphenylmethanol. Analyze the crude and recrystallized product by TLC on silica gel (*see* Chapter 8), developing the plate with a 1:5 mixture of dichloromethane and petroleum ether. An infrared (IR) spectrum can be determined in chloroform solution or by preparing a mull or KBr disk (*see* Chapter 11). Compare the apparatus used in this experiment with the research-type apparatus shown in Figure 38.7.

Cleaning Up. Combine the acidic aqueous layer and saturated sodium chloride layers, dilute with water, neutralize with sodium carbonate, and flush down the drain with excess water. Ether is allowed to evaporate from the drying agent in the hood, and the drying agent is then discarded in the nonhazardous solid waste container. If local regulations do not allow for evaporating solvents in a hood, the wet drying agent should be discarded in a special container. The petroleum ether and 2-propanol or ether-hexanes mother liquor are placed in the organic solvents container.

3. Benzoic Acid

> **IN THIS EXPERIMENT** the Grignard reagent prepared in Experiment 1 is squirted onto a piece of dry ice. The resulting white carboxylate salt is hydrolyzed with hydrochloric acid, releasing benzoic acid, which is extracted into the ether layer. The ether solution could be dried and evaporated to give the product, but a better product is obtained by adding base to make the benzoate salt and then adding acid to this basic solution to cause benzoic acid to crystallize. It can be recrystallized from hot water.

Phenylmagnesium bromide

Carbon dioxide
MW 44.01
mp $-78.5°C$ (sublimes)

Benzoic acid
MW 122.12
mp 123°C

CAUTION: Handle dry ice with a towel or gloves. Contact with the skin can cause frostbite because dry ice sublimes at $-78.5°C$.

Prepare 2 mmol of phenylmagnesium bromide exactly as described in Experiment 1. Wipe off the surface of a small piece of dry ice (solid carbon dioxide) with a dry towel to remove frost and place it in a dry 30-mL beaker. Remove the pressure-relief needle from the reaction tube; then insert a syringe through the septum, turn the tube upside down, and draw into the syringe as much of the reagent solution as possible. Squirt this solution onto the piece of dry ice; then, using a clean needle, rinse out the reaction tube with 1 mL of anhydrous diethyl ether and squirt this onto the dry ice. Allow excess dry ice to sublime; then hydrolyze the salt by adding 2 mL of 3 M hydrochloric acid.

Transfer the mixture from the beaker to a reaction tube and shake it thoroughly. Two homogeneous layers should result. Add 1–2 mL of acid or ordinary (not anhydrous) ether if necessary. Remove the aqueous layer and shake the ether layer with 1 mL of water, which is removed and discarded. Then extract the benzoic acid by adding to the ether layer 0.7 mL of 3 M sodium hydroxide solution, shaking the mixture thoroughly, and withdrawing the aqueous layer, which is placed in a very small beaker or vial. The extraction is repeated with another 0.5-mL portion of base and finally 0.5 mL of water. Now that the extraction is complete, the ether, which can be discarded, contains primarily biphenyl, the byproduct formed during the preparation of phenylmagnesium bromide.

The combined aqueous extracts are heated briefly to about 50°C to drive off dissolved ether from the aqueous solution and then made acidic by adding

Online Study Center
Video: Extraction with Ether

concentrated hydrochloric acid (test with indicator paper). Cool the mixture thoroughly in an ice bath. Collect the benzoic acid on a Hirsch funnel and wash it with about 1 mL of ice water while on the funnel. A few crystals of this crude material are saved for a melting-point determination; the remainder of the product is recrystallized from boiling water.

The solubility of benzoic acid in water is 68 g/L at 95°C and 1.7 g/L at 0°C. Dissolve the acid in very hot water. Let the solution cool slowly to room temperature; then cool it in ice for several minutes before collecting the product by vacuum filtration on a Hirsch funnel. Use the ice-cold filtrate in the filter flask to complete the transfer of benzoic acid from the reaction tube. Turn the product out onto a piece of filter paper, squeeze out excess water, and allow it to dry thoroughly. Once dry, weigh it, calculate the percent yield, and determine the melting point along with the melting point of the crude material. The IR spectrum may be determined as a solution in chloroform (1 g of benzoic acid dissolves in 4.5 mL of chloroform) or as a mull or KBr disk (*see* Chapter 11).

Cleaning Up. Combine all aqueous layers, dilute with a large quantity of water, and flush the slightly acidic solution down the drain.

4. Phenylmagnesium Bromide (Phenyl Grignard Reagent)

Br + Mg $\xrightarrow[\text{ether}]{\text{anhydrous}}$ MgBr

Bromobenzene
MW 157.02
bp 156°C
den. 1.491

Magnesium
At Wt
24.31

Phenylmagnesium bromide
not isolated, used *in situ*

Diethyl ether can be kept anhydrous by storing it over Linde 5A molecular sieves. Discard the ether after 90 days because of peroxide formation.

All equipment and reagents must be *absolutely dry*. The Grignard reagent is prepared in a dry, 100-mL round-bottomed flask fitted with a long reflux condenser. A calcium chloride drying tube inserted in a cork that will fit either the flask or the top of the condenser is also made ready (Fig. 38.8a). The flask, condenser, and magnesium (2.00 g = 0.082 mol of magnesium turnings) should be as dry as possible to begin with and then should be further dried in a 110°C oven for at least 35 min. Alternatively, the magnesium is placed in the flask, the calcium chloride tube is attached directly, and the flask is heated gently but thoroughly with a cool luminous flame.[1] Do not overheat the magnesium. It will become deactivated through oxidation or, if strongly overheated, can burn. The flask on cooling pulls dry air through the calcium chloride. Cool to room temperature before proceeding! Extinguish all flames! Ether vapor is denser than air and can travel along bench tops and into sinks. Use care.

CAUTION: Ether is extremely flammable. Extinguish all flames before using ether.

1. Alternatively, if nitrogen gas is available, the reaction can be run under nitrogen using a bubbler.

■ FIG. 38.8
(a) A calcium chloride drying tube fitted with a rubber stopper. Store for future use with a cork in the top and a pipette bulb on the bottom. (b) An apparatus for refluxing the Grignard reaction.

Cotton
or glass wool

8 Mesh
CaCl$_2$

Cotton

(a)

Calcium
chloride tube

Water out

Water in

Round-bottom
flask

Thermowell

(b)

Specially dried ether is required.

Prepare an ice bath in case control of the reaction becomes necessary, although this is usually not the case. Remove the drying tube and fit it to the top of the condenser. Then pour into the flask through the condenser 15 mL of *absolute* ether (absolutely dry, anhydrous) and 9 mL (13.5 g = 0.086 mol) of bromobenzene. Be sure the graduated cylinders used to measure the ether and bromobenzene are absolutely dry. (More ether is to be added as soon as the reaction starts, but the concentration of bromobenzene is kept high at the outset to promote easy starting.) If there is no immediate sign of reaction, insert a *dry* stirring rod with a flattened end and crush a piece of magnesium firmly against the bottom of the flask under the surface of the liquid, giving a twisting motion to the rod. When this is done properly, the liquid becomes slightly cloudy, and ebullition commences at the surface of the compressed metal. Be careful not to punch a hole in the bottom of the flask. Attach the condenser at once and swirl the flask to provide fresh surfaces for contact. As soon as you are sure that the reaction has started, add an additional 25 mL of absolute ether through the top of the condenser before spontaneous boiling becomes too vigorous (replace the drying tube). Note the volume of ether in the flask. Cool in ice if necessary to slow the reaction but do not overcool the mixture; the reaction can be stopped by too much cooling. Any difficulty in initiating the reaction can be dealt with by trying the following prompts in succession.

Starting the Grignard reaction

1. Warm the flask with your hands or in a beaker of warm water. Then see if boiling continues when the flask (condenser attached) is removed from the warmth.
2. Try further mashing of the metal with a dry stirring rod.
3. Add a tiny crystal of iodine as a starter (in this case the ethereal solution of the final reaction product should be washed with sodium bisulfite solution to remove the yellow color).
4. Add a few drops of a solution of phenylmagnesium bromide or methylmagnesium iodide (which can be made in a test tube).
5. Start afresh, taking greater care with the dryness of apparatus, measuring tools, and reagents, and sublime a crystal or two of iodine on the surface of the magnesium to generate Gattermann's activated magnesium before beginning the reaction again.

Use caution when heating to avoid condensation on the outside of the condenser.

Once the reaction begins, spontaneous boiling in the diluted mixture may be slow or become slow. If so, mount the flask and condenser in a heating mantle or Thermowell (one clamp supporting the condenser suffices; Fig. 38.8b) and reflux gently until the magnesium has disintegrated and the solution has acquired a cloudy or brownish appearance. The reaction is complete when only a few remnants of metal (or metal contaminants) remain. Check to see that the volume of ether has not decreased. If it has, add more anhydrous ether. Because the solution of Grignard reagent deteriorates on standing, Experiment 5 should be started at once.

5. Triphenylmethanol from Methyl Benzoate

Phenylmagnesium bromide

Methyl benzoate
MW 136.15
bp 198–199°C

Triphenylmethanol
MW 260.34
mp 164.2°C

Mix 5 g (0.037 mol) of methyl benzoate and 15 mL of absolute ether in a separatory funnel, cool the flask containing the phenylmagnesium bromide solution briefly in an ice bath, remove the drying tube, and insert the stem of a separatory funnel into the top of the condenser. Run in the methyl benzoate solution *slowly* with only such cooling as is required to control the mildly exothermic reaction, which affords an intermediate salt that separates as a white solid. Replace the calcium chloride tube; swirl the flask until it is at room temperature and the reaction has subsided. Go to Experiment 7.

6. Triphenylmethanol from Benzophenone

| Phenylmagnesium bromide | Benzophenone
MW 182.22
mp 48°C | | | Triphenylmethanol
MW 260.34
mp 164.2°C |

Dissolve 6.75 g (0.037 mol) of benzophenone in 25 mL of absolute ether in a separatory funnel and cool the flask containing *half* the phenylmagnesium bromide solution (0.041 mol) briefly in an ice bath. (The other half can be used to make benzoic acid.) Remove the drying tube and insert the stem of the separatory funnel into the top of the condenser. Add the benzophenone solution *slowly* with swirling and only such cooling as is required to control the mildly exothermic reaction, which gives a bright-red solution and then precipitates a white salt. Replace the calcium chloride tube; swirl the flask until it is at room temperature and the reaction has subsided. Go to Experiment 7.

7. Completion of Grignard Reaction

This is a suitable stopping point.

In this part of the experiment, ordinary (not anhydrous) diethyl ether or *t*-butyl methyl ether may be used.

The reaction is then completed by either refluxing the mixture for 30 min or stoppering the flask with the calcium chloride tube and letting the mixture stand overnight (subsequent refluxing is then unnecessary).[2]

Pour the reaction mixture into a 250-mL Erlenmeyer flask containing 50 mL of 10% sulfuric acid and about 25 g of ice and use both ordinary ether and 10% sulfuric acid to rinse the flask. Swirl well to promote hydrolysis of the addition compound; basic magnesium salts are converted into water-soluble neutral salts;

---

2. A rule of thumb for organic reactions: A 10°C rise in temperature will double the rate of the reaction.

triphenylmethanol is distributed into the ether layer. An additional amount of ordinary ether may be required. Pour the mixture into a separatory funnel (rinse the flask with ether), shake, and draw off the aqueous layer. Shake the ether solution with 10% sulfuric acid to further remove magnesium salts and wash with saturated sodium chloride solution to remove water that has dissolved in the ether. The amounts of liquid used in these washing operations are not critical. In general, an amount of wash liquid equal to one-third of the ether volume is adequate.

Saturated aqueous sodium chloride solution removes water from ether.

To effect final drying of the ether solution, pour the ether layer out of the neck of the separatory funnel into an Erlenmeyer flask, add about 5 g of calcium chloride pellets, swirl the flask intermittently, and after 5 min remove the drying agent by gravity filtration (using a filter paper and funnel) into a tared Erlenmeyer flask. Rinse the drying agent with a small amount of ether. Add 25 mL of 66°C–77°C hexanes and concentrate the ether-hexanes solutions (steam bath or hot plate) in an Erlenmeyer flask under an aspirator tube (*see* Fig. 9.6 on page 206). Evaporate slowly until crystals of triphenylmethanol just begin to separate; then let crystallization proceed, first at room temperature and then at 0°C. The product should be colorless and should melt at no lower than 160°C. Concentration of the mother liquor may yield a second crop of crystals. A typical student yield is 5.0 g. Evaporate the mother liquors to dryness and save the residue for later isolation of the components by chromatography.

Perform a TLC analysis of the first crop of triphenylmethanol and the residue from the evaporation of the mother liquors. Dissolve equal quantities of the two solids (a few crystals) and also biphenyl in equal quantities of dichloromethane (1 or 2 drops). Using a microcapillary, spot equal quantities of material on silica gel TLC plates and develop the plates in an appropriate solvent system. Try a 1:3 dichloromethane–petroleum ether mixture first and adjust the relative quantities of solvent as needed. The spots can be seen by examining the TLC plate under a fluorescent lamp or by treating the TLC plate with iodine vapor. From this analysis decide how pure each of the solids is and whether it would be worthwhile to attempt to isolate more triphenylmethanol from the mother liquors.

Turn in the product in a vial labeled with your name, the name of the compound, its melting point, and the overall percent yield from benzoic acid.

Cleaning Up. Combine the acidic aqueous layer and saturated sodium chloride layers, dilute with water, neutralize with sodium carbonate, and flush down the drain with excess water. Ether is allowed to evaporate from the drying agent in the hood, and the drying agent is then discarded in the nonhazardous solid waste container. If local regulations do not allow for evaporating solvents in a hood, the wet drying agent should be discarded in a special container. The ether-hexanes mother liquor is placed in the organic solvents container.

Dispose of recovered and waste solvents in the appropriate containers.

8. Benzoic Acid

Wipe the frost from a piece of dry ice, transfer the ice to a cloth towel, and crush it with a hammer. Without delay (so moisture will not condense on the cold solid), transfer about 10 g of dry ice to a 250-mL beaker. Cautiously pour one-half of the

Online Study Center

Video: Macroscale
Crystallization

solution of phenylmagnesium bromide prepared in Experiment 1 onto the dry ice. A vigorous reaction will ensue. Allow the mixture to warm up and stir it until the dry ice has evaporated. To the beaker add 20 mL of 3 *M* hydrochloric acid; then heat the mixture over a steam bath in the hood to boil off the ether. Cool the beaker thoroughly in an ice bath and collect the solid product by vacuum filtration on a Büchner funnel.

Transfer the solid back to the beaker and dissolve it in a minimum quantity of saturated sodium bicarbonate solution (2.8 *M*). Note that a small quantity of a byproduct remains suspended and floating on the surface of the solution. Note the odor of the mixture. Transfer it to a separatory funnel and shake it briefly with about 15 mL of ether. Discard the ether layer, place the clear aqueous layer in the beaker, and heat it briefly to drive off dissolved ether. Carefully add 3 *M* hydrochloric acid to the mixture until the solution tests acidic to pH paper. Cool the mixture in ice and collect the product on a Büchner funnel. Recrystallize it from a minimum quantity of hot water and isolate it in the usual manner. Determine the melting point and the weight of the benzoic acid; calculate its yield based on the weight of magnesium used to prepare the Grignard reagent.

Cleaning Up. Combine all aqueous layers, dilute with a large quantity of water, and flush the slightly acidic solution down the drain. The ether-hexanes mother liquor from the recrystallization goes in the organic solvents container. The TLC developer, which contains dichloromethane, is placed in the halogenated organic waste container. Calcium chloride from the drying tube should be dissolved in water and flushed down the drain.

QUESTIONS

1. Triphenylmethanol can also be prepared by reacting ethyl benzoate with phenylmagnesium bromide and by reacting diethylcarbonate with phenylmagnesium bromide. Write stepwise reaction mechanisms for these two reactions.

$$\overset{\displaystyle O}{\underset{\displaystyle C_2H_5OCOC_2H_5}{\|}}$$

2. If the ethyl benzoate used to prepare triphenylmethanol is wet, what byproduct is formed?
3. Exactly what weight of dry ice is needed to react with 2 mmol of phenylmagnesium bromide? Would an excess of dry ice be harmful?
4. In the synthesis of benzoic acid, benzene is often detected as an impurity. How does this come about?
5. In Experiment 3, the benzoic acid could have been extracted from the ether layer using sodium bicarbonate solution. Write equations showing how this might be done and how the benzoic acid would be regenerated. What

practical reason makes this extraction method less desirable than sodium hydroxide extraction?

6. What is the weight of frost (ice) on the dry ice that will react with all of the Grignard reagent used in Experiment 8?

7. How many moles of carbon dioxide are contained in 10 g of dry ice?

8. Just after the dry ice has evaporated from the beaker, what is the white solid remaining?

9. Write an equation for the reaction of the white solid with 3 *M* hydrochloric acid.

10. Write an equation for the reaction of the product with sodium bicarbonate.

11. Would you expect sodium benzoate to have an odor? Why or why not?

12. What odor do you detect after the product has dissolved in sodium bicarbonate solution?

13. What is the purpose of the ether extraction?

14. "Isolate the product in the usual way." What is the meaning of this sentence?

Online Study Center

General Resources
Web Links

The Wittig and Wittig-Horner Reactions

Online Study Center

This icon will direct you to techniques, equipment setups, and online resources at http://college.hmco.com/ PIC/williamsonMMOE5e.

PRELAB EXERCISE: Account for the fact that the Wittig-Horner reaction of cinnamaldehyde gives almost exclusively the *E,E*-butadiene with very little contaminating *E,Z*-product.

$(C_6H_5)_3P$ + ClH_2C—⟨⟩ ⟶ $(C_6H_5)_3\overset{+}{P}CH_2$—⟨⟩ Cl^- $\xrightarrow{\text{Base} \atop \text{(50% NaOH)}}$

Triphenylphosphine	Benzyl chloride	Benzyltriphenylphosphonium
(1)	(2)	chloride
		(3)

$(C_6H_5)_3P{=}CH$—⟨⟩ $\xleftrightarrow{\text{The Wittig reagent,} \atop \text{an ylide}}$ $(C_6H_5)_3\overset{+}{P}$—$\overset{-}{C}H$—⟨⟩ ⟶

(4)

9-Anthraldehyde
(5)

4-Anthranyl-2,2,2,3-tetraphenyl-
1,2-oxaphosphetane
(6)

⟶ $(C_6H_5)_3P{=}O$ +

Triphenylphosphine
oxide
(7)

trans-9-(2-Phenylethenyl)anthracene
(8)

The Wittig reaction affords an invaluable method for converting a carbonyl compound to an olefin; for example, the conversion of 9-anthraldehyde (**5**) and benzyl chloride (**2**) by means of the Wittig reagent (**4**) through a four-centered intermediate to the product (**8**). Because the active reagent, an ylide, is unstable, it is generated in the presence of a carbonyl compound by dehydrohalogenation of the phosphonium chloride (**3**) with base. Usually a very strong base, such as phenyllithium in dry ether, is employed, but in the experiments in this chapter, 50% sodium hydroxide is employed. The existence of the four-membered ring intermediate was proved by nuclear magnetic resonance (NMR) in 1984.[1] The phenylethenylanthracene product produces a green fluorescence with Cyalume, a chemiluminescent substance, in the light stick reaction (*see* Chapter 61).

The light stick reaction

Simplified Wittig reaction

When the halogen compound employed in the first step has an activated halogen atom ($RCH{=}CHCH_2X$, $C_6H_5CH_2X$, XCH_2CO_2H), a simpler procedure known as the *Horner phosphonate modification* of the Wittig reaction is applicable. When benzyl chloride is heated with triethyl phosphite, chloroethane is eliminated from the initially formed phosphonium chloride with the production of diethyl benzylphosphonate. This phosphonate is stable, but in the presence of a strong base, such as the sodium methoxide used here, it condenses with a carbonyl component in the same way that a Wittig ylide condenses. Thus it reacts with benzaldehyde to give *E*-stilbene and with cinnamaldehyde to give *E,E*-1,4-diphenyl-1,3-butadiene.

Benzyl chloride
bp 179°C, MW 126.59
den. 1.10, n_D^{20} 1.5380

Triethyl phosphite
bp 156°C, MW 166.16
den. 0.94, n_D^{20} 1.4130

Benzyltriethylphosphonium chloride

Diethyl benzylphosphonate
bp 156°C/9 torr
MW 228.23, den. 1.045
n_D^{20} 1.4970

Chloroethane
bp 12.3°C
MW 64.52, den. 0.891

1. Maryanoff, B. E.; Reitz, A. B.; Mutter, M. S. *J. Am. Chem. Soc.* **1984**, *106*, 1873.

Diethyl benzylphosphonate + $CH_3O^- Na^+$ $\longrightarrow$

Sodium methoxide
MW 52.02

Ylide

Ylide + Cinnamaldehyde $\longrightarrow$ *E,E*-1,4-Diphenyl-1,3-butadiene + $Na^+ \bar{O} - P$

Cinnamaldehyde
MW 132.16, den. 1.11
bp 248°C

***E,E*-1,4-Diphenyl-1,3-butadiene**
mp 153°C, MW 206.27

The energy-minimized conformation of *E,E*-1,4-diphenyl-1,3-butadiene. Because of steric hindrance, the molecule is not flat.

$\equiv$

EXPERIMENTS

1. Synthesis of *trans*-9-(2-Phenylethenyl)anthracene[2]

Microscale Procedure

IN THIS EXPERIMENT a phosphonium chloride is reacted with base to form the Wittig reagent. An aldehyde in the same solution reacts with the Wittig reagent to give the alkene product. The solvent, dichloromethane, is dried and evaporated to give the product that is, in turn, recrystallized from 1-propanol.

To a reaction tube add 200 mg of benzyltriphenylphosphonium chloride, 115 mg of 9-anthraldehyde, 0.6 mL of dichloromethane, and a magnetic stirring bar. With rapid magnetic stirring, 0.26 mL of 50% sodium hydroxide solution is added

---

2. For macroscale syntheses of *trans*-9-(2-phenylethenyl)anthracene, see Becker, H. D.; Andersson, K. *J. Org. Chem.* **1983**, *48*, 4552. Merkl, G.; Merz, A. *Synthesis* **1973**, 295. Silversmith, E. F. *J. Chem. Educ.* **1986**, *63*, 645.

■ **FIG. 39.1**
An apparatus for removing
a solvent under a vacuum.

To
aspirator

dropwise from a Pasteur pipette. After stirring vigorously for 30 min, 1.5 mL of dichloromethane and 1.5 mL of water are added; then the tube is capped and shaken. The organic layer is removed and placed in another reaction tube, and the aqueous layer is extracted with 1 mL of dichloromethane. The combined dichloromethane extracts are dried over calcium chloride pellets, the dichloromethane is removed, the drying agent is washed with more solvent, and the solvent is removed under vacuum in the filter flask (Fig. 39.1). To the solid remaining in the filter flask add 3 mL of 1-propanol, heat and transfer the hot solution to an Erlenmeyer flask to crystallize. After cooling spontaneously to room temperature, cool the flask in ice and collect the product on a Hirsch funnel. The triphenylphosphine oxide remains in the propanol solution. The reported melting point of the product is 131°C–132°C.

Macroscale Procedure

Into a 10-mL round-bottomed flask place 0.97 g of benzyltriphenylphosphonium chloride, 0.57 g of 9-anthraldehyde, 3 mL of dichloromethane, and a stirring bar. Clamp the flask over a magnetic stirrer and stir the mixture at high speed while adding 1.3 mL of 50% sodium hydroxide solution dropwise from a Pasteur pipette. After the addition is complete, continue the stirring for 30 min; then transfer the contents of the flask to a 50-mL separatory funnel using 10 mL of water and 10 mL of dichloromethane to complete the transfer. Shake the mixture, remove the organic layer, and then extract the aqueous layer once more with 5 mL of dichloromethane. Dry the combined organic layers with anhydrous calcium chloride pellets, transfer the solution to a 50-mL Erlenmeyer flask, evaporate it to dryness on a steam bath, and recrystallize the yellow partially crystalline residue from 15 mL of 2-propanol. The product recrystallizes as thin yellow plates (mp 131°C–132°C). Save the product for use as a fluorescer in the Cyalume chemiluminescence experiment (*see* Chapter 61). Examine a dilute ethanol solution of the product under an ultraviolet (UV) lamp.

2. Synthesis of 1,4-Diphenyl-1,3-Butadiene

> **IN THIS EXPERIMENT** benzyl chloride and triethyl phosphite are reacted with each other to give a phosphonate salt. This salt, on reaction with the strong base, sodium methoxide, gives a Wittig reagent-like ylide that reacts with an aldehyde to give the product alkene, diphenylbutadiene. It is isolated by filtration and can be recrystallized, if necessary, from methylcyclohexane.

CAUTION: Take care to keep organophosphorus compounds off the skin.

Use freshly prepared or opened sodium methoxide; keep the bottle closed.

CAUTION: Handle benzyl chloride in the hood. Severe lachrymator (tear producer) and irritant of the respiratory tract.

N,N-Dimethylformamide (DMF)
MW 73.10, bp 153°C
n_D^{20} 1.4310

A highly polar solvent capable of dissolving ionic compounds such as sodium methoxide yet miscible with water.

CAUTION: Avoid skin contact with dimethylformamide.

The success of this reaction is strongly dependent on the purity of the starting materials.[3] Benzyl chloride and triethyl phosphite are usually pure enough as received from the supplier. Cinnamaldehyde from a new, previously unopened bottle should be satisfactory, but because it air oxidizes extremely rapidly, it should be distilled, preferably under nitrogen or at reduced pressure, if there is any doubt about its quality. Sodium methoxide, direct from reputable suppliers, has been found on occasion to be completely inactive. No easy method exists for determining its activity; therefore, it is best prepared using the procedure given in *Organic Syntheses*.[4]

To a 10 mm × 100-mm reaction tube add 316 mg (0.0025 mol) of benzyl chloride (α-chlorotoluene), 415 mg (0.44 mL, 0.0025 mol) of triethyl phosphite, and a boiling chip (Fig. 39.2). Because the triethyl phosphite has an offensive odor, obtain this material from the dispenser that has been calibrated to deliver the correct quantity. Place the reaction tube to a depth of about 1 cm in a sand bath that has been preheated to 210°C to 220°C. Reflux the reaction mixture for 1 h. The vapors condense on the cool upper portion of the reaction tube, so a condenser is not necessary. At an internal temperature of about 140°C (which you need not monitor), ethyl chloride is evolved; by the end of the reflux period, the temperature of the reaction mixture will be 200°C to 220°C. At the end of the reaction period, remove the tube from the sand bath, cool it to room temperature, and then add the contents to 160 mg (0.003 mol) of sodium methoxide in a 10-mL Erlenmeyer flask using 1 mL of dry dimethylformamide (DMF) to complete the transfer. Cool the mixture in ice, mix the contents of the flask thoroughly, then add 330 mg (0.0025 mol) of freshly distilled cinnamaldehyde in 1 mL of dry DMF dropwise with thorough mixing in the ice bath. Allow the mixture to come to room temperature. Note the changes that take place over the next few minutes.

After a *minimum* of 10 min, add 2 mL of methanol to the Erlenmeyer flask with thorough stirring. Then almost fill the flask with water and stir the mixture until it is homogeneous in color. The hydrocarbon precipitates from the reaction

---

3. The instructor should try out this experiment before assigning it to a class.

4. For enough sodium methoxide for 50 microscale or 2 macroscale reactions, add 3.5 g of sodium spheres to 50 mL of anhydrous methanol in a 100-mL flask equipped with a condenser. Add the sodium a few pieces at a time through the top of the condenser at a rate so as to keep the reaction under control. It is safest to wait for complete reaction of one portion of sodium before adding the next. After all the sodium has reacted, remove the methanol on a rotary evaporator, first over a steam bath and then over a bath heated to 150°C. The sodium methoxide will be a free-flowing white powder that should keep for several weeks in a desiccator. The yield should be 8.2 g. Source: *Org. Synth.* Col. Vol. IV, **1963**, 651.

■ **FIG. 39.2**
A microscale reflux apparatus.

Cool part of tube

Refluxing liquid (Air condenser)

Sand

Heated area

Boiling liquid

Boiling chip

Electric flask heater

■ **FIG. 39.3**
A Hirsch funnel for filtration.

Filter paper, 12 mm dia.

Polyethylene filter disk (frit), 10 mm dia.

Hirsch funnel

To aspirator

25-mL Filter flask

mixture after adding the methanol and water. Collect the product by vacuum filtration on a Hirsch funnel (Fig. 39.3) and wash the crystals: first with water to remove the red color and then with ice-cold methanol to remove the yellow color. The hydrocarbon is completely insoluble in water and only sparingly soluble in methanol. Weigh the dry product, which should be faint yellow in color, determine its melting point, and calculate the crude yield. If the melting point is below 150°C, recrystallize the product from methylcyclohexane (10 mL/g), and again determine the melting point and yield. Turn in the product in a labeled vial, giving crude and recrystallized weights, melting points, and yields.

Cleaning Up. The filtrate and washings from this reaction are dark, oily, and smell bad. The mixture contains DMF and could contain traces of all starting materials. Keep the volume as small as possible and place it in the hazardous waste container for organophosphorus compounds. If methylcyclohexane was used for recrystallization, place the mother liquor in the organic solvents container.

3. Synthesis of 1,4-Diphenyl-1,3-Butadiene

The success of this reaction is strongly dependent on the purity of the starting materials.

CAUTION: Keep organophosphorus compounds off the skin. Handle benzyl chloride in the hood. It is a severe lachrymator (tear producer) and respiratory tract irritant.

Use freshly prepared or opened sodium methoxide; keep the bottle closed.

Avoid skin contact with dimethylformamide.

N,N-Dimethylformamide (DMF)
MW 73.10, bp 153°C
n_D^{20} 1.4310

A highly polar solvent capable of dissolving ionic compounds such as sodium methoxide yet miscible with water.

With the aid of pipettes and a pipetter, measure into a 25 × 150-mm test tube 5 mL of benzyl chloride (α-chlorotoluene) and 7.7 mL of triethyl phosphite. Add a boiling stone, insert a cold finger condenser, and gently reflux the liquid with a flask heater for 1 h. Alternatively, carry out the reaction in a 25-mL round-bottomed flask equipped with a reflux condenser. (Elimination of ethyl chloride starts at about 130°C and, in the time period specified, the temperature of the liquid rises to 190°C–200°C.) Let the phosphonate ester cool to room temperature, pour it into a 125-mL Erlenmeyer flask containing 2.4 g of sodium methoxide, and add 40 mL of dimethylformamide (DMF), using a part of this solvent to rinse the test tube. Swirl the flask vigorously in a water-ice bath to thoroughly chill the contents and continue swirling while running in 5 mL of cinnamaldehyde by pipette. The mixture soon turns deep red; then crystalline hydrocarbon starts to separate. When there is no further change (about 2 min), remove the flask from the cooling bath and let it stand at room temperature for about 10 min. Then add 20 mL of water and 10 mL of methanol, swirl vigorously to dislodge crystals, and finally collect the product on a suction funnel using the red mother liquor to wash the flask. Wash the product with water until the red color of the product is completely replaced by a yellow color. Then wash with methanol to remove the yellow impurity and continue until the wash liquor is colorless. The yield of the crude, faintly yellow hydrocarbon (mp 150°C–151°C) should be about 5.7 g. This material is satisfactory for use in Chapter 50 (1.5 g required). A good solvent for recrystallization of the remaining product is methylcyclohexane (bp 101°C, 10 mL/g; use more if the solution requires filtration). Pure *E,E*-1,4-diphenyl-1,3-butadiene melts at 153°C.

Cleaning Up. The filtrate and washings from this reaction are dark, oily, and smell bad. The mixture contains DMF and could contain traces of all starting materials. Keep the volume as small as possible and place it in the hazardous waste container for organophosphorus compounds. If methylcyclohexane was used for recrystallization, place the mother liquor in the organic solvents container.

QUESTIONS

1. Show how 1,4-diphenyl-1,3-butadiene might be synthesized from benzaldehyde and an appropriate halogenated compound.
2. Explain why the methyl groups of trimethyl phosphite give two peaks in the ^{1}H NMR spectrum (Fig. 39.4).
3. Write the equation for the reaction between sodium methoxide and moist air.

■ FIG. 39.4
The ^{1}H NMR spectrum of trimethyl
phosphite (90 MHz).

PPM (δ)

4. The Wittig reaction usually gives a mixture of *cis* and *trans* isomers. Using
a molecular mechanics program, calculate the steric energies or heats of
formation of both possible products in Experiment 1 or 2. Are these
compounds planar? Are the most stable molecules produced in these two
experiments? If not, why not?

Aldehydes and Ketones

PRELAB EXERCISE: Outline a logical series of experiments designed to identify an unknown aldehyde or ketone with the least effort. Consider the time required to complete each identification reaction.

The carbonyl group occupies a central place in organic chemistry. Aldehydes and ketones—compounds such as formaldehyde, acetaldehyde, acetone, and 2-butanone—are very important industrial chemicals used by themselves and as starting materials for a host of other substances. For example, more than 10 billion pounds (4.5 billion kilograms) of formaldehyde-containing plastics are produced in the United States each year.

The carbonyl carbon is sp^2 hybridized, the bond angles between adjacent groups are 120°, and the four atoms R, R′, C, and O lie in one plane:

$$
\overset{\ddot{\text{O}}:}{\underset{R \qquad R'}{\overset{\|}{C}}}
$$

The electronegative oxygen polarizes the carbon-oxygen bond, rendering the carbon electron deficient and hence subject to nucleophilic substitution.

$$
\diagdown\!C\!=\!\ddot{\text{O}}: \quad \longleftrightarrow \quad \overset{+}{\diagdown}\!C\!-\!\ddot{\text{O}}:^- \quad \text{or} \quad \overset{\delta+}{\diagdown}\!C\!=\!\overset{\delta-}{\ddot{\text{O}}}:
$$

Geometry of the carbonyl group

Attack on the sp^2 hybridized carbon occurs via the π-electron cloud above and below the plane of the carbonyl group:

Reactions of the Carbonyl Group

Many reactions of carbonyl groups are acid catalyzed. The acid attacks the electronegative oxygen, which bears a partial negative charge, to create a carbocation that subsequently reacts with the nucleophile:

The strength of the nucleophile and the structure of the carbonyl compound determine whether the equilibrium lies on the side of the carbonyl compound or the tetrahedral adduct. Water, a weak nucleophile, does not usually add to the carbonyl group to form a stable compound:

In the special case of trichloroacetaldehyde, however, the electron-withdrawing trichloromethyl group allows a stable hydrate to form:

A stable hydrate: chloral hydrate

The compound so formed, chloral hydrate, was discovered by Justus von Liebig in 1832 and was introduced as one of the first sedatives and hypnotics (sleep-inducing substances) in 1869. It is now most commonly encountered in detective fiction as a "Mickey Finn" or "knockout drops."

Reaction with an alcohol; hemiacetals

In an analogous manner, an aldehyde or ketone can react with an alcohol. The product, a hemiacetal or hemiketal, is usually not stable, but in the case of certain cyclic hemiacetals the product can be isolated. Glucose is an example of a stable hemiacetal.

Hemiacetal
usually not stable

Glucose
a stable cyclic hemiacetal

Bisulfite Addition

The bisulfite ion is a strong nucleophile but a weak acid. It will attack the unhindered carbonyl group of an aldehyde or methyl ketone to form an addition product:

Because these bisulfite addition compounds are ionic water-soluble compounds and can be formed in up to 90% yield, they serve as a useful means of separating aldehydes and methyl ketones from mixtures of organic compounds. At high sodium bisulfite concentrations these adducts crystallize and can be isolated by filtration. The aldehyde or ketone can be regenerated by adding either a strong acid or base:

Cyanide Addition

A similar reaction occurs between aldehydes and ketones and hydrogen cyanide, which, like bisulfite, is a weak acid but a strong nucleophile. The reaction is hazardous to carry out because of the toxicity of cyanide, but the cyanohydrins are useful synthetic intermediates:

Cyanohydrin formation
and reactions

Amines are good nucleophiles and readily add to the carbonyl group:

The reaction is strongly dependent on the pH. In acid the amine is protonated (RN^+H_3) and is no longer a nucleophile. In strong base there are no protons available to catalyze the reaction. But in weak acid solution (pH 4–6) the equilibrium between acid and base (**a**) is such that protons are available to protonate the carbonyl (**b**), and yet there is free amine present to react with the protonated carbonyl (**c**):

(a) $CH_3\ddot{N}H_2 + HCl \rightleftharpoons CH_3\overset{+}{N}H_3 + Cl^-$

(b)   (chemical structures: acetaldehyde + HCl in equilibrium with protonated carbonyl resonance forms + Cl⁻)

(c)   (chemical structures: protonated carbonyl + CH₃NH₂ in equilibrium with tetrahedral adduct, then −H⁺ to give hydroxyamino adduct)

Schiff Bases

The intermediate hydroxyamino form of the adduct is not stable and spontaneously dehydrates under the mildly acidic conditions of the reaction to give an imine, commonly referred to as a *Schiff base*:

(chemical structures showing dehydration to form Schiff base)

Schiff base

Imine or Schiff base formation

The biosynthesis of most amino acids proceeds through Schiff base intermediates.

Oximes, Semicarbazones, and 2,4-Dinitrophenylhydrazones

Three rather special amines form useful stable imines:

$$H_2\ddot{N}\ddot{O}H + \underset{R'}{\overset{R}{\diagdown}}C=\ddot{O}: \xrightarrow{-H_2O} \rightleftharpoons \underset{R'}{\overset{R}{\diagdown}}C=\ddot{N}\overset{\diagup O-H}{}$$

| Hydroxylamine | Oxime |

$$\underset{}{H_2NNH\overset{\overset{O}{\|}}{C}NH_2} + \underset{R'}{\overset{R}{\diagdown}}C=O \xrightarrow{-H_2O} \rightleftharpoons \underset{R'}{\overset{R}{\diagdown}}C=N-\underset{H}{N}-\overset{\overset{O}{\|}}{C}-NH_2$$

| Semicarbazide | Semicarbazone |

$$H_2NNH-\underset{}{\overset{NO_2}{\bigcirc}}-NO_2 + \underset{R'}{\overset{R}{\diagdown}}C=O \xrightarrow{-H_2O} \rightleftharpoons \underset{R'}{\overset{R}{\diagdown}}C=N-\underset{H}{N}-\underset{}{\overset{NO_2}{\bigcirc}}-NO_2$$

2,4-Dinitrophenylhydrazine   **2,4-Dinitrophenylhydrazone**

These imines are solids and are useful for the characterization of aldehydes and ketones. For example, IR (infrared) and NMR (nuclear magnetic resonance) spectroscopies may indicate that a certain unknown is acetaldehyde. It is difficult to determine the boiling point of a few milligrams of a liquid, but if it can be converted to a solid derivative, the melting point *can* be determined with that amount. The 2,4-dinitrophenylhydrazones are usually the derivatives of choice because they are crystalline compounds with well-defined melting or decomposition points, and they increase the molecular weight by 180. Ten milligrams of acetaldehyde will give 51 mg of the 2,4-dinitrophenylhydrazone.

$$CH_3\overset{\overset{O}{\|}}{C}\underset{H}{} + H_2NNH-\underset{}{\overset{NO_2}{\bigcirc}}-NO_2 \rightleftharpoons CH_3\underset{H}{C}=N-\underset{H}{N}-\underset{}{\overset{NO_2}{\bigcirc}}-NO_2$$

Acetaldehyde
MW 44.05
bp 20.8°C

2,4-Dinitrophenylhydrazine
MW 198.14
mp 196°C

Acetaldehyde 2,4-dinitrophenylhydrazone
MW 224.19
mp 168.5°C

Tollens' Reagent

Before the advent of NMR and IR spectroscopy and mass spectrometry, the chemist was often called on to identify aldehydes and ketones by purely chemical means. Aldehydes can be distinguished chemically from ketones by their ease of oxidation to carboxylic acids. The oxidizing agent, an ammoniacal solution of silver nitrate, Tollens' reagent, is reduced to metallic silver, which is deposited on the inside of a test tube as a silver mirror.

$$2\ Ag(NH_3)_2OH + R-\overset{\overset{\displaystyle O}{\|}}{C}-H \longrightarrow 2\ Ag + R-\overset{\overset{\displaystyle O}{\|}}{C}\underset{O^-}{} \ NH_4^+ + H_2O + 3\ NH_3$$

Schiff's Reagent

Another way to distinguish aldehydes from ketones is to use Schiff's reagent. This is a solution of the red dye Basic Fuchsin, which is rendered colorless on treatment with sulfur dioxide. In the presence of an aldehyde, the colorless solution turns magenta.

Basic Fuchsin, p-rosaniline hydrochloride   **Schiff's reagent, colorless**   **Magenta in color**

Iodoform Test

A test for methyl ketones

$$\overset{\overset{\displaystyle O}{\|}}{CH_3C-}$$
Methyl ketone

Methyl ketones can be distinguished from other ketones by the iodoform test. The methyl ketone is treated with iodine in a basic solution. Introduction of the first iodine atom increases the acidity of the remaining methyl protons, so halogenation stops only when the triiodo compound has been produced. The base then allows the relatively stable triiodomethyl carbanion to leave, and a subsequent proton transfer gives iodoform, a yellow crystalline solid with a melting point of 119°C–123°C. The test is also positive for fragments or compounds easily oxidized to methyl ketones, such as the fragment $CH_3\overset{|}{C}HOH$ or the compound ethanol. Acetaldehyde also gives a positive test because it is both a methyl ketone and an aldehyde.

$$R-\overset{\overset{\displaystyle \ddot{O}:}{\|}}{C}-CH_3 + OH^- \rightleftharpoons R-\overset{\overset{\displaystyle \ddot{O}:}{\|}}{C}-\overset{..}{\overset{-}{C}}H_2 + H_2O$$

$$R-\overset{\overset{\displaystyle \ddot{O}:}{\|}}{C}-\overset{-}{\overset{..}{C}}H_2 + I_2 \longrightarrow R-\overset{\overset{\displaystyle O}{\|}}{C}-CH_2I + I^- \xrightarrow[\text{}]{OH^-}\xrightarrow[\text{}]{I_2}\xrightarrow[\text{}]{OH^-}\xrightarrow[\text{}]{I_2} R-\overset{\overset{\displaystyle \ddot{O}:}{\|}}{C}-CI_3$$

$$R-\overset{\overset{\displaystyle \ddot{O}:}{\|}}{C}-CI_3 + OH^- \longrightarrow R-\overset{\overset{\displaystyle :\ddot{O}:^-}{|}}{\underset{:OH}{C}}-CI_3 \longrightarrow R-\overset{\displaystyle :\ddot{O}}{\underset{:O-H}{C}} + :\overset{-}{C}I_3 \longrightarrow R-\overset{\displaystyle :\ddot{O}}{\underset{\ddot{O}:^-}{C}} + CHI_3$$

Iodoform
mp 123°C

***

EXPERIMENTS

1. Unknowns

You will be given an unknown that may be any of the aldehydes or ketones listed in Table 36.1. At least one derivative of the unknown is to be submitted to your instructor; but if you first do the bisulfite and iodoform characterizing tests, the results may suggest derivatives whose melting points will be particularly revealing.

You can further characterize the unknown by determining its boiling point, which is best done with a digital thermometer and a reaction tube (*see* Chapter 5). The boiling points of the unknowns are given on this book's website.

In conducting the following tests, you should perform three tests simultaneously: on a compound known to give a positive test, on a compound known to give a negative test, and on the unknown. In this way you will be able to determine whether the reagents are working as they should as well as interpret a positive or a negative test.

Carry out three tests:

Known positive
Known negative
Unknown

2. 2,4-Dinitrophenylhydrazones

$$\underset{R'}{\overset{R}{\diagdown}}C=\ddot{O}: + H_2\ddot{N}-\underset{H}{\overset{\displaystyle \ddot{N}}{|}}\!\!-\!\!\left\langle\!\!\begin{array}{c} NO_2 \\ \\ \end{array}\!\!\right\rangle\!\!-NO_2 \xrightarrow{H^+} \underset{R'}{\overset{R}{\diagdown}}C=\ddot{N}\underset{\underset{H}{|}}{\diagdown}\!\overset{..}{N}\!-\!\!\left\langle\!\!\begin{array}{c} NO_2 \\ \\ \end{array}\!\!\right\rangle\!\!-NO_2$$

An easily prepared derivative of aldehydes and ketones

To 5 mL of the stock solution[1] of 2,4-dinitrophenylhydrazine in phosphoric acid add about 0.05 g of the compound to be tested. Five milliliters of the 0.1 *M* solution contains 0.5 mmol (0.0005 mol) of the reagent. If the compound to be tested

***

1. Dissolve 2.0 g of 2,4-dinitrophenylhydrazine in 50 mL of 85% phosphoric acid by heating, cool, add 50 mL of 95% ethanol, cool again, and clarify by suction filtration from a trace of residue.

| TABLE 36.1 • **Melting Points of Derivatives of Some Aldehydes and Ketones** | | | | | | | |

					Melting Points (°C)		
Compound[a]	Formula	n_D^{20}	MW	Water Solubility	Phenyl-hydrazone	2,4-dinitro-phenyl-hydrazone	Semi-carbazone
Acetone	CH_3COCH_3	1.3590	58.08		42	126	187
n-Butanal	$CH_3CH_2CH_2CHO$	1.3790	72.10	4 g/100 g	Oil	123	95 (106)[b]
3-Pentanone (diethyl ketone)	$CH_3CH_2COCH_2CH_3$	1.3920	86.13	4.7 g/100 g	Oil	156	138
2-Furaldehyde (furfural)	$C_4H_3O \cdot CHO$	1.5260	96.08	9 g/100 g	97	212 (230)[b]	202
Benzaldehyde	C_6H_5CHO	1.5450	106.12	Insol.	158	237	222
Hexane-2,5-dione	$CH_3COCH_2CH_2COCH_3$	1.4260	114.14	∞	120[c]	257[c]	224[c]
2-Heptanone	$CH_3(CH_2)_4COCH_3$	1.4080	114.18	Insol.	Oil	89	123
3-Heptanone	$CH_3(CH_2)_3COCH_2CH_3$	1.4080	114.18	Insol.	Oil	81	101
n-Heptanal	$n\text{-}C_6H_{13}CHO$	1.4125	114.18	Insol.	Oil	108	109
Acetophenone	$C_6H_5COCH_3$	1.5325	120.66	Insol.	105	238	198
2-Octanone	$CH_3(CH_2)_5COCH_3$	1.4150	128.21	Insol.	Oil	58	122
Cinnamaldehyde	$C_6H_5CH{=}CHCHO$	1.6220	132.15	Insol.	168	255	215
Propiophenone	$C_6H_5COCH_2CH_3$	1.5260	134.17	Insol.	About 48	191	182

[a]Visit this book's website for data on additional aldehydes and ketones.

[b]Both melting points have been found, depending on crystalline form of derivative.

[c]Monoderivative or diderivative.

Online Study Center

Video: Microscale
Crystallization

has a molecular weight of 100, then 0.05 g is 0.5 mmol. Warm the reaction mixture for a few minutes in a water bath and then let crystallization proceed. Collect the product by suction filtration (Fig. 36.1), wash the crystals with a large amount of water to remove all of the phosphoric acid, press a piece of moist litmus paper onto the crystals, and wash them with more water if they are acidic. Press the product between sheets of filter paper until it is as dry as possible and recrystallize from ethanol. Occasionally a high molecular weight derivative will not dissolve in a reasonable quantity (10 mL) of ethanol. In that case cool the hot suspension and isolate the crystals by suction filtration. The boiling ethanol treatment removes impurities so that an accurate melting point can be obtained on the isolated material.

An alternative procedure is applicable when the 2,4-dinitrophenylhydrazone is known to be sparingly soluble in ethanol. Measure 0.5 mmol (0.1 g) of crystalline 2,4-dinitrophenylhydrazine into a 50-mL Erlenmeyer flask, add 15 mL of 95% ethanol, digest on a steam bath until all the solid particles are dissolved, and then add 0.5 mmol of the compound to be tested and continue warming. If there is no immediate change, add, from a Pasteur pipette, 3–4 drops of concentrated hydrochloric acid as a catalyst and note the result. Warm for a few minutes, then

■ **FIG. 36.1**
A Hirsch funnel filtration apparatus.

Filter paper,
12 mm dia.

Polyethylene
filter disk (frit),
10 mm dia.

Hirsch
funnel

To aspirator

25-mL Filter
flask

cool and collect the product. This procedure would be used for an aldehyde like cinnamaldehyde ($C_6H_5CH{=}CHCHO$).

The alternative procedure strikingly demonstrates the catalytic effect of hydrochloric acid, but it is not applicable to a substance like diethyl ketone, whose 2,4-dinitrophenylhydrazone is much too soluble to crystallize from the large volume of ethanol. The first procedure is obviously the one to use for an unknown.

Cleaning Up. The filtrate from the preparation of the 2,4-dinitrophenylhydrazone should have very little 2,4-dinitrophenylhydrazine in it, so after dilution with water and neutralization with sodium carbonate, it can be flushed down the drain. Similarly, the mother liquor from crystallization of the phenylhydrazone should have very little product in it and so should be diluted and flushed down the drain. If solid material is detected, it should be collected by suction filtration, the filtrate flushed down the drain, and the filter paper placed in the solid hazardous waste container because hydrazines are toxic.

3. Semicarbazones

Semicarbazide hydrochloride   Pyridine   Semicarbazone   Pyridine
                                                                        hydrochloride

Semicarbazide (mp 96°C) is not very stable in the free form and is used as the crystalline hydrochloride (mp 173°C). Because this salt is insoluble in methanol or ethanol and does not react readily with typical carbonyl compounds in alcohol-water mixtures, pyridine, a basic reagent, is added to liberate free semicarbazide.

To 0.5 mL of the stock solution[2] of semicarbazide hydrochloride, which contains 1 mmol of the reagent, add 1 mmol of the compound to be tested and enough methanol (1 mL) to produce a clear solution; then add 10 drops of pyridine (a twofold excess) and warm the solution gently on the steam bath for a few minutes. Cool the solution slowly to room temperature. It may be necessary to scratch the inside of the test tube in order to induce crystallization. Cool the tube in ice, collect the product by suction filtration, and wash it with water followed by a small amount of cold methanol. Recrystallize the product from methanol, ethanol, or ethanol/water. The product can easily be collected on a Wilfilter.

Cleaning Up. Combine the filtrate from the reaction and the mother liquor from the crystallization, dilute with water, make very slightly acidic with dilute hydrochloric acid, and flush the mixture down the drain.

Online Study Center
Photo: Use of the Wilfilter

4. Tollens' Test

Test for aldehydes

$$R-C(\!=\!O)H + 2\ Ag(NH_3)_2OH \longrightarrow 2\ Ag + RCOO^-NH_4^+ + H_2O + 3\ NH_3$$

Clean four or five test tubes by adding a few milliliters of 3 M sodium hydroxide solution to each and heating them in a water bath while preparing the Tollens' reagent.

To 2.0 mL of 0.03 M silver nitrate solution, add 1.0 mL of 3 M sodium hydroxide in a test tube. To the gray precipitate of silver oxide, Ag_2O, add 0.5 mL of a 2.8% aqueous ammonia solution (10 mL of concentrated ammonium hydroxide diluted to 100 mL). Stopper the tube and shake it. Repeat the process until *almost* all of the precipitate dissolves (3.0 mL of ammonia at most); then dilute the solution with water to 10 mL. Empty the test tubes of sodium hydroxide solution, rinse them, and add 1 mL of Tollens' reagent to each. Add 1 drop (no more) of the substance to be tested by allowing it to run down the inside of the inclined test tube. Set the tubes aside for a few minutes without agitating the contents. If no reaction occurs, warm the mixture briefly on a water bath. As a known aldehyde, try 1 drop of a 0.1 M solution of glucose. A more typical aldehyde to test is benzaldehyde.

At the end of the reaction, promptly destroy any excess Tollens' reagent with nitric acid: It can form an explosive fulminate on standing. Nitric acid can also be used to remove silver mirrors from test tubes.

2. Prepare a stock solution by dissolving 1.11 g of semicarbazide hydrochloride in 5 mL of water; 0.5 mL of this solution contains 1 mmol of reagent.

Cleaning Up. Place all solutions used in this experiment in a beaker (unused ammonium hydroxide, sodium hydroxide solution used to clean out the tubes, Tollens' reagent from all tubes). Remove any silver mirrors from reaction tubes with a few drops of nitric acid, which is added to the beaker. Make the mixture acidic with nitric acid to destroy unreacted Tollens' reagent and then neutralize the solution with sodium carbonate and add some sodium chloride solution to precipitate silver chloride (about 40 mg). The whole mixture can be flushed down the drain, or the silver chloride can be collected by suction filtration, and the filtrate flushed down the drain. The silver chloride would go in the nonhazardous solid waste container.

5. Schiff's Test

Very sensitive test for aldehydes

Add 3 drops of the unknown to 2 mL of Schiff's reagent.[3] A magenta color will appear within 10 min with aldehydes. As in all of these tests, compare the colors produced by a known aldehyde, a known ketone, and the unknown compound.

Cleaning Up. Neutralize the solution with sodium carbonate and flush it down the drain. The amount of *p*-rosaniline in this mixture is negligible (1 mg).

6. Iodoform Test

$$\underset{\textbf{A methyl ketone}}{R-\overset{\overset{\ddots}{\underset{\|}{O}}}{C}-CH_3} + 3\,I_2 + 4\,OH^- \longrightarrow R-\overset{\overset{\ddots}{O}}{\underset{\underset{\ddots}{O:^-}}{C}} + CHI_3 + 3\;\ddot{\underset{\ddots}{I}:^- + 3\,H_2O}$$

Iodoform
mp 119–123°C

Test for methyl ketones

The reagent contains iodine in potassium iodide solution[4] at a concentration such that 2 mL of solution, on reaction with excess methyl ketone, will yield 174 mg of iodoform. If the substance to be tested is water soluble, dissolve 4 drops of a liquid or an estimated 50 mg of a solid in 2 mL of water in a 20 × 150-mm test tube; add 2 mL of 3 *M* sodium hydroxide, and then slowly add 3 mL of the iodine solution. In a positive test the brown color of the reagent disappears, and yellow iodoform separates. If the substance to be tested is insoluble in water, dissolve it in 2 mL of 1,2-dimethoxyethane, proceed as above, and at the end dilute with 10 mL of water.

Suggested test substances are hexane-2,5-dione (water soluble), *n*-butyraldehyde (water soluble), and acetophenone (water insoluble).

---

3. Schiff's reagent is prepared by dissolving 0.1 g Basic Fuchsin (*p*-rosaniline hydrochloride) in 100 mL of water and then adding 4 mL of a saturated aqueous solution of sodium bisulfite. After 1 h, add 2 mL of concentrated hydrochloric acid.

4. Dissolve 25 g of iodine in a solution of 50 g of potassium iodide in 200 mL of water.

Online Study Center

Videos: Microscale Filtration
on the Hirsch Funnel,
Extraction with Dichloromethane;
Photo: Use of the Wilfilter

Iodoform can be recognized by its odor and yellow color and, more securely, from its melting point (119°C–123°C). The substance can be isolated by suction filtration of the test suspension or by adding 0.5 mL of dichloromethane, shaking the stoppered test tube to extract the iodoform into the small lower layer, withdrawing the clear part of this layer with a Pasteur pipette, and evaporating it in a small tube on a steam bath. The crude solid is crystallized from a methanol-water mixture (*see* Chapter 4). It can be collected on a Wilfilter.

Cleaning Up. Combine all reaction mixtures in a beaker, add a few drops of acetone to destroy any unreacted iodine in potassium iodide reagent, remove the iodoform by suction filtration, and place the iodoform in the halogenated organic waste container. The filtrate can be flushed down the drain after neutralization (if necessary).

7. Bisulfite Test

Forms with unhindered carbonyls

$$\underset{H}{\overset{R}{\diagdown}}C=\overset{..}{O}: \ + \ Na^+SO_3H^- \ \rightleftharpoons \ R-\overset{\overset{\textstyle :\overset{..}{O}H}{|}}{\underset{\underset{\textstyle H}{|}}{C}}-SO_3^-Na^+$$

Put 1 mL of the stock solution[5] into a 13 × 100-mm test tube and add 5 drops of the substance to be tested. Shake each tube during the next 10 min and note the results. A positive test will result from aldehydes, unhindered cyclic ketones such as cyclohexanone, and unhindered methyl ketones.

If the bisulfite test is applied to a liquid or solid that is very sparingly soluble in water, formation of the addition product is facilitated by adding a small amount of methanol before the addition to the bisulfite solution.

Cleaning Up. Dilute the bisulfite solution or any bisulfite addition products (they will dissociate) with a large volume of water and flush the mixture down the drain. The amount of organic material being discarded is negligible.

8. IR and NMR Spectroscopy

IR spectroscopy is extremely useful in analyzing all carbonyl-containing compounds, including aldehydes and ketones (Fig. 36.4 and Fig. 36.11). Refer to the extensive discussion in Chapter 11. In the modern laboratory, spectroscopy has almost completely supplanted the qualitative tests described in this chapter. Figures 36.4 through 36.11 present IR and NMR spectra of typical aldehydes and ketones. Compare these spectra with those of your unknown. Also compare the IR and ^{1}H NMR spectra of the hydrocarbon fluorene (Fig. 36.2 and Fig. 36.3) with those of the ketone derivative, fluorenone (Fig. 36.4 and Fig. 36.5).

---

5. Prepare a stock solution from 50 g sodium bisulfite dissolved in 200 mL of water with brief swirling.

■ **FIG. 36.2**
The IR spectrum of fluorene in CS_2.

■ **FIG. 36.3**
The ^1H NMR spectrum of fluorene (250 MHz).

■ **FIG. 36.4**
The IR spectrum of fluorenone
(KBr disk).

■ **FIG. 36.5**
The ¹H NMR spectrum
of fluorenone (250 MHz).

A peak at 9.6–10 ppm in the ¹H NMR spectrum is highly characteristic of aldehydes because almost no other peaks appear in this region (Fig. 36.7 and Fig. 36.10). Similarly, a sharp singlet at 2.2 ppm is very characteristic of methyl ketones; beware of contamination of the sample by acetone, which is often used to clean glassware.

■ **FIG. 36.6**
The ¹H NMR spectrum of 2-butanone, $CH_3COCH_2CH_3$ (90 MHz).

PPM (δ)

■ **FIG. 36.7**
The ¹H NMR spectrum of crotonaldehyde, $CH_3CH{=}CHCHO$ (90 MHz).

PPM (δ)

■ FIG. 36.8
The ^{13}C NMR spectrum of
2-butanone, $CH_3COCH_2CH_3$
(22.6 MHz).

■ FIG. 36.9
The ^{13}C NMR spectrum of
crotonaldehyde (22.6 MHz).

QUESTIONS

1. What is the purpose of making derivatives of unknowns?
2. Why are 2,4-dinitrophenylhydrazones better derivatives than phenylhydrazones?
3. Using chemical tests, how would you distinguish among 2-pentanone, 3-pentanone, and pentanal?
4. Draw the structure of a compound with the empirical formula C_5H_8O that gives a positive iodoform test and does not decolorize permanganate.
5. Draw the structure of a compound with the empirical formula C_5H_8O that gives a positive Tollens' test and does not react with bromine in dichloromethane.

■ **FIG. 36.10**
The ¹H NMR spectrum of
benzaldehyde (250 MHz).

■ **FIG. 36.11**
The IR spectrum of benzaldehyde
(thin film).

6. Draw the structure of a compound with the empirical formula C_5H_8O that reacts with phenylhydrazine, decolorizes bromine in dichloromethane, and does not give a positive iodoform test.

7. Draw the structure of two geometric isomers with the empirical formula C_5H_8O that give a positive iodoform test.

8. What vibrations cause the peaks at about 3.6 μm (2940 cm^{-1}) in the IR spectrum of fluorene (Fig. 36.2)?

9. Locate the carbonyl peak in Figure 36.4.

10. Assign the various peaks in the ^{1}H NMR spectrum of 2-butanone to specific protons in the molecule (Fig. 36.6).

11. Assign the various peaks in the ^{1}H NMR spectrum of crotonaldehyde to specific protons in the molecule (Fig. 36.7).

Esterification and Hydrolysis

$$\overset{\overset{\displaystyle O}{\|}}{R-C}-O-R'$$

The ester group

Flavors and fragrances

> **PRELAB EXERCISE:** Write the detailed mechanism for the acid-catalyzed hydrolysis of methyl benzoate.

The ester group is an important functional group that can be synthesized in a variety of ways. The low molecular weight esters have very pleasant odors and indeed comprise the major flavor and odor components of a number of fruits. Although a natural flavor may contain nearly 100 different compounds, single esters approximate the natural odors and are often used in the food industry for artificial flavors and fragrances (Table 40.1).

Esters can be prepared by reacting a carboxylic acid with an alcohol in the presence of a catalyst such as concentrated sulfuric acid, hydrogen chloride, *p*-toluenesulfonic acid, or the acid form of an ion exchange resin. For example, methyl acetate can be prepared as follows:

$$\underset{\textbf{Acetic acid}}{\overset{\overset{\displaystyle O}{\|}}{CH_3C}-OH} \;+\; \underset{\textbf{Methanol}}{CH_3OH} \;\overset{H^+}{\rightleftharpoons}\; \underset{\textbf{Methyl acetate}}{\overset{\overset{\displaystyle O}{\|}}{CH_3C}-OCH_3} \;+\; H_2O$$

Fischer esterification

The Fischer esterification reaction reaches equilibrium after a few hours of refluxing. The position of the equilibrium can be shifted by adding more of the acid or of the alcohol, depending on cost or availability. The mechanism of the reaction involves initial protonation of the carboxyl group, attack by the nucleophilic hydroxyl, a proton transfer, and loss of water followed by loss of the catalyzing proton to give the ester. Each of these steps is completely reversible, so this process is also, in reverse, the mechanism for the hydrolysis of an ester:

TABLE 40.1 • Boiling Points and Fragrances of Esters

Ester	Formula	bp (°C)	Fragrance
2-Methylpropyl formate	$\overset{O}{\underset{\parallel}{HC}}-OCH_2\overset{CH_3}{\underset{\mid}{CH}}CH_3$	98.4	Raspberry
1-Propyl acetate	$\overset{O}{\underset{\parallel}{CH_3C}}-OCH_2CH_2CH_3$	101.7	Pear
Methyl butyrate	$CH_3CH_2CH_2\overset{O}{\underset{\parallel}{C}}-OCH_3$	102.3	Apple
Ethyl butyrate	$CH_3CH_2CH_2\overset{O}{\underset{\parallel}{C}}-OCH_2CH_3$	121	Pineapple
2-Methylpropyl propionate	$CH_3CH_2\overset{O}{\underset{\parallel}{C}}-OCH_2\overset{CH_3}{\underset{\mid}{CH}}CH_3$	136.8	Rum
3-Methylbutyl acetate	$CH_3\overset{O}{\underset{\parallel}{C}}-OCH_2CH_2\overset{CH_3}{\underset{\mid}{CH}}CH_3$	142	Banana
Benzyl acetate	$CH_3\overset{O}{\underset{\parallel}{C}}-OCH_2C_6H_5$	213.5	Peach
Octyl acetate	$CH_3\overset{O}{\underset{\parallel}{C}}-OCH_2(CH_2)_6CH_3$	210	Orange
Methyl salicylate	$C_6H_4(OH)\overset{O}{\underset{\parallel}{C}}-OCH_3$	222	Wintergreen

Other methods are available for synthesizing esters, most of which are more expensive but readily carried out on a small scale. For example, alcohols react with anhydrides and with acid chlorides:

$$CH_3CH_2OH + CH_3\overset{O}{\underset{||}{C}}-O-\overset{O}{\underset{||}{C}}CH_3 \longrightarrow CH_3\overset{O}{\underset{||}{C}}-OCH_2CH_3 + CH_3\overset{O}{\underset{||}{C}}-OH$$

Ethanol   **Acetic anhydride**   **Ethyl acetate**   **Acetic acid**

$$CH_3CH_2CH_2OH + CH_3\overset{O}{\underset{||}{C}}-Cl \longrightarrow CH_3\overset{O}{\underset{||}{C}}-OCH_2CH_2CH_3 + HCl$$

1-Propanol   **Acetyl chloride**   **n-Propyl acetate**

In the latter reaction, an organic base such as pyridine is usually added to react with the hydrogen chloride.

Other ester syntheses

Other methods can also be used to synthesize the ester group. Among these are the addition of 2-methylpropene to an acid to form *t*-butyl esters, the addition of ketene to make acetates, and the reaction of a silver salt with an alkyl halide:

$$CH_2=\overset{CH_3}{\underset{|}{C}}CH_3 + CH_3CH_2\overset{O}{\underset{||}{C}}-OH \xrightarrow{H^+} CH_3CH_2\overset{O}{\underset{||}{C}}-O\overset{CH_3}{\underset{\underset{CH_3}{|}}{\overset{|}{C}}}CH_3$$

2-Methylpropene   **Propionic acid**   **t-Butyl propionate**
(isobutylene)

$$CH_2=C=O + HOCH_2-\langle\bigcirc\rangle \longrightarrow CH_3\overset{O}{\underset{||}{C}}-OCH_2-\langle\bigcirc\rangle$$

Ketene   **Benzyl alcohol**   **Benzyl acetate**

$$CH_3\overset{O}{\underset{||}{C}}-OAg + BrCH_2CH_2\overset{CH_3}{\underset{|}{C}}HCH_3 \longrightarrow CH_3\overset{O}{\underset{||}{C}}-OCH_2CH_2\overset{CH_3}{\underset{|}{C}}HCH_3$$

Silver acetate   **1-Bromo-3-methylbutane**   **3-Methylbutyl acetate**

As noted previously, Fischer esterification is an equilibrium process. Consider the reaction of acetic acid with 1-butanol to give *n*-butyl acetate:

$$CH_3\overset{O}{\underset{||}{C}}-OH + HOCH_2CH_2CH_2CH_3 \rightleftharpoons CH_3\overset{O}{\underset{||}{C}}-OCH_2CH_2CH_2CH_3 + H_2O$$

The equilibrium constant is as follows:

$$K_{eq} = \frac{[n\text{-BuOAc}][H_2O]}{[n\text{-BuOH}]\,[HOAc]}$$

For primary alcohols reacting with unhindered carboxylic acids, $K_{eq} \approx 4$. If equal quantities of 1-butanol and acetic acid are allowed to react at equilibrium, the theoretical yield of ester is only 67%. To upset the equilibrium we can, by Le Chatelier's principle, increase the concentration of either the alcohol or acid. If either one is doubled, the theoretical yield increases to 85%. When one is tripled, the yield goes to 90%. But note that in the example cited the boiling point of the relatively nonpolar ester is only about 8°C higher than the boiling points of the polar acetic acid and 1-butanol, so a difficult separation problem exists if the product must be isolated by distillation after the starting materials are increased in concentration.

Another way to upset the equilibrium is to remove water. This can be done by adding to the reaction mixture molecular sieves (an artificial zeolite), which preferentially adsorb water. Most other drying agents, such as anhydrous sodium sulfate or calcium chloride pellets, will not remove water at the temperatures used to make esters.

Azeotropic distillation

A third way to upset the equilibrium is to preferentially remove the water as an azeotrope (a constant-boiling mixture of water and an organic liquid). The information in Table 40.2 can be found in a chemistry handbook table of ternary (three-component) azeotropes. These data tell us that vapor that distills from a mixture of 1-butanol, n-butyl acetate, and water will boil at 90.7°C and that the vapor contains 8% alcohol, 63% ester, and 29% water. The vapor is homogeneous, but when it condenses, it separates into two layers. The upper layer is composed of 11% alcohol, 86% ester, and 3% water, but the lower layer consists of 97% water with only traces of alcohol and ester. If some ingenious way can be devised to remove the lower layer from the condensate and still return the upper layer to the reaction mixture, then the equilibrium can be upset, and nearly 100% of the ester can be produced in the reaction flask.

The apparatus shown in Figure 40.1, modeled after that of Ernest W. Dean and David D. Stark, achieves the desired separation of the two layers. The mixture of equimolar quantities of 1-butanol and acetic acid is placed in the flask along with an acid catalyst. Stirring reduces bumping. The vapor, the temperature of

TABLE 40.2 • The Ternary Azeotrope of Boiling Point 90.7°C

Compound	Boiling Point of Pure Compound (°C)	Percentage Composition of Azeotrope		
		Vapor Phase	*Upper Layer*	*Lower Layer*
1-Butanol	117.7	8.0	11.0	2.0
n-Butyl acetate	126.7	63.0	86.0	1.0
Water	100.0	29.0	3.0	97.0

■ **FIG. 40.1**
A microscale Dean-Stark azeotropic esterification apparatus. A cork is used instead
of a septum so that layer separation can be observed clearly.

■ **FIG. 40.2**
A macroscale azeotropic distillation
apparatus, with a Dean-Stark trap where
water collects.

Reflux condenser

Ester +
alcohol layer

Water layer

Cork

Reaction mixture

Hot sand bath

Stirring bar
and catalyst

which is 90.7°C, condenses and runs down to the sidearm, which is closed with a
cork. The layers separate, with the denser water layer remaining in the sidearm
and the lighter ester plus alcohol layer running down into the reaction flask. As
soon as the theoretical quantity of water has collected, the reaction is over, and the
product in the flask should contain an ester of high purity. The macroscale apparatus is illustrated in Figure 40.2.

Esterification using a carboxylic acid and an alcohol requires an acid catalyst.
In the first experiment, the acid form of an ion-exchange resin is used. This resin,
in the form of small beads, is a cross-linked polystyrene that bears sulfonic acid
groups on some of the phenyl groups. It is essentially an immobilized form of
p-toluenesulfonic acid, an organic-substituted sulfuric acid.

$$\text{+(CH}-\text{CH}_2-\text{CH}-\text{CH}_2-\text{CH)}_n\text{+}$$

(Three benzene rings each bearing $SO_3^- H^+$)

An ion-exchange catalyst

This catalyst has the distinct advantage that at the end of the reaction it can be easily removed by filtration. Immobilized catalysts of this type are becoming more and more common in organic synthesis.

If concentrated sulfuric acid were used as the catalyst, it would be necessary to dilute the reaction mixture with ether; wash the ether layer successively with water, sodium carbonate solution, and saturated sodium chloride solution; and then dry the ether layer with anhydrous calcium chloride pellets before evaporating the ether.

EXPERIMENTS

1. *n*-Butyl Acetate by Azeotropic Distillation of Water

$$\underset{\substack{\text{Acetic acid}}}{CH_3\overset{\displaystyle O}{\overset{\|}{C}}-OH} \;+\; \underset{\substack{\text{1-Butanol}}}{HOCH_2CH_2CH_2CH_3} \;\overset{H^+}{\rightleftharpoons}\; \underset{\substack{\textit{n}\text{-Butyl acetate}}}{CH_3\overset{\displaystyle O}{\overset{\|}{C}}-OCH_2CH_2CH_2CH_3} \;+\; H_2O$$

Acetic acid
MW 60.05
bp 117.9°C, den 1.049
n_D^{20} 1.3720

1-Butanol
MW 74.12
bp 117.7°C, den 0.810
n_D^{20} 1.3990

n-Butyl acetate
MW 116.16
bp 126.5°C, den 0.882
n_D^{20} 1.3940

MW 18

IN THIS EXPERIMENT acetic acid is esterified with butanol in the presence of an acid catalyst attached to very small polystyrene beads. Because esterification is an equilibrium reaction, the equilibrium is upset by removing the water formed in a unique apparatus patterned after the Dean-Stark water separator. The product is isolated simply by withdrawing it from the reaction flask with a Pasteur pipette, leaving the catalyst behind. It can be further purified by simple distillation.

Ion-exchange resin catalyst

A cork instead of a septum allows the accumulation of water to be observed.

In a 5-mL short-necked, round-bottomed flask, place 0.2 g of Dowex 50X2-100 ion-exchange resin,[1] 0.60 g (0.58 mL; 0.01 mol) of acetic acid, 0.74 g (0.91 mL; 0.01 mol) of 1-butanol, and a stirring bar. Attach the addition port with the sidearm corked and an empty distilling column, as shown in Figure 40.1, and clamp the apparatus at the angle shown. Heat the flask while stirring on a hot sand

1. The Dowex resin as received should be washed with water by decantation to remove much of its yellow color. It is then collected by vacuum filtration on a Büchner funnel and returned, in a slightly damp state, to the reagent bottle.

bath and bring the reaction mixture to a boil. Stirring the mixture prevents it from bumping. As an option, you might hold a thermometer just above the boiling liquid and note a temperature of about 91°C. Remove the thermometer and allow the reaction mixture to reflux in a manner such that the vapors condense about one-third of the way up the empty distilling column, which is functioning as an air condenser. Note that the material that condenses is not homogeneous, as droplets of water begin to collect in the upper part of the apparatus. As the sidearm fills with condensate, it is cloudy at first and then two layers separate. When the volume of the lower aqueous layer does not appear to increase, the reaction is over. This will take about 20–30 min. Carefully remove the apparatus from the heat, allow it to cool, and then tip the apparatus very carefully to allow all the upper layer in the sidearm to run back into the reaction flask. Disconnect the apparatus.

Remove the product from the reaction flask with a Pasteur pipette, determine its weight and boiling point, and assess its purity by thin-layer chromatographic (TLC) analysis and infrared (IR) spectroscopy. The product can be analyzed by gas chromatography on a 10-ft (3-m) Carbowax column. At 152°C, the 1-butanol has a retention time of 2.1 min, the *n*-butyl acetate 2.5 min, and the acetic acid 7.5 min. Look for the presence of hydroxyl and carboxyl absorption bands in the IR spectrum. The product can easily be purified by simple distillation (*see* Figure 5.7 on page 97).

Cleaning Up. Place the catalyst in the solid hazardous waste container.

2. Isobutyl Propionate (2-Methylpropyl propanoate) by Fischer Esterification

$$
\underset{\substack{\text{Propanoic acid} \\ \text{MW 74.08} \\ \text{bp 141°C}}}{CH_3CH_2\overset{\displaystyle O}{\overset{\|}{C}}OH} + \underset{\substack{\text{2-Methyl-1-propanol} \\ \text{MW 74.12} \\ \text{bp 108°C}}}{HOCH_2\overset{\displaystyle CH_3}{\overset{|}{C}HCH_3}} \underset{}{\overset{H^+}{\rightleftharpoons}} \underset{\substack{\text{Isobutyl propionate} \\ \text{MW 130.19} \\ \text{bp 136.8°C}}}{CH_3CH_2\overset{\displaystyle O}{\overset{\|}{C}}OCH_2\overset{\displaystyle CH_3}{\overset{|}{C}HCH_3}} + H_2O
$$

> **IN THIS EXPERIMENT** a propionate ester is prepared by reacting excess propanoic acid with an alcohol in the presence of an acid catalyst on polystyrene beads (Dowex 50X). The excess acid serves to drive the equilibrium reaction toward formation of the product. The excess propanoic acid is removed by reaction with potassium carbonate, and the water is adsorbed by silica gel when the reaction mixture is chromatographed.

Procedure

To a reaction tube add 112 mg of 2-methyl-1-propanol (isobutyl alcohol), 148 mg of propanoic acid (propionic acid), 50 mg of Dowex 50X2-100 ion-exchange resin, and a boiling chip. Attach the empty distilling column as an air condenser (Fig. 40.3). Reflux the resulting mixture for 1 h or more, cool it to room temperature, remove the product mixture from the resin with a Pasteur pipette, and chromatograph the product (2-methyl-1-propyl propanoate) on a silica gel column.

■ FIG. 40.3
An esterification apparatus.

Wet pipe
cleaner —

■ FIG. 40.4
A chromatographic column
for esters.

Funnel —

Glass
column —

— Anhydrous
potassium
carbonate

— Silica gel

Micro
Büchner
funnel

— Polyethylene
frit

10-mL
Erlenmeyer
flask

CAUTION: Carry out this part
of the experiment in a hood.
Dichloromethane is a suspected
carcinogen.

Chromatography Procedure

Assemble the column as depicted in Figure 40.4, being sure that it is clamped in a
vertical position. Close the valve and fill the column with dichloromethane to the
bottom of the funnel. In a small beaker prepare a slurry of 1 g of silica gel in 4 mL
of dichloromethane. Stir the slurry gently to remove air bubbles and gently swirl,
pour, and scrape the slurry into the funnel, which has a capacity of 10 mL. After

some of the silica gel has been added to the column, open the stopcock and allow solvent to drain slowly into an Erlenmeyer flask. Use this dichloromethane to rinse the beaker containing the silica gel. As the silica gel is being added, tap the column with a glass rod or pencil so the adsorbent will pack tightly into the column. Continue to tap the column while cycling the dichloromethane through the column once more; then add 1 g of anhydrous potassium carbonate to the top of the silica gel. The potassium carbonate will remove water from the esterification mixture as well as react with any carboxylic acid present. Allow the solvent to flow until it reaches the top of the potassium carbonate layer.

Adding the Sample

The solvent is drained just to the surface of the potassium carbonate. Using a Pasteur pipette, add the sample to the column and let it run into the adsorbent, stopping when the solution reaches the top of the potassium carbonate. The flask and ion-exchange resin are rinsed twice with 0.5-mL portions of dichloromethane that are run into the column, with the eluent being collected in a tared reaction tube. The elution is completed with 1 mL more of dichloromethane.

Analysis of the Product

Evaporate the dichloromethane under a stream of air or nitrogen in the hood and remove the last traces by connecting the reaction tube to a water aspirator. Because the dichloromethane boils at 40°C and the product boils at 137°C, separation of the two is easily accomplished. Determine the weight of the product and its boiling point and calculate the yield. The ester should be a perfectly clear, homogeneous liquid. Obtain an IR spectrum and analyze it for the presence of unreacted alcohol and carboxylic acid. Check the purity of the product by TLC and/or gas chromatography.

Cleaning Up. Place the catalyst in the hazardous waste container. Any dichloromethane should be placed in the halogenated organic waste container. The contents of the chromatography column, if free of solvent, can be placed in the nonhazardous solid waste container; otherwise, this material is classified as a hazardous waste and must go in the container so designated.

3. Benzyl Acetate from Acetic Anhydride

Benzyl alcohol	Acetic anhydride	Benzyl acetate	Acetic acid
MW 108.14	MW 102.09	MW 150.18	MW 60.06
bp 205°C	bp 138–140°C	bp 213.5°C	bp 117–118°C
n_D^{20} 1.5400	n_D^{20} 1.3900	n_D^{20} 1.5020	n_D^{20} 1.3720

To a reaction tube add 108 mg of benzyl alcohol, 102 mg of acetic anhydride, and a boiling chip. Reflux the mixture for at least 1 h, cool the mixture to room temperature, and chromatograph the liquid in exactly the same manner described in Experiment 2. Analyze the product by TLC and by IR spectroscopy as a thin film between salt or silver chloride plates. Note the presence or absence of hydroxyl and carboxyl bands.

This ester cannot be prepared by Fischer esterification using Dowex. Polymerization seems to occur.

Cleaning Up. Place the catalyst in the hazardous waste container. Any dichloromethane should be placed in the halogenated organic waste container. The contents of the chromatography column, if free of solvent, can be placed in the nonhazardous solid waste container; otherwise, this material is classified as a hazardous waste and must go in the container so designated.

Other Esterifications

This experiment lends itself to wide-ranging experimentation. All three methods of esterification previously described can, in principle, be applied to any unhindered primary or secondary alcohol. These methods work well for most of the esters in Table 40.1 and for hundreds of others as well.

4. Methyl Benzoate by Fischer Esterification

$$O\!=\!C\!-\!OH + CH_3OH \xrightarrow[\text{H}_2\text{SO}_4]{} O\!=\!C\!-\!O\!-\!CH_3 + H_2O$$

Benzoic acid	**Methanol**	**Methyl benzoate**
mp 122°C	bp 64.6°C	bp 198–199°C
MW 122.12	den. 0.791	den. 1.094
	MW 32.04	MW 136.15

IN THIS EXPERIMENT benzoic acid and excess methanol are refluxed in the presence of a catalytic amount of sulfuric acid. Water and ether are added; the water layer is withdrawn; and the ether layer is washed with water, bicarbonate, and saturated salt solutions. After drying over calcium chloride, the ether is evaporated. Finally, the product, ethyl benzoate, is distilled.

Place 10.0 g of benzoic acid and 25 mL of methanol in a 125-mL round-bottomed flask, cool the mixture in ice, pour 3 mL of concentrated sulfuric acid *slowly and carefully down the walls of the flask*, then swirl to mix the components.

■ **FIG. 40.5**
An apparatus for refluxing
a reaction mixture.

■ **FIG. 40.5**
An apparatus for refluxing
a reaction mixture.

Water out

Water in

Do not use water in the
circulating jacket.

Attach a reflux condenser, add a boiling chip, and reflux the mixture gently for 1 h. (Fig. 40.5 illustrates this apparatus.) Cool the solution, decant it into a separatory funnel containing 50 mL of water, and rinse the flask with 35 mL of ether. Add this ether to the separatory funnel, shake thoroughly, and drain off the water layer, which contains the sulfuric acid and the bulk of the methanol. Wash the ether in the separatory funnel with 25 mL of water followed by 25 mL of 0.5 M sodium bicarbonate to remove unreacted benzoic acid. Again shake, with frequent release of pressure by inverting the separatory funnel and opening the stopcock, until no further reaction is apparent; then drain off the bicarbonate layer into a beaker. If this aqueous material is made strongly acidic with hydrochloric acid, unreacted benzoic acid may be observed. Wash the ether layer in the separatory funnel with saturated sodium chloride solution and dry the solution over anhydrous calcium chloride in an Erlenmeyer flask. Add sufficient calcium chloride pellets so that it no longer clumps together on the bottom of the flask. After 10 min decant the dry ether solution into a flask, wash the drying agent with an additional 5 mL of ether, and decant again.

Remove the ether by simple distillation or by evaporation on a steam bath under an aspirator tube. Use the methods illustrated in Fig. 4.22 (on page 79) or Fig. 5.10 (on page 100), or use a rotary evaporator (*see* Fig. 9.8 on page 207). When evaporation ceases, add 2–3 g of anhydrous calcium chloride pellets to the residual oil and heat for about 5 min longer. Then decant the methyl benzoate into a 50-mL round-bottomed flask, attach a stillhead, dry out the ordinary condenser and use it without water circulating in the jacket, and distill. The boiling point of the ester is so high (199°C) that a water-cooled condenser is liable to crack. Use a tared 25-mL Erlenmeyer flask as the receiver to collect material boiling above 190°C. A typical student yield is about 7 g. *See* Chapter 28 for the nitration of methyl benzoate and Chapter 38 for its use in the Grignard synthesis of triphenylmethanol.

IR and nuclear magnetic resonance (NMR) spectra of benzoic acid and methyl benzoate are found at the end of the chapter (Figs. 40.6 to 40.11).

Cleaning Up. Pour the sulfuric acid layer into water, combining it with the bicarbonate layer, neutralize it with sodium carbonate, and flush the solution down the drain with excess water. The saturated sodium chloride layer can also be flushed down the drain. If the calcium chloride is free of ether and methyl benzoate, it can be placed in the nonhazardous solid waste container; otherwise it must go into the hazardous waste container. Ether goes into the organic solvents container, along with the pot residues from the final distillation.

5. Hydrolysis (Saponification): The Preparation of Soap

In general, the reversal of esterification is called *hydrolysis*. In the case of the hydrolysis of a fatty acid ester, it is called . In this experiment, the saturated fat made from hydrogenated olive oil in Chapter 25 will be saponified to give a soap, which, in this case, will be primarily sodium stearate.

$$
\begin{array}{c}
\underset{\displaystyle CH_2OC(CH_2)_{16}CH_3}{\overset{\displaystyle O}{\overset{\|}{}}} \\[2mm]
\underset{\displaystyle CHOC(CH_2)_{16}CH_3}{\overset{\displaystyle O}{\overset{\|}{}}} \xrightarrow[H_2O]{NaOH} \\[2mm]
\underset{\displaystyle CH_2OC(CH_2)_{16}CH_3}{\overset{\displaystyle O}{\overset{\|}{}}}
\end{array}
\qquad
\begin{array}{c}
CH_2OH \\[2mm]
CHOH \;+\; 3Na^+\;\overset{O}{\overset{\|}{\underset{}{}}}\;\overline{O}C(CH_2)_{16}CH_3 \\[2mm]
CH_2OH
\end{array}
$$

Glycerol tristearate   **Glycerol   Sodium stearate (soap)**

Microscale Procedure

> **IN THIS EXPERIMENT** a saturated fat is heated with sodium hydroxide in a water-ethanol micture. The resulting soap is precipitated in salt solution and collected on a Hirsch funnel, where it is washed free of base and salt.

Online Study Center

Video: Microscale Filtration on the Hirsch Funnel

Place 0.18 g of the saturated triglyceride prepared in Chapter 25, Experiment 4, in a 5-mL short-necked, round-bottomed flask. Add 1.5 mL of a 50:50 water-ethanol solution that contains 0.18 g of solid sodium hydroxide (weigh this quickly). Add an air condenser and gently reflux the mixture on a sand bath for 30 min, taking care not to boil away the ethanol. At the end of the reaction period, some of the soap will have precipitated. Transfer the mixture to a 10-mL Erlenmeyer flask containing a solution of 0.8 g of sodium chloride in 3 mL of water. Collect the precipitated soap on a Hirsch funnel and wash it free of excess sodium hydroxide and salt using 4 mL of distilled ice water.

Test the soap by adding a very small piece (about 5–15 mg) to a centrifuge or test tube along with 3–4 mL of distilled water. Cap the tube and shake it vigorously. Note the height and stability of the bubbles. Add a crystal of magnesium chloride or calcium chloride to the tube. Shake the tube again and note the results. For comparison, do these same tests with a few grains of a detergent instead of the soap.

Macroscale Procedure

In a 100-mL round-bottomed flask, place 5 g of hydrogenated olive oil (Chapter 25) or lard or solid shortening (e.g., Crisco). Add 20 mL of ethanol and a hot solution of 5 g of sodium hydroxide in 20 mL of water. This solution, prepared in a beaker, will become very hot as the sodium hydroxide dissolves. Fit the flask with a water-cooled condenser and reflux the mixture on a sand bath for 30 min. At the end of the reaction period, some of the soap may precipitate from the reaction mixture. Transfer the mixture to a 250-mL Erlenmeyer flask containing an ice-cold solution of 25 g of sodium chloride in 90 mL of distilled water. Collect the precipitated soap on a Büchner funnel and wash it free of excess sodium hydroxide and salt using no more than 100 mL of distilled ice water.

Test the soap by adding a small piece to a test tube along with about 5 mL of water. Cap the tube and shake it vigorously. Note the height and stability of the bubbles formed. Add a few crystals of magnesium chloride or calcium chloride to the tube. Shake the tube again and note the results. For comparison, do these same tests with an amount of detergent equal to that of the soap used.

QUESTIONS

1. In the preparation of methyl benzoate, what is the purpose of (a) washing the organic layer with sodium bicarbonate solution? (b) washing the organic layer with saturated sodium chloride solution? (c) treating the organic layer with anhydrous calcium chloride pellets?

2. Assign the resonances in Figure 40.8 to specific protons in methyl benzoate.

3. Figures 40.9 and 40.10 each have two resonances that are very small. What do the carbons causing these peaks have in common?

■ **FIG. 40.6**
The IR spectrum of benzoic acid (KBr disk).

■ **FIG. 40.7**
The ^{1}H NMR spectrum of benzoic acid (250 MHz).

■ FIG. 40.8
The ^{1}H NMR spectrum of methyl benzoate (250 MHz).

■ FIG. 40.9
The ^{13}C NMR spectrum of benzoic acid (22.6 MHz).

■ **FIG. 40.10**

The ^{13}C NMR spectrum of methyl benzoate (22.6 MHz).

■ **FIG. 40.11**

The IR spectrum of methyl benzoate.

CHAPTER
37

Dibenzalacetone by the Aldol Condensation

Online Study Center

This icon will direct you to techniques, equipment setups, and online resources at http://college.hmco.com/PIC/williamsonMMOE5e.

PRELAB EXERCISE: Calculate the volumes of benzaldehyde and acetone needed for the macroscale version of this reaction, taking into account the densities of the liquids and the number of moles of each required.

Benzaldehyde
MW 106.13, bp 178°C
den. 1.04

Acetone
(2-Propanone)
MW 58.08, bp 56°C
den. 0.790

Dibenzalacetone
(1,5-Diphenyl-1,4-pentadien-3-one)
MW 234.30

The base catalyzed reaction of an aldehyde with a ketone is a mixed aldol condensation, known as the Claisen–Schmidt reaction. Dibenzalacetone is readily prepared by the condensation of acetone with two equivalents of benzaldehyde. The aldehyde carbonyl is more reactive than that of the ketone and, therefore, reacts rapidly with the anion of the ketone to give a β-hydroxyketone, which easily undergoes base-catalyzed dehydration. Depending on the relative quantities of the reactants, the reaction can give either mono- or dibenzalacetone.

Dibenzalacetone is innocuous; its spectral properties (ultraviolet [UV] absorbance) indicate why it is used in sunscreens and sunblock preparations. In the present experiment sufficient ethanol is present as a solvent to readily dissolve the starting material, benzaldehyde, and also the intermediate, benzalacetone. The benzalacetone, once formed, can then easily react with another mole of benzaldehyde to give the product, dibenzalacetone. The mechanism for the formation of benzalacetone is as follows:

297

$$CH_3CCH_3 + OH^- \longrightarrow \left[CH_3C-CH_2^- \leftrightarrow CH_3C=CH_2 \right] + H_2O$$

$$CH_3CCH_2^- + \overset{H}{\underset{O}{C}} \rightleftharpoons CH_3CCH_2C \overset{H}{\underset{O^-}{}} \overset{H_2O}{\rightleftharpoons} CH_3CCH_2C \overset{H}{\underset{OH}{}} + OH^-$$

$$CH_3C-C-C \longrightarrow CH_3C-C=C + H_2O + OH^-$$

A β-hydroxyketone

Benzalacetone
(4-Phenyl-3-butene-2-one)
mp 42°C

EXPERIMENT

Synthesis of Dibenzalacetone[1]

Microscale Procedure

> **IN THIS EXPERIMENT** an ethanolic solution of acetone and benzaldehyde is added to aqueous sodium hydroxide. The product, dibenzalacetone, crystallizes after a few minutes. The product is filtered from the mixture, washed, pressed dry, and recrystallized from an ethanol-water mixture. This very important reaction is easily carried out.

If sodium hydroxide gets on the skin, wash until the skin no longer has a soapy feeling.

Into a 10 × 100-mm reaction tube place 2 mL of 3 *M* sodium hydroxide solution. To this solution add 1.6 mL of 95% ethanol and 0.212 g of benzaldehyde.[2] Then add 0.058 g of acetone to the reaction mixture. Alternatively, your instructor may provide a solution that contains 58 mg of acetone in 1.6 mL of ethanol. Cap the tube immediately and shake the mixture vigorously. The benzaldehyde, initially insoluble, goes into solution, resulting in a water-clear, pale-yellow solution. After a minute or so it suddenly becomes cloudy, and a yellow precipitate of the

---

1. Ask your instructor for an alternative procedure for carrying out this experiment, which is found in the *Instructor's Guide.*

2. The benzaldehyde should be pure. Because it is easily air oxidized to benzoic acid on standing in the lab, it should be freshly purified or a newly purchased bottle.

■ FIG. 37.1
The Pasteur pipette filtration technique. Solvent is removed between the pipette tip and the bottom of tube, which leaves crystals in the reaction tube.

Pasteur pipette

Reaction tubes

Note square, flat tip

■ FIG. 37.2
A Hirsch funnel filtration apparatus.

Filter paper, 12 mm dia.

Polyethylene filter disk (frit), 10 mm dia.

Hirsch funnel

To aspirator

25-mL Filter flask

■ FIG. 37.3
The drying of crystals under vacuum.

Online Study Center

Videos: Microscale Filtration on the Hirsch Funnel, Formation of an Oil Instead of Crystals, Filtration of Crystals Using the Pasteur Pipette, Microscale Crystallization

product forms. Continue to shake the tube from time to time for the next 30 min. If the product fails to crystallize, open the tube and scratch the inside of the tube with a glass rod. Remove the liquid from the tube using a Pasteur pipette by squeezing the bulb of the pipette, pressing the tip against the bottom of the tube, and bringing the liquid into the pipette, leaving the crystals in the tube (Fig. 37.1). Add 3 mL of water, cap, and shake the tube vigorously. Remove the wash liquid as before and wash the crystals twice more with 3-mL portions of water.

After the final washing, add 3 mL of water to the tube and collect the crystals on a Hirsch funnel using vacuum filtration. Use the filtrate to complete the transfer of the crystals. Squeeze the product between sheets of filter paper to dry it and then recrystallize the crude dibenzalacetone from a 70:30 ethanol-water mixture. During the recrystallization process (*see* Chapter 4), insert a wooden boiling stick to promote even boiling when heating the solute in the solvent. Remove the tube from the hot sand bath and place it in an insulated container to cool slowly to room temperature. Should the product separate as an oil, obtain a seed crystal, heat the solution to dissolve the oil, and add the seed crystal as the solution cools. If the product continues to oil out, add a bit more ethanol. After cooling the tube for several minutes in ice, collect the product by removing the solvent with a pipette (Fig. 37.1) and washing once with about 0.5 mL of ice-cold 70% ethanol while the tube is in ice. Alternatively, collect the crystals on a Hirsch funnel (Fig. 37.2) or Wilfilter and wash once with ice-cold 70% ethanol. Dry the product under vacuum by attaching the tube to an aspirator (Fig. 37.3). Determine the weight of the dibenzalacetone and its melting point and calculate the percent yield. In a typical experiment, the yield will be 0.10 g (mp 110.5°C–112°C).

Cleaning Up. Dilute the filtrate from the reaction mixture with water and neutralize it with dilute hydrochloric acid before flushing down the drain. The ethanol filtrate from the recrystallization should be placed in the organic solvents container.

Macroscale Procedure

In a 125-mL Erlenmeyer flask containing a magnetic stirring bar, mix 0.05 mol of benzaldehyde with the theoretical quantity of acetone, and add one-half the mixture to a solution of 5 g of sodium hydroxide dissolved in 50 mL of water and 40 mL of ethanol at room temperature (<25°C). After 15 min of stirring, add the remainder of the aldehyde-ketone mixture and rinse the container with a little ethanol to complete the transfer. Stir the mixture for 30 min; then collect the product by suction filtration on a Büchner funnel. Break the suction and carefully pour 100 mL of water on the product. Reapply the vacuum. Repeat this process three times in order to remove all traces of sodium hydroxide. Finally, press the product as dry as possible on the filter using a cork and then press it between sheets of filter paper to remove as much water as possible. Save a small sample for a melting-point determination; then recrystallize the product from ethanol using about 10 mL of ethanol for each 4 g of dibenzalacetone. The yield after recrystallization should be about 4 g.

Cleaning Up. Dilute the filtrate from the reaction mixture with water and neutralize it with dilute hydrochloric acid before flushing down the drain. The ethanol filtrate from the recrystallization should be placed in the organic solvents container.

Molecular Modeling

The name *dibenzalacetone* does not completely characterize the molecule made in this experiment. There are actually three isomeric dibenzalacetones: one melting at 110°C to 111°C, λ_{max} = 330 nm, ε = 34,300; another melting at 60°C, λ_{max} = 295 nm, ε = 20,000; and a third, a liquid with λ_{max} = 287 nm, ε = 11,000.

Both the melting points and the UV spectral data give some hints regarding the structures of these molecules. The first one is very symmetrical and can pack well into a crystal lattice. The long wavelength of the UV light absorption maximum and the high value of the molar absorbance (ε) indicate a long, planar conjugated system (*see* Chapter 14). The other two molecules are increasingly less able to pack nicely into a crystal lattice or to have a planar conjugated system. In the last step of the aldol condensation, the loss of water from the β-hydroxyketone can form molecules in which the alkene hydrogen atoms are either *cis* or *trans* to each other. Write the structures of the three geometric isomers of dibenzalacetone and assign each one to the three molecules described above.

If sodium hydroxide gets on the skin, wash until the skin no longer has a soapy feeling.

Online Study Center

Video: Macroscale Crystallization

■ **FIG. 37.4**
Single bond isomers
of benzalacetone.

(a)   (b)   (c)

Enter the structures of these three isomers into a molecular modeling program and carry out an energy minimization or semiempirical calculation to find the relative steric energies or heats of formation of each molecule. Note: Once the calculation is complete, the lowest energy conformation of each isomer will be as planar as possible so that there can be maximum overlap of the p orbitals on each sp^2 hybridized carbon. To test this idea, calculate the steric energy or heat of formation of benzalacetone (Fig. 37.4a) using the usual energy minimization procedure. The result should be an almost planar molecule. Then deliberately hold the dihedral angle defined by atoms 1, 2, 3, and 4 at 90° (Fig. 37.4b) and again calculate the energy of the molecule. In the latter conformation, the p orbitals of the carbonyl group are orthogonal to the p orbitals of the alkene.

As you may have discovered in calculating the energies of the three geometric isomers of dibenzalacetone, there is still another form of isomerization entering into the conformations of these molecules: single-bond *cis* and *trans* isomers, exemplified by two of the isomers of benzalacetone (Fig. 37.4a and Fig. 37.4c). Both of these conformers are planar in order to achieve maximum overlap of p orbitals, but in 37.4a the carbonyl group is *cis* to the alkene bond, whereas in 37.4c it is *trans*. The barrier to rotation about the single bond is not very high, so these isomers cannot be isolated at room temperature. If your molecular modeling program has a dihedral driver routine, you can calculate the heats of formation of benzalacetone as a function of the dihedral angle defined by atoms 1, 2, 3, and 4 and thus determine the barrier to rotation around this bond in kilocalories per mole.

Online Study Center

General Resources
Additional Experiments

QUESTIONS

1. Why is it important to maintain equivalent proportions of reagents in this reaction?
2. Which side products do you expect in this reaction? How are they removed?
3. What evidence do you have that your product consists of a single geometric isomer or a mixture of isomers? Does the melting point give such information?
4. From the ^{1}H NMR spectrum of dibenzalacetone (Fig. 37.5), can you deduce which geometric isomer(s) is (are) formed? (*See* Table 12.1 on page 255.)
5. How would you change the procedures in this chapter if you wished to synthesize benzalacetone ($C_6H_5CH{=}CHCOCH_3$) or benzalacetophenone ($C_6H_5CH{=}CHCOC_6H_5$)?

■ FIG. 37.5
The ^{1}H NMR spectrum of
dibenzalacetone (250 MHz). (An
expanded spectrum appears
above the normal spectrum.)

■ FIG. 37.6
The IR spectrum of
dibenzalacetone (KBr disk).

6. Assign the infrared (IR) peak at 1651 cm^{-1} in Figure 37.6.

7. Write the structures of the three geometric isomers of dibenzalacetone and assign each one to the three molecules described. Disregard single bond *cis* and *trans* isomerism.

8. Draw the structures of all the single bond *cis* and *trans* isomers for each of the three geometric isomers of dibenzalacetone. There are 10 such isomers. Pick out the one you regard as the most stable and calculate its steric energy. Which three or four are represented by the solid with a melting point of 110°C–111°C, the solid with a melting point of 60°C, and the liquid?

9. Carry out a molecular mechanics or semiempirical calculation to determine the relative steric energies or heats of formation of 3 of the 10 possible isomeric dibenzalacetones.

10. (a) Calculate the steric energy or heat of formation for one single bond isomer of *trans*-benzalacetone using the usual energy minimization procedure. The result should be a planar molecule. (b) Then deliberately hold the dihedral angle defined by atoms 1, 2, 3, and 4 at 0°, 90°, and 180° and again calculate the energies of the molecule. What is the approximate barrier to rotation about the single bond?

11. Pick out the isomer you regard as the most stable from Question 7 and calculate its steric energy (if this was not done in Question 8).

CHAPTER

44

The Sandmeyer Reaction: 1-Bromo-4-chlorobenzene, 2-Iodobenzoic Acid, and 4-Chlorotoluene

Online Study Center

This icon will direct you to techniques, equipment setups, and online resources at http://college.hmco.com/PIC/williamsonMMOE5e.

PRELAB EXERCISE: Using the Sandmeyer reaction as one step, outline the steps necessary to prepare 4-bromotoluene, 4-iodotoluene, and 4-fluorotoluene from benzene.

The Sandmeyer reaction is a versatile means of replacing the amine group of a primary aromatic amine with a variety of different substituents:

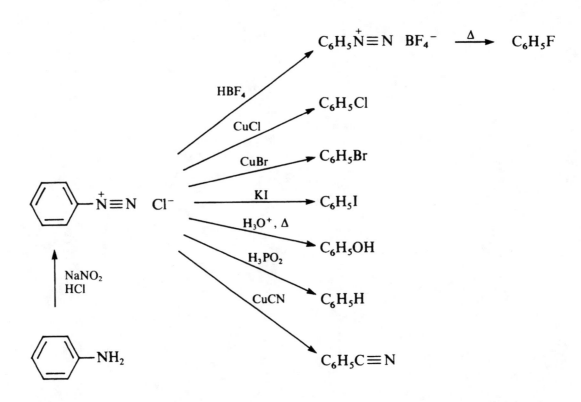

The benzene diazonium salt is formed by reacting nitrous acid with the amine in acid solution. Nitrous acid is not stable and must be prepared in situ; in strong acid it dissociates to form nitroso ions, $:N=O$, which attack the nitrogen of the amine. The intermediate so formed loses a proton, rearranges, and finally loses water to form the resonance-stabilized diazonium ion.

$$NaNO_2 + HCl \rightleftharpoons HONO + Na^+Cl^-$$

Sodium nitrite   **Nitrous acid**

$$H_3O^+ + HONO \rightleftharpoons H_2O + H_2\overset{+}{O}NO \rightleftharpoons 2\ H_2O + :\overset{+}{N}=O$$

Primary aromatic amine

$$C_6H_5-N=N-OH \underset{H^+}{\rightleftharpoons} C_6H_5-N=N-\overset{+}{O}H_2 \underset{-H_2O}{\rightleftharpoons} [C_6H_5-\overset{+}{N}\equiv N \leftrightarrow C_6H_5-N=\overset{+}{N}]$$

Diazonium ion

The benzene diazonium ion is reasonably stable in aqueous solution at 0°C; on warming it will form the phenol. A versatile functional group, it will undergo all the reactions depicted on the previous page as well as coupling to aromatic rings activated with substituents such as amino and hydroxyl groups to form the huge class of azo dyes (*see* Chapter 46).

Benzenediazonium   **N,N-Dimethylaniline**   **A diazo compound**
chloride

Diazonium salts are not ordinarily isolated because the dry solid is explosive.

Three Sandmeyer Reactions

$$NaNO_2 + HCl \longrightarrow Na^+Cl^- + HONO$$

Sodium nitrite
MW 69.01

Nitrous acid

4-Bromoaniline
MW 172.03, mp 62–64°C

4-Bromoaniline hydrochloride

4-Bromobenzenediazonium chloride

1-Bromo-4-chlorobenzene
MW 191.46, mp 68°C

In the first microscale procedure (Experiments 1, 2, and 3), after the copper(I) chloride is prepared, 4-bromoaniline is dissolved in the required amount of hydrochloric acid, two more equivalents of acid are added, and the mixture is cooled in ice to produce a paste of the crystalline amine hydrochloride. When this salt is treated with one equivalent of sodium nitrite at 0°C–5°C, nitrous acid is generated and reacts to produce the diazonium salt. The excess hydrochloric acid (beyond the two equivalents required to form the amine hydrochloride and react with sodium nitrite) maintains sufficient acidity to prevent formation of the diazo-amino compound and rearrangement of the diazonium salt. The diazonium salt reacts with copper(I) chloride to give the easily sublimed 1-bromo-4-chlorobenzene.

$$\text{NaNO}_2 + \text{HCl} \xrightarrow{0°C} \text{HONO} + \text{NaCl}$$

Sodium nitrite
MW 69.01

Nitrous
acid

Experiments 6, 7, and 8

p-Toluidine
MW 107.15, mp 45°C

p-Toluidine
hydrochloride

p-Methylbenzenediazonium
chloride

Experiments 4 and 5

CAUTION: *p*-Toluidine, like many aromatic amines, is highly toxic. *o*-Toluidine is not only highly toxic but is also a suspected carcinogen.

Copper(I) chloride
MW 98.99

4-Chlorotoluene
MW 126.58, bp 162°C

The second procedure (Experiment 4 microscale, Experiment 5 macroscale) employs potassium iodide, which reacts with a diazonium salt to give an iodobenzoic acid.

The third procedure is a macroscale synthesis of 4-chlorotoluene (Experiments 6, 7, and 8). *p*-Toluidine is dissolved in the required amount of hydrochloric acid, two more equivalents of acid are added, and the mixture is cooled in ice to produce a paste of the crystalline amine hydrochloride. When this salt is treated with one equivalent of sodium nitrite at 0°C–5°C, nitrous acid is liberated and reacts to produce the diazonium salt. The excess hydrochloric acid, beyond the two equivalents required to form the amine hydrochloride and react with sodium nitrite, maintains sufficient acidity to prevent formation of the diazo-amino compound and rearrangement of the diazonium salt. The diazonium salt reacts with copper(I) chloride to give liquid 4-chlorotoluene.

Copper(I) chloride is made by reducing copper(II) sulfate with sodium sulfite (which is produced as required from the cheaper sodium bisulfite). The white solid is left covered with the reducing solution for protection against air oxidation until it is to be used and then dissolved in hydrochloric acid. When the diazonium salt solution is added, a complex forms and rapidly decomposes to give *p*-chlorotoluene and nitrogen. The mixture is very discolored, but steam distillation leaves behind most of the impurities and all salts and yields material substantially pure except for the presence of a trace of yellow pigment, which can be eliminated by distilling the dried oil.

EXPERIMENTS

1. Copper(I) Chloride Solution

$$2\,CuSO_4 \cdot 5\,H_2O + 4\,NaCl + NaHSO_3 + NaOH \;\rightarrow\; 2\,CuCl + 3\,Na_2SO_4 + 2\,HCl + 10\,H_2O$$
MW 249.71   MW 58.45   MW 104.97   MW 40.01   MW 99.02

> **IN THIS EXPERIMENT** an aqueous solution of copper sulfate, sodium chloride, sodium bisulfite and sodium hydroxide react to give a precipitate of copper(I) chloride. Immediately before use this white salt is dissolved in hydrochloric acid.

NaHSO$_3$, sodium bisulfite (sodium hydrogen sulfite), not Na$_2$S$_2$O$_4$, sodium hydrosulfite

In a reaction tube dissolve 0.30 g of copper(II) sulfate crystals (CuSO$_4$ · 5 H$_2$O) in 1.0 mL of water by boiling and then add 140 mg of sodium chloride, which may give a small precipitate of basic copper(II) chloride. Prepare a solution of sodium sulfite from 70 mg of sodium bisulfite and 0.4 mL of 3 *M* sodium hydroxide solution (or use 57 mg of sodium sulfite in 0.4 mL of water). Add this solution dropwise to the hot copper(II) sulfate solution. Rinse the tube that contained the sulfite with a couple drops of water and add it to the copper(I) chloride mixture. Shake the reaction mixture well; then allow it to cool in ice while preparing the diazonium salt (Experiment 2). When you are ready to use the copper(I) chloride (in Experiment 3), remove the water above the solid, wash the white solid once with water, remove the water, and dissolve the solid in 0.45 mL of concentrated hydrochloric acid. This solution is susceptible to air oxidation and should not stand for an appreciable time before use.

CAUTION: Do not measure hydrochloric acid in a syringe that has a metal needle.

Cleaning Up. Combine the filtrate and washings, neutralize with sodium carbonate, and flush down the drain.

2. Diazotization of 4-Bromoaniline

> **IN THIS EXPERIMENT** an ice-cold acidic solution of an aromatic amine is treated with solid sodium nitrite to give a solution of the diazonium salt.

In a 10-mL Erlenmeyer flask place 172 mg of 4-bromoaniline and 0.50 mL of 3 *M* hydrochloric acid. Warm the mixture on a sand bath to dissolve the amine and ensure transformation into hydrochloride. Cool the flask in ice (the hydrochloride will crystallize) and add an ice-cold solution of 70 mg of fresh sodium nitrite in 0.2 mL of water. Use a drop of water to complete the transfer of the nitrite solution. Mix the solid and the sodium sulfite thoroughly. The result should be a homogeneous yellow solid/liquid mixture. Do not allow this mixture to warm above 0°C.

3. Sandmeyer Reaction: Synthesis of 1-Bromo-4-Chlorobenzene

> **IN THIS EXPERIMENT** the cold copper(I) chloride solution is combined with the cold diazonium salt solution made from 4-bromoaniline in Experiment 2. Nitrogen gas bubbles off, and the diazonium ion is replaced with a chlorine atom to give the product, 1-bromo-4-chlorobenzene.

Online Study Center

Video: Microscale Filtration on the Hirsch Funnel; Photo: Sublimation Apparatus

The extraction can be carried out in the microscale separatory funnel (*see* Fig. 7.7 on page 145).

Online Study Center

Video: Extraction with Ether, Filtration of Crystals Using the Pasteur Pipette; Photo: Filtration Using a Pasteur Pipette

Online Study Center

Photo: Sublimation Apparatus

Cool the copper(I) chloride solution (from Experiment 1) in ice and add it to the diazonium chloride solution dropwise with a Pasteur pipette and with thorough mixing. Rinse the tube that contained the copper(I) chloride with a drop of water. Allow the reaction mixture to warm to room temperature and observe the reaction mixture closely. It bubbles as nitrogen gas is evolved. Heat the mixture on a steam or a sand bath to complete the reaction. Cool the mixture thoroughly in ice and collect the dark solid on a Hirsch funnel. Squeeze the product between sheets of filter paper to dry it and then sublime the bromochlorobenzene on a steam or sand bath. After initial sublimation, scrape the residue in the filter flask to sublime more product.

Another way to isolate the product is to extract the product with three 0.5-mL portions of ether and wash the ether extract with 0.2 mL of 3 *M* sodium hydroxide solution, which will remove any 4-bromophenol, and then with 0.5 mL of saturated sodium chloride solution. Dry the ether solution over anhydrous calcium chloride pellets. Add sufficient drying agent so that it no longer clumps together. After 5–10 min, remove the ether with a Pasteur pipette, wash the drying agent with ether, and evaporate the ether solutions in a small, tared filter flask. Use care in this evaporation because the product is volatile. Determine the weight of the crude product; then purify it by sublimation at atmospheric pressure.

The 15-mL centrifuge tube is filled with ice water while the filter flask is heated on a sand or steam bath (refer to the sublimation apparatus in Fig. 6.21 on page 130). Close the sidearm with a rubber pipette bulb. Roll the flask in the sand and/or use a heat gun to drive product from the sides of the flask to the centrifuge tube. Replace the ice water in the centrifuge tube with room-temperature water before removing it so that moisture will not condense on the tube. Scrape the product onto a piece of weighing paper, determine the weight and the melting point, and analyze it for purity by thin-layer chromatography (TLC) and infrared (IR) spectroscopy in a chloroform solution.

Cleaning Up. Combine all aqueous filtrates and washings, neutralize with sodium carbonate, and flush down the drain. Allow the ether to evaporate from the drying agent in the hood before the drying agent is placed in the nonhazardous solid waste container. If local regulations do not allow for the evaporation of solvents in a hood, the wet solid should be disposed in a special container.

4. Sandmeyer Reaction: Synthesis of 2-Iodobenzoic Acid

2-Iodobenzoic acid
MW 248.02
mp 162–164°C

2-Aminobenzoic acid
MW 137.14, mp 144–148°C

$$\text{2-Aminobenzoic acid} + NaNO_2 + 2\ HCl \longrightarrow \text{(diazonium)} + Na^+Cl^- + 2\ H_2O$$

CAUTION: Do not measure hydrochloric acid in a syringe that has a metal needle.

To a reaction tube containing 137 mg of 2-aminobenzoic acid (anthranilic acid), add 1 mL of water and 0.25 mL of concentrated hydrochloric acid. Heat to dissolve the amino acid and form the hydrochloride; then cool the tube in ice. Cap the tube with a septum; then, with the tube in an ice bath, add a solution of 75 mg of sodium nitrite dissolved in 0.3 mL of water using a syringe equipped with a needle. This addition should be made dropwise with thorough agitation or magnetic stirring of the reaction. Rinse the syringe with 0.1 mL of water, which is also injected into the reaction mixture. After 5 min, a solution of 0.17 g of potassium iodide in 0.25 mL of water is added when a brown complex partially separates.

An empty distilling column is added to the top of the reaction tube to catch any foam. The mixture is allowed to stand without cooling for 5 min and then cautiously warmed to 40°C. At this point a vigorous reaction begins, with nitrogen gas evolution, foaming, and separation of a tan-colored solid. After reacting for 10 min, the mixture is heated in a beaker of boiling water for 10 min and then cooled in ice. A few milligrams of sodium sulfite are added to destroy any iodine present, and the granular tan-colored product is collected and washed with water.

The still-moist product is dissolved in 0.7 mL of ethanol; 0.35 mL of water is added; and the hot, brown solution is treated with enough granular Norit to remove most of the color. The solution is transferred to another reaction tube to remove the decolorizing charcoal, diluted at the boiling point with 0.35–0.40 mL of water, and allowed to stand. 2-Iodobenzoic acid separates in large, slightly yellow needles. The yield should be about 150 mg with a melting point near 164°C.

Online Study Center

Video: Microscale
Crystallization

Cleaning Up. The reaction mixture filtrate and mother liquor from the crystallization are combined, neutralized with sodium carbonate, and flushed down the drain. Norit is placed in the nonhazardous solid waste container.

5. Sandmeyer Reaction: Synthesis of 2-Iodobenzoic Acid

COOH NH_2 $\xrightarrow[\text{HCl, 0°C}]{\text{NaNO}_2}$ COOH $\overset{+}{N}_2Cl^-$ $\xrightarrow{\text{KI}}$ COOH I

2-Aminobenzoic acid
(Anthranilic acid)
MW 137.14, mp 144–148°C

2-Iodobenzoic acid
MW 248.02, mp 162–164°C

Online Study Center

Video: Macroscale
Crystallization

A 100-mL round-bottomed flask containing 3.4 g of anthranilic acid, 25 mL of water, and 6 mL of concentrated hydrochloric acid is heated until the solid is dissolved. The mixture is then cooled in ice while bubbling in nitrogen to displace the air. When the temperature reaches 0°C–5°C, a solution of 1.8 g of sodium nitrite in 6 mL of water is added slowly. After 5 min, a solution of 4.25 g of potassium iodide in 6 mL of water is added when a brown complex partially separates. This mixture is allowed to stand without cooling for 5 min (under nitrogen) and then warmed to 40°C, at which point a vigorous reaction ensues (gas evolution and separation of a tan-colored solid). After reacting for 10 min, the mixture is heated on a steam or sand bath for 10 min and then cooled in ice. A pinch of sodium bisulfite is added to destroy any iodine present, and the granular tan-colored product is collected and washed with water. The still-moist product is dissolved in 18 mL of 95% ethanol; 9 mL of hot water is added; and the brown solution is treated with decolorizing charcoal, filtered, diluted at the boiling point with 9–10 mL of water, and allowed to stand. 2-Iodobenzoic acid separates in large, slightly yellow needles (mp 164°C); yield is approximately 4.3 g (72%).

Cleaning Up. The reaction mixture, filtrate, and mother liquor from the crystallization are combined, neutralized with sodium carbonate, and flushed down the drain with a large excess of water. Decolorizing charcoal is placed in the nonhazardous solid waste container.

6. Copper(I) Chloride Solution

$$2 \, CuSO_4 \cdot 5 \, H_2O + 4 \, NaCl + NaHSO_3 + NaOH \rightarrow 2 \, CuCl + 3 \, Na_2SO_4 + 2 \, HCl + 10 \, H_2O$$
MW 249.71   MW 58.45   MW 104.97   MW 40.01   MW 99.02

In a 250-mL round-bottomed flask (to be used later for steam distillation) dissolve 15 g of copper(II) sulfate crystals ($CuSO_4 \cdot 5 \, H_2O$) in 50 mL of water by boiling; then add 7 g of sodium chloride, which may give a small precipitate of basic copper(II) chloride. Prepare a solution of sodium sulfite from 3.5 g of sodium bisulfite, 2.25 g of sodium hydroxide, and 25 mL of water; add this, not too rapidly, to the hot copper(II) sulfate solution (rinse flask and neck). Shake well, put the flask in a pan of cold water in a slanting position favorable for decantation, and

$NaHSO_3$, sodium bisulfite (sodium hydrogen sulfite), not $Na_2S_2O_4$, sodium hydrosulfite

One may stop here.

let the mixture stand to cool and settle during the diazotization. When you are ready to use the copper(I) chloride for Experiment 8, decant the supernatant liquid, wash the white solid once with water by decantation, and dissolve the solid in 23 mL of concentrated hydrochloric acid. This solution is susceptible to air oxidation and should not stand for an appreciable time before use.

 ## 7. Diazotization of *p*-Toluidine

> **IN THIS EXPERIMENT** a solid amine is dissolved in hydrochloric acid. The ice-cold solution is treated with solid sodium nitrite to diazotize the amine.

CAUTION: *p*-Toluidine is toxic. Handle with care.

Put 5.5 g of *p*-toluidine and 7.5 mL of water in a 50-mL Erlenmeyer flask. Measure 12.5 mL of concentrated hydrochloric acid and add 5 mL of it to the flask. Heat over a hot plate and swirl to dissolve the amine to ensure that it is all converted into the hydrochloride. Add the remaining acid, cool thoroughly in an ice bath, and let the flask stand in the bath while preparing a solution of 3.5 g of sodium nitrite in 10 mL of water. To maintain a temperature of 0°C–5°C during diazotization, add a few pieces of ice to the amine hydrochloride suspension and add more later as the first ones melt. Pour in the nitrite solution in portions during 5 min with swirling in the ice bath. The solid should dissolve to a clear solution of the diazonium salt. After 3–4 min, test for excess nitrous acid: Dip a stirring rod in the solution, touch off the drop on the wall of the flask, put the rod in a small test tube, and add a few drops of water. Then insert a strip of starch-iodide paper; an instantaneous deep-blue color due to a starch-iodine complex indicates the desirable presence of a slight excess of nitrous acid. (The sample tested is diluted with water because strong hydrochloric acid alone produces the same color on starch-iodide paper, after a slight induction period.) Leave the solution in an ice bath.

 ## 8. Sandmeyer Reaction: Synthesis of 4-Chlorotoluene

> **IN THIS EXPERIMENT** the ice-cold diazonium salt solution from Experiment 7 is poured into the copper(I) chloride solution prepared in Experiment 6. Nitrogen gas is evolved, and the product, 4-chlorotoluene, separates as oil. It is isolated by steam distillation; the distillate is extracted with ether; and the ether is washed, dried, and evaporated to leave crude product that is purified by simple distillation.

Complete the preparation of copper(I) chloride solution from Experiment 6, cool it in an ice bath, pour in the solution of diazonium chloride through a long-stemmed funnel, and rinse the flask. Swirl occasionally at room temperature for 10 min. You should observe initial separation of a complex of the two components followed by its decomposition with the liberation of nitrogen and the separation of an oil. Arrange for steam distillation (*see* Fig. 6.4 on page 112) or generate steam in situ simply by boiling the flask contents with a Thermowell using the apparatus for simple distillation (*see* Fig. 5.10 on page 100; add more water during the distillation). Do not start the distillation until bubbling in the mixture has practically ceased and an oily layer has separated. Then steam distill and note that *p*-chlorotoluene, although lighter than the solution of inorganic salts in which it was produced, is heavier (den. 1.07) than water. Extract the distillate with a little ether, wash the extract with 3 *M* sodium hydroxide solution to remove any *p*-cresol ($CH_3C_6H_4OH$) present, and then wash with saturated sodium chloride solution. Dry the ether solution over about 2.5 g of anhydrous calcium chloride pellets and filter or decant it into a tared flask, evaporate the ether, and determine the yield and percent yield of product (your crude yield should be about 4.5 g). Pure *p*-chlorotoluene, the IR and nuclear magnetic resonance (NMR) spectra of which are shown in Figures 44.1 through 44.3, is obtained after simple distillation of this crude product. Analyze your crude and distilled product by TLC (using a 3:1 mixture of hexane and dichloromethane as the eluent), IR spectroscopy, and gas chromatography using a Carbowax column. Is it pure?

Cleaning Up. Combine the pot residue from the steam distillation with the aqueous washings, neutralize with sodium carbonate, dilute with water, and flush down the drain. Allow the ether to evaporate from the drying agent in the hood; then place the drying agent in the nonhazardous solid waste container.

⚠️

CAUTION: Use aspirator tube.

Dispose of copper salts and solutions in the container provided.

■ **FIG. 44.1**
The IR spectrum of *p*-chlorotoluene in carbon disulfide.

■ **FIG. 44.2**
The ¹H NMR spectrum of *p*-chlorotoluene (90 MHz).

■ **FIG. 44.3**
The ^{13}C NMR spectrum
of *p*-chlorotoluene (22.6 MHz).

QUESTIONS

1. Nitric acid is generated by the action of sulfuric acid on sodium nitrate. Nitrous acid is prepared by the action of hydrochloric acid on sodium nitrite. Why is nitrous acid prepared in situ rather than obtained from the reagent shelf?

2. Which byproduct would be obtained in high yield if the diazotization of *p*-toluidine were carried out at 30°C instead of 0°C–5°C?

3. How would 4-bromoaniline be prepared from benzene?